Edexcel International GCSE
Chemistry

No doubt about it, Edexcel International GCSE Chemistry is tough. But never fear — this brilliant all-in-one CGP book has the whole course covered!

There are smashing notes, examples and exam-style questions for every topic, plus a full set of realistic practice papers at the end of the book. Everything you need.

It's great for the Chemistry parts of Edexcel's International GCSE Science Double Award too — if you're studying this course, you'll only need to learn the Paper 1 topics.

How to access your free Online Edition

This book includes a free Online Edition to read on your PC, Mac or tablet. You'll just need to go to **cgpbooks.co.uk/extras** and enter this code:

0489 7250 4754 7197

By the way, this code only works for one person. If somebody else has used this book before you, they might have already claimed the Online Edition.

Complete
Revision & Practice
Everything you need to pass the exams!

Contents

Throughout this book you'll see grade stamps like these:

These grade stamps help to show how difficult the questions are.
Remember — to get a top grade you need to be able to answer **all** the questions, not just the hardest ones.

Section 5 — Physical Chemistry

Section 6 — Organic Chemistry

Describing Experiments

Edexcel International GCSE Exam Information

1) For the Edexcel International GCSE in Chemistry, you'll sit two exam papers at the end of your course.

2) Paper 1 is 2 hours long and worth 110 marks. Paper 2 is 1 hour 15 minutes long and worth 70 marks.

3) Some material in the specification will only be tested in Paper 2. The Paper 2 material in this book is marked with a green 'Paper 2' box. The 'Warm-Up' and Revision Summary questions that cover Paper 2 material are printed in green, and the 'Exam Questions' are marked with this stamp: PAPER 2

If you're doing a Science (Double Award) qualification you don't need to learn the Paper 2 material.

Practice Exams

Published by CGP

From original material by Paddy Gannon.

Editors: Alex Billings, Ellen Burton, Emma Clayton, Mary Falkner, Emily Forsberg, Charles Kitts, Sam Mann, Claire Plowman, Caroline Purvis, Ethan Starmer-Jones

Contributors: Mike Bossart, Mike Thompson

With thanks to Katherine Faudemer and Karen Wells for the proofreading.

With thanks to Ana Pungartnik for the copyright research.

Graph to show trend in Atmospheric CO_2 Concentration and global temperature on page 70
based on data by EPICA community members 2004 and Siegenthaler et al 2005.

ISBN: 978 1 78908 083 4

Printed by Elanders Ltd, Newcastle upon Tyne.
Clipart from Corel®
Illustrations by: Sandy Gardner Artist, email sandy@sandygardner.co.uk

Based on the classic CGP style by Richard Parsons.

States of Matter

You can explain quite a bit of the stuff in chemistry if you can get your head around this lot.

The **Three States of Matter** — Solid, Liquid and Gas

1) Materials come in <u>three</u> different forms — <u>solid</u>, <u>liquid</u> and <u>gas</u>. These are the <u>Three States of Matter</u>.

2) Which <u>state</u> you get (<u>solid</u>, <u>liquid</u> or <u>gas</u>) depends on how <u>strong</u> the forces of attraction are between the particles of the material.

3) How strong the forces are depends on <u>THREE THINGS</u>:
   - the <u>material</u>
   - the <u>temperature</u>
   - the <u>pressure</u>.

Solids

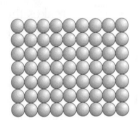

1) In solids, there are <u>strong forces</u> of attraction between particles, which hold them <u>close together</u> in <u>fixed positions</u> to form a very regular <u>lattice arrangement</u>.

2) The particles <u>don't move</u> from their positions, so all solids keep a <u>definite shape</u> and <u>volume</u>, and don't flow like liquids.

3) The particles <u>vibrate</u> about their positions — the <u>hotter</u> the solid becomes, the <u>more</u> they vibrate (causing solids to <u>expand</u> slightly when heated).

Liquids

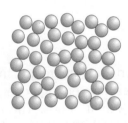

1) In liquids, there is a <u>weak force</u> of attraction between the particles. They're randomly arranged and <u>free</u> to <u>move</u> past each other, but they tend to <u>stick closely together</u>.

2) Liquids have a definite volume but <u>don't</u> keep a <u>definite shape</u>, and will flow to fill the bottom of a container.

3) The particles are <u>constantly</u> moving with <u>random motion</u>. The <u>hotter</u> the liquid gets, the <u>faster</u> they move. This causes liquids to <u>expand</u> slightly when heated.

Gases

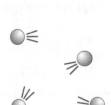

1) In gases, the force of attraction between the particles is <u>very weak</u> — they're <u>free</u> to <u>move</u> and are <u>far apart</u>. The particles in gases travel in <u>straight lines</u>.

2) Gases <u>don't</u> keep a definite <u>shape</u> or <u>volume</u> and will always <u>fill</u> any container.

3) The particles move <u>constantly</u> with <u>random motion</u>. The <u>hotter</u> the gas gets, the <u>faster</u> they move. Gases either <u>expand</u> when heated, or their <u>pressure increases</u>.

States of Matter

Materials don't just stay in one state. They can <u>change</u> between all three. Clever eh. It all depends on how much <u>energy</u> they have. Read on...

Substances Can **Change** from **One State to Another**

<u>Physical changes</u> don't change the particles — just their <u>arrangement</u> or their <u>energy</u>.

3) At a <u>certain temperature</u>, the particles have enough energy to <u>break free</u> from their positions. This is called <u>MELTING</u> and the <u>solid</u> turns into a <u>liquid</u>.

4) When a liquid is <u>heated</u>, the particles get even <u>more</u> energy.

2) This makes the particles vibrate <u>more</u>, which <u>weakens</u> the <u>forces</u> that hold the solid together. This makes the solid <u>expand</u>.

5) This energy makes the particles move <u>faster</u>, which <u>weakens</u> and <u>breaks</u> the bonds holding the liquid together.

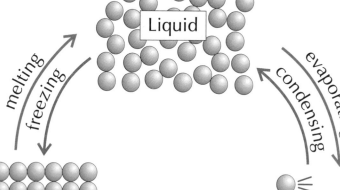
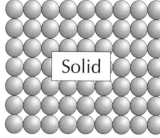
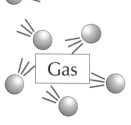

1) When a solid is <u>heated</u>, its particles gain more <u>energy</u>.

6) At a <u>certain temperature</u>, the particles have <u>enough</u> energy to <u>break</u> their bonds. This is called <u>EVAPORATING</u> and the <u>liquid</u> turns into a <u>gas</u>.

A red arrow means heat is supplied

A blue arrow means heat is given out

Changing the energy of particles can cause a change of state
Make sure you can describe what happens to the <u>energy</u> of the particles, and the <u>forces</u> between them, as a substance is <u>heated</u> and <u>cooled</u>. Remember the terms for each <u>state change</u> too.

Movement of Particles

There are many nifty <u>experiments</u> you can do to <u>observe chemistry</u> at work. Read on to find out more...

Diffusion is the Movement of Particles Through a Liquid or Gas

1) <u>Diffusion</u> is the <u>gradual movement</u> of particles from places where there are <u>lots</u> of them to places where there are <u>fewer</u> of them. It's just the <u>natural tendency</u> for stuff to <u>spread out</u>.

2) You can use the experiment below to demonstrate diffusion...

Potassium Manganate(VII) and Water

<u>Potassium manganate(VII)</u> is great for this experiment because it's <u>bright purple</u>.

1) If you take a beaker of <u>water</u> and place some potassium manganate(VII) at the bottom, the purple colour <u>slowly spreads</u> out to fill the beaker.

2) This is chemistry in action... The particles of potassium manganate(VII) are <u>diffusing</u> out among the particles of water.

There are some more experiments that you can use to demonstrate diffusion on the next page.

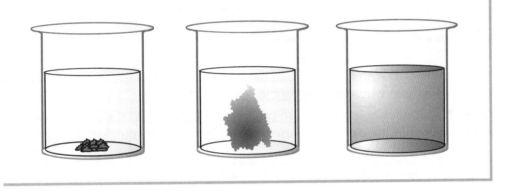

3) It's the <u>random motion</u> of particles in a liquid (see the previous page) that causes the purple colour to eventually be <u>evenly spread out</u> throughout the water.

Potassium Manganate(VII) Solution can be Diluted by Adding Water

If you were to <u>add more water</u> to the final purple solution, the potassium manganate(VII) particles would <u>spread even further apart</u> and the solution would be <u>less purple</u>. This is called <u>dilution</u>.

Particles tend to spread out to areas where there are fewer of them

A bad smell tends not to stay in one corner of a room forever — it'll eventually <u>spread out</u> to other parts of the room. And now you know what to blame. Yep, that's right... the <u>random movement of particles</u>.

Movement of Particles

Here are a couple more <u>experiments</u> that demonstrate <u>diffusion</u>...

Ammonia and Hydrogen Chloride

1) Aqueous ammonia (NH_3) gives off <u>ammonia gas</u>.
   Hydrochloric acid (HCl) gives off <u>hydrogen chloride gas</u>.

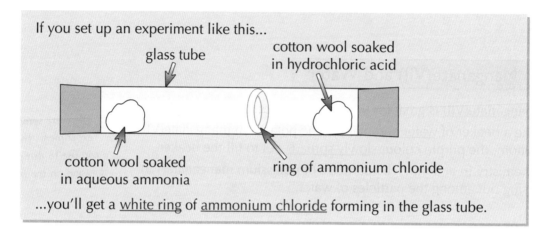

If you set up an experiment like this...

glass tube

cotton wool soaked in hydrochloric acid

cotton wool soaked in aqueous ammonia

ring of ammonium chloride

...you'll get a <u>white ring</u> of <u>ammonium chloride</u> forming in the glass tube.

2) The NH_3 gas <u>diffuses</u> from one end of the tube and the HCl gas <u>diffuses</u> from the other. When they meet they <u>react</u> to form ammonium chloride.

3) The ring doesn't form exactly in the middle of the glass tube — it forms nearest the end of the tube where the <u>hydrochloric acid</u> was.

4) This is because the particles of ammonia are <u>smaller</u> and <u>lighter</u> than the particles of hydrogen chloride, so they diffuse through the air more <u>quickly</u>.

Since ammonia diffuses more quickly, it will travel further than HCl in the same amount of time.

Bromine Gas and Air

1) Bromine gas is a <u>brown</u>, strongly smelling gas. You can use it to demonstrate diffusion in gases.

2) Fill half a <u>gas jar</u> full of <u>bromine gas</u>, and the other half full of air — separate the gases with a glass plate.

3) When you <u>remove</u> the glass plate, you'll see the brown bromine gas <u>slowly diffusing</u> through the air.

4) The <u>random motion</u> of the particles means that the bromine will eventually diffuse right through the air.

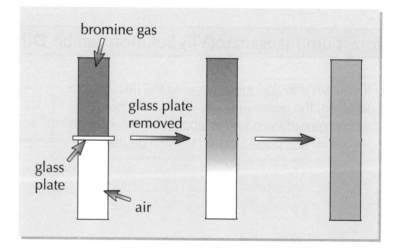

bromine gas

glass plate removed

glass plate

air

If only all this revision could just diffuse into my brain...

Make sure you know how the <u>particles move about</u> in these experiments — it'll help you to <u>explain the results</u>.

Solutions

This page is all about <u>solutions</u>. Study it carefully and you might even get some solutions to exam questions.

A Solution is a **Mixture** of **Solvent** and **Solute**

When you add a <u>solid</u> (the <u>solute</u>) to a <u>liquid</u> (the <u>solvent</u>) the bonds holding the solute molecules together <u>sometimes break</u> and the molecules then <u>mix</u> with the molecules in the liquid — forming a <u>solution</u>. This is called <u>dissolving</u>. Make sure you learn these important <u>definitions</u>:

1) <u>Solution</u> – is a mixture of a solute and a solvent that does not separate out.
2) <u>Solute</u> – is the substance being dissolved.
3) <u>Solvent</u> – is the liquid it's dissolving into.
4) <u>Saturated solution</u> – a solution where the maximum amount of solute has been dissolved, so no more solute will dissolve in the solution.

Solubility is How Much **Solute** will **Dissolve** in a **Solvent**

1) The ability of a <u>substance</u> to <u>dissolve</u> in a solvent is known as its <u>solubility</u>.
2) Solubility is often measured in <u>grams of solute</u> per <u>100 grams of solvent</u>.
3) For example, if 23 grams of a substance can dissolve in 100 grams of water before the solution becomes <u>saturated</u>, that substance has a solubility of 23 g per 100 g of water.
4) The <u>solubility</u> of most solid substances <u>increases</u> as you increase the <u>temperature</u>.
5) A graph of solubility versus temperature is known as a <u>solubility curve</u>:

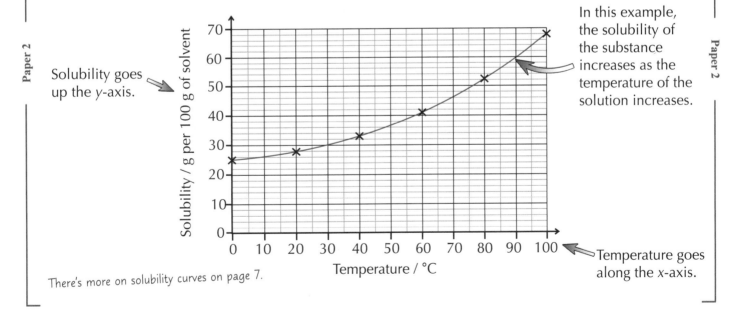

Solubility goes up the *y*-axis.

In this example, the solubility of the substance increases as the temperature of the solution increases.

Temperature goes along the *x*-axis.

There's more on solubility curves on page 7.

A solute dissolves in a solvent to form a solution

Learning all the <u>definitions</u> in chemistry can be a right pain, but it's worth it for a <u>few easy marks</u> in the exam.

 **Investigating Solubility**

You can measure <u>solubility</u> by <u>evaporating</u> away all the water in a solution. Sounds weird, but trust me...

You can **Investigate** how **Temperature** Affects **Solubility**

Here's how you would investigate how the <u>solubility</u> of <u>ammonium chloride</u> (a solid) is affected by <u>temperature</u>:

1) Make a <u>saturated solution</u> by adding an <u>excess</u> of ammonium chloride to 10 cm³ of <u>water</u> in a boiling tube. You will know when ammonium chloride is in excess because it will start to <u>sink</u> to the bottom of the tube.

2) Give the solution a good <u>stir</u> and place the boiling tube in a <u>water bath</u> set to 25 °C.

3) After <u>5 minutes</u>, check that <u>all</u> of the excess solid has sunk to the <u>bottom</u> of the tube and use a <u>thermometer</u> to check that the solution has reached 25 °C.

4) <u>Weigh</u> an <u>empty evaporating basin</u>. Pour some of the solution into the basin, making sure not to pour in any of the <u>undissolved solid</u>.

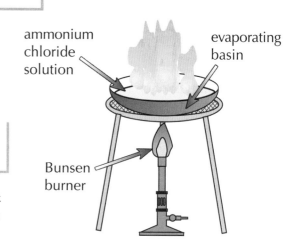

ammonium chloride solution

evaporating basin

Bunsen burner

5) <u>Re-weigh</u> the basin and its contents, then <u>gently heat</u> it using a <u>Bunsen burner</u> to remove all the water.

If you heat the basin <u>too strongly</u>, some of the ammonium chloride might turn into a <u>gas</u> and escape. This will cause the <u>mass of solid</u> in the basin to <u>decrease</u>, and your <u>solubility value</u> will be <u>lower</u> than it should be.

6) Once all the water has <u>evaporated</u>, you're left with <u>pure ammonium chloride</u>. <u>Re-weigh</u> the evaporating basin and its contents.

7) <u>Repeat</u> steps 1-6 twice more, but with the water bath at <u>different</u> temperatures (e.g. 35 °C and 45 °C).

8) You can use the different masses to work out the <u>solubility</u> at each <u>temperature</u> — see the next page.

9) You could plot the results on a <u>graph</u> like the one on the previous page.

  The solubility of a substance can change with temperature...

It's important that you make sure the <u>solute</u> is <u>in excess</u> in this experiment, so that you end up with a <u>saturated solution</u>. If the solution is <u>unsaturated</u>, it means that <u>more solute</u> can be <u>dissolved</u> in the solvent, so the <u>calculated solubility</u> will be <u>less than the true value</u>.

Section 1 — Particles and Mixtures

Investigating Solubility

Solubility can be Calculated from the Masses of the Solid and Water

You can use the following equation to calculate the solubility from the results of the experiment on the previous page:

PRACTICAL

$$\text{solubility (g per 100 g of solvent)} = \frac{\text{mass of solid (g)}}{\text{mass of water removed (g)}} \times 100$$

Example: A student dries a saturated solution of ammonium chloride that was prepared at 25 °C. Use the following experimental data to find the solubility of ammonium chloride at 25 °C.

Mass of evaporating basin	78.6 g
Mass of evaporating basin + saturated solution	89.3 g
Mass of evaporating basin + solid	81.5 g

Method:
1) Find the mass of solid left over in the basin:
   mass of solid = (mass of evaporating basin + solid) − mass of evaporating basin
   = 81.5 g − 78.6 g = 2.9 g
2) Find the mass of water removed during evaporation:
   mass of water removed = (mass of basin + saturated solution) − (mass of basin + solid)
   = 89.3 g − 81.5 g = 7.8 g
3) Use the equation above to calculate the solubility:
   solubility = (mass of solid ÷ mass of water removed) × 100
   = (2.9 ÷ 7.8) × 100 = 37.1794... = 37 g per 100 g of water

Solubility at a Set Temperature can be Read off a Solubility Curve

1) The results of the experiment on the previous page can be plotted on a solubility curve.

2) You can use solubility curves to see the solubility of a substance at a specific temperature.

3) To do this, draw a line from the temperature that you're interested in (on the x-axis) up to the curve. Then, read across from the curve to the y-axis to find the solubility of the substance at that particular temperature.

On the graph on the right, the solubility at 25 °C is 32 g per 100 g of solvent.

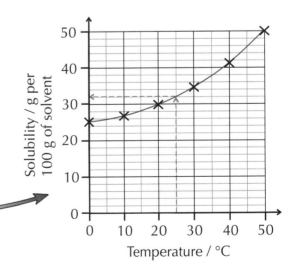

Check your final answer makes sense when doing calculations

E.g. if you've got a solubility that's far higher than you would expect, something might have gone wrong in your working — you might have got the equation upside-down or the units wrong.

Warm-Up & Exam Questions

Hooray, you've made it through the first pages of content. Here are a couple of pages of questions to check you've learnt it all. Have a go at the warm-up questions, then get stuck into some proper exam practice.

Warm-Up Questions

1) True or false? The particles in a solid material have more energy than the particles in a liquid of the same material.

2) Name the change of state that occurs when a liquid turns into a solid.

3) What is meant by a 'solute'? How about a 'solvent'?

4) When drawing a solubility curve, what is plotted on the *x*-axis?

Exam Questions

1 Substances can exist in three states of matter: solid, liquid or gas.

   (a)   In which of these three states of matter are the forces of attraction between the particles **strongest**?

[1 mark]

   (b)   Name the state of matter illustrated in the diagram below.

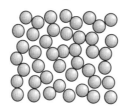

[1 mark]

   (c)   Describe the movement of particles in a gas.

[1 mark]

2 The diagram below shows a substance changing between solid, liquid and gas states.

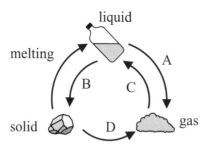

   (a)   Give the letter of the arrow that represents **subliming**.

[1 mark]

   (b)   Give the name of the process represented by arrow **A**.

[1 mark]

   (c)   Describe what happens to the particles in a solid when it is heated to the point of melting.

[4 marks]

Exam Questions

3   A student is preparing a solution of sodium chloride in a beaker of water.   (Grade 4-6)

     (a)   Define the term '**solution**'.

[2 marks]

     (b)   The student keeps adding sodium chloride to the beaker and stirring the solution. Eventually, the sodium chloride starts to settle at the bottom of the beaker. Explain why.

[1 mark]

4   In the experiment shown in the diagram on the right, a gas jar full of brown bromine gas is separated from a gas jar full of air by a glass plate.   (Grade 4-6)

     The glass plate is then removed. Describe and explain the appearance of the gas jars after an hour.

[2 marks]

bromine

glass plate

air

PAPER 2   **PRACTICAL**

5   A student is carrying out an experiment to find the solubility of a substance at 30 °C.   (Grade 6-7)

     (a)   The student starts by heating a saturated solution to 30 °C. Which of the following pieces of apparatus would be most suitable for evenly heating the solution?

       ☐   **A**   Desiccator   ☐   **C**   Evaporating dish

       ☐   **B**   Water bath   ☐   **D**   Bunsen burner

[1 mark]

     (b)   The student then heats a known mass of the saturated solution until all the water has evaporated. Suggest a hazard that could be associated with this experiment, and give **one** way that the student could reduce the risk involved with this hazard.

[2 marks]

     (c)   The student's results are shown in the table below.

Mass of solid obtained / g	12.2
Mass of water removed / g	32.8

       Calculate the solubility, in grams per 100 g solute, of potassium chloride at 30 °C. Give your answer to three significant figures.

[2 marks]

     (d)   Suggest **one** way that the student could improve the reliability of the experiment.

[1 mark]

     (e)   State the dependent variable in the experiment.

[1 mark]

Atoms

All substances are made of <u>atoms</u>. They're really <u>tiny</u> — too small to see, even with a microscope.

Atoms Contain **Protons, Neutrons** and **Electrons**

The atom is made up of three <u>subatomic particles</u> — protons, neutrons and electrons.

- <u>Protons</u> are <u>heavy</u> and <u>positively charged</u>.
- <u>Neutrons</u> are <u>heavy</u> and <u>neutral</u>.
- <u>Electrons</u> have <u>hardly any mass</u> and are <u>negatively charged</u>.

Relative mass (measured in atomic mass units) measures mass on a scale where the mass of a proton or neutron is 1.

Particle	Relative mass	Relative charge
Proton	1	+1
Neutron	1	0
Electron	0.0005	−1

The Nucleus

1) It's in the <u>middle</u> of the atom.
2) It contains <u>protons</u> and <u>neutrons</u>.
3) It has a <u>positive charge</u> because of the protons.
4) Almost the <u>whole</u> mass of the atom is <u>concentrated</u> in the nucleus.
5) Compared to the overall size of the atom, the nucleus is <u>tiny</u>.

Protons and neutrons are still teeny tiny — they're just heavy compared to electrons.

The Electrons

1) Electrons move <u>around</u> the nucleus in energy levels called <u>shells</u>.
2) They're <u>negatively charged</u>.
3) They're <u>tiny</u>, but their orbitals cover <u>a lot of space</u>.
4) The <u>size</u> of their orbitals determines the size of the atom.
5) Electrons have virtually <u>no</u> mass (so small that it's sometimes given as zero).

Number of Electrons **Equals** Number of Protons

1) Neutral atoms have <u>no charge</u> overall.
2) The <u>charge</u> on the electrons is the <u>same</u> size as the charge on the <u>protons</u> — but <u>opposite</u>.
3) This means the <u>number</u> of <u>electrons</u> always equals the <u>number</u> of <u>protons</u> in a <u>neutral atom</u>.
4) If some electrons are <u>added or removed</u>, the atom becomes <u>charged</u> and is then an <u>ion</u>.

Atomic Number and **Mass Number** Describe an Atom

These two numbers tell you how many of each kind of particle an atom has.

1) The <u>atomic number</u> tells you how many <u>protons</u> there are.
2) Atoms of the <u>same</u> element all have the <u>same</u> number of <u>protons</u> — so atoms of <u>different</u> elements will have <u>different</u> numbers of <u>protons</u>.

Mass number → 23
Atomic number → 11
Na ← Element symbol

3) The <u>mass number</u> is the total of <u>protons</u> and <u>neutrons</u> in the atom.
4) To get the number of <u>neutrons</u>, just <u>subtract</u> the <u>atomic number</u> from the <u>mass number</u>.

Molecules are **Groups** of Atoms

Molecules are held together by covalent bonds (see pages 34-38 for more).

1) Atoms can join together to form <u>molecules</u>.
2) Some molecules are made from just <u>one element</u> (e.g. H_2, N_2), while others are made up of <u>more than one element</u> (e.g. H_2O, CO_2).

Isotopes

Atoms were reasonably straightforward weren't they? Well, here come <u>isotopes</u> to confuse everything.

Isotopes are the Same Except for an Extra **Neutron** or Two

A favourite exam question is: "<u>Explain the meaning of the term isotope</u>"
The trick is that it's impossible to explain what one isotope is.
You have to outsmart them and always start your answer "Isotopes are..."   <u>LEARN the definition</u>:

> <u>Isotopes</u> are <u>different atomic forms</u> of the <u>same element</u>, which have
> the <u>same number of protons</u> but <u>different numbers of neutrons</u>.

1) The upshot is: isotopes must have the <u>same</u> proton number but <u>different</u> mass numbers.

2) <u>If</u> they had <u>different</u> proton numbers, they'd be <u>different</u> elements altogether.

3) A very popular example of a pair of isotopes is <u>carbon-12</u> and <u>carbon-13</u>.

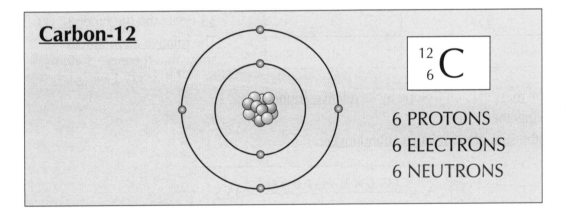

Carbon-12

$^{12}_{6}\text{C}$

6 PROTONS
6 ELECTRONS
6 NEUTRONS

Remember — the number of neutrons is just the mass number minus the atomic number.

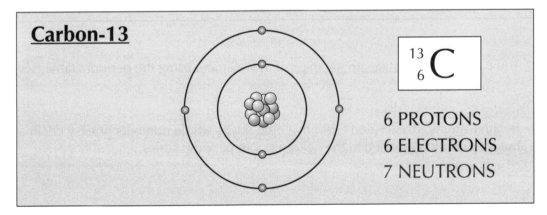

Carbon-13

$^{13}_{6}\text{C}$

6 PROTONS
6 ELECTRONS
7 NEUTRONS

Isotopes of an element have different numbers of neutrons

If you're struggling to recall how an isotope is defined, try using the letters in 'isotope' as a memory aid — i**S**oto**P**es of the same element have the **Same Proton** number but <u>different mass numbers</u>.

Relative Atomic Mass

Relative atomic mass isn't as bad as it sounds, I promise. Take a look for yourself...

Relative Atomic Mass Takes All Stable Isotopes into Account

1) Relative atomic mass (A_r) is just a way of saying how heavy different atoms are compared with the mass of an atom of carbon-12. So carbon-12 has an A_r of exactly 12.

2) It's the average mass of all the isotopes of an element. It has to allow for the relative mass of each isotope and its relative abundance.

3) Relative abundance just means how much there is of each isotope compared to the total amount of the element in the world. This can be a ratio, a fraction or a percentage.

For example, you could calculate the relative atomic mass of chlorine using the info in the table below:

Element	Relative mass of isotope	Relative abundance
chlorine	35.0	3
	37.0	1

The data in the table shows that there are 2 isotopes of chlorine. One has a relative mass of 35 (^{35}Cl) and the other 37 (^{37}Cl).

The relative abundances show that there are 3 atoms of ^{35}Cl to every 1 of ^{37}Cl.

1) Multiply the mass of each isotope by its relative abundance.
2) Add those together.
3) Divide by the sum of the relative abundances.

$$A_r = \frac{(35.0 \times 3) + (37.0 \times 1)}{3 + 1} = \underline{35.5}$$

4) You can find the relative atomic mass of any element using the periodic table (see p.24).

5) Relative atomic masses don't usually come out as whole numbers or easy decimals, but they're often rounded to the nearest 0.5 in periodic tables.

Relative atomic mass is the average atomic mass of an element

Relative atomic mass takes into account all isotopes of an element — this is different to the mass number, which is the mass of a specific isotope of an element. It's easy to get them muddled up, but fortunately for you, there's a handy way to remember it — relative atomic mass has the symbol $\underline{A_r}$ and is an average mass. See, not so difficult when you know how...

Elements, Compounds and Mixtures

There are only about <u>100 or so</u> different kinds of atoms, which doesn't sound too bad.
But they can <u>join together</u> in <u>loads</u> of different combinations, which makes life more complicated.

Elements Consist of One Type of Atom Only

Quite a lot of everyday substances are <u>elements</u>:

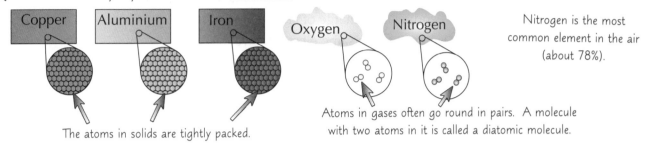

Nitrogen is the most common element in the air (about 78%).

The atoms in solids are tightly packed.

Atoms in gases often go round in pairs. A molecule with two atoms in it is called a diatomic molecule.

Compounds are Chemically Bonded

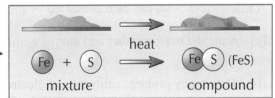

carbon + oxygen ⟹ carbon dioxide

1) A <u>compound</u> is a substance that is made of <u>two or more</u> <u>different elements</u> which are <u>chemically joined</u> (<u>bonded</u>) together.

2) For example, <u>carbon dioxide</u> is a <u>compound</u> formed from a <u>chemical reaction</u>. One carbon atom reacts with two oxygen atoms to form a <u>molecule</u> of carbon dioxide, with the <u>formula</u> CO_2.

3) It's <u>very difficult</u> to <u>separate</u> the two original elements out again.

4) The <u>properties</u> of a compound are often <u>totally different</u> from the properties of the <u>original elements</u>.

5) For example, if a mixture of iron and sulfur is <u>heated</u>, the iron and sulfur atoms react to form the compound <u>iron sulfide</u> (FeS).

6) Iron sulfide is not much like iron (e.g. it's not attracted to a magnet), nor is it much like sulfur (e.g. it's not yellow in colour).

heat

Fe + S ⟹ Fe S (FeS)
mixture   compound

Mixtures are Easily Separated — Not Like Compounds

1) Unlike in a compound, there's <u>no chemical bond</u> between the different parts of a mixture. The parts can be separated out by <u>physical methods</u> such as distillation (see pages 19-20).

2) The <u>properties</u> of a mixture are just a <u>mixture</u> of the properties of the <u>separate parts</u>. E.g. a <u>mixture</u> of <u>iron powder</u> and <u>sulfur powder</u> will show the properties of <u>both iron and sulfur</u>. It will contain grey magnetic bits of iron and bright yellow bits of sulfur.

Iron and sulfur mixed together, but unreacted.

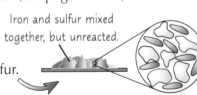

A Mixture Isn't a Pure Substance

1) In chemistry, a substance is <u>pure</u> if it's completely made up of a <u>single element or compound</u>.

2) Every <u>pure</u> substance has a <u>specific, sharp melting point</u> and <u>boiling point</u>. For example, pure ice melts at 0 °C, and pure water boils at 100 °C.

3) A <u>mixture</u> is <u>not</u> pure — it will melt or boil <u>gradually</u> over a <u>range</u> of temperatures.

Warm-Up & Exam Questions

So, you reckon you know your elements from your compounds...? Have a go at these questions and see how you do. If you get stuck on something just flick back and give it another read through.

Warm-Up Questions

1) Name the two types of subatomic particles found in the nucleus of an atom.
2) What is the relative mass and relative charge of an electron?
3) True or false? Different isotopes of the same element have the same number of neutrons but a different number of protons.
4) What is the definition of an element?

Exam Questions

1   Copper can be made extremely pure. The melting points of two samples of copper were measured. Sample **A** had a melting point of 1085 °C and sample **B** melted over the range 900 – 940 °C.

  Suggest which of the samples, **A** or **B**, was the **most pure**. Explain your answer.

  [2 marks]

2   A manganese atom can be represented by the nuclear symbol $^{55}_{25}$Mn.

  (a)   State the mass number and atomic number of $^{55}_{25}$Mn.

  [2 marks]

  (b)   How many protons, neutrons and electrons does an atom of $^{55}_{25}$Mn have?

  [3 marks]

3   The relative atomic mass of every element can be found in the periodic table.

  (a)   Give the definition of the **relative atomic mass** of an element.

  [2 marks]

  (b)   Suggest why some elements have relative atomic masses that are not whole numbers.

  [1 mark]

4   Gallium can exist as two stable isotopes: Ga-69 and Ga-71.

  60.1% of gallium atoms are Ga-69 atoms, and the rest are Ga-71 atoms. Calculate the relative atomic mass of gallium.

  [3 marks]

Filtration and Crystallisation

The components of a mixture <u>aren't chemically joined</u> (see p.13), so can be <u>separated</u> by <u>physical methods</u>.

Filtration is Used to Separate an Insoluble Solid from a Liquid

1) If the <u>product</u> of a reaction is an <u>insoluble solid</u>, you can use <u>filtration</u> to separate it out from the <u>liquid reaction mixture</u>.

2) It can be used in <u>purification</u> as well. For example, <u>solid impurities</u> can be separated out from a reaction mixture using <u>filtration</u>.

3) All you do is pop some <u>filter paper</u> into a <u>funnel</u> and pour your mixture into it. The liquid part of the mixture <u>runs through</u> the paper, leaving behind a <u>solid residue</u>.

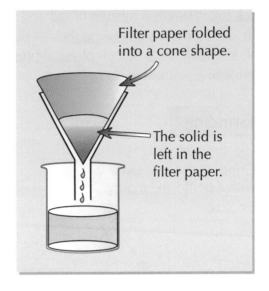

Filter paper folded into a cone shape.

The solid is left in the filter paper.

Crystallisation Separates a Soluble Solid from a Solution

Here's how you <u>crystallise</u> a product...

1) Pour the solution into an <u>evaporating dish</u> and gently <u>heat</u> the solution. Some of the <u>water</u> will evaporate and the solution will get more <u>concentrated</u>.

2) Once some of the water has evaporated, <u>or</u> when you see crystals start to form (the <u>point of crystallisation</u>), remove the dish from the heat and leave the solution to <u>cool</u>.

3) The salt should start to form <u>crystals</u> as it becomes <u>insoluble</u> in the cold, highly concentrated solution.

4) <u>Filter</u> the crystals out of the solution, and leave them in a warm place to <u>dry</u>. You could also use a <u>drying oven</u> or a <u>desiccator</u> (a desiccator contains chemicals that remove water from the surroundings).

evaporating dish

Crystallisation is for soluble solids...

... and filtration is for insoluble solids in a mixture. It's important to <u>remember</u> the <u>difference</u>.

Filtration and Crystallisation

Here's how you can put <u>filtration</u> and <u>crystallisation</u> to good use. <u>Separating rock salt</u>...

You Can Use **Filtration** and **Crystallisation** to Separate **Rock Salt**

1) <u>Rock salt</u> is simply a <u>mixture</u> of <u>salt</u> and <u>sand</u> (they spread it on the roads in winter).
2) Salt and sand are both <u>compounds</u> — but <u>salt dissolves</u> in water and <u>sand doesn't</u>. This <u>vital difference</u> in their <u>physical properties</u> gives a great way to <u>separate</u> them.
3) Here's how you would do it:

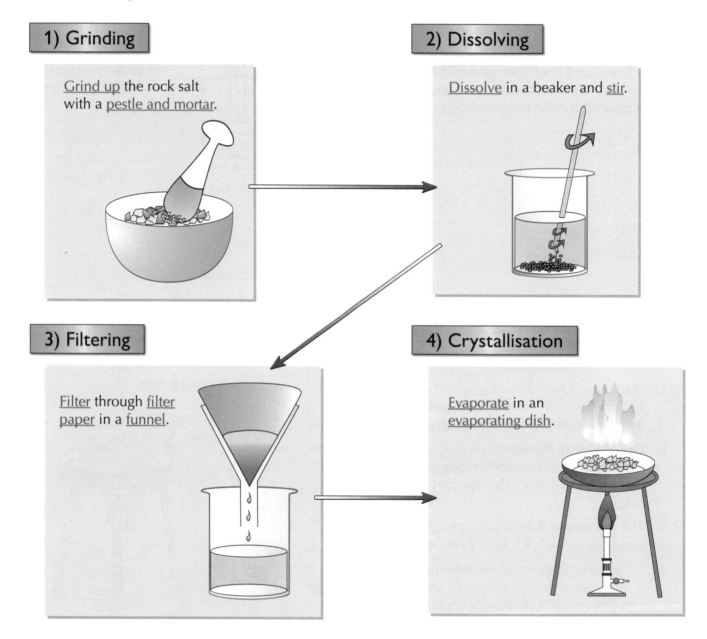

1) Grinding

<u>Grind up</u> the rock salt with a <u>pestle and mortar</u>.

2) Dissolving

<u>Dissolve</u> in a beaker and <u>stir</u>.

3) Filtering

<u>Filter</u> through <u>filter paper</u> in a <u>funnel</u>.

4) Crystallisation

<u>Evaporate</u> in an <u>evaporating dish</u>.

4) The sand doesn't dissolve (it's <u>insoluble</u>), so it stays as <u>big grains</u>. These <u>won't fit</u> through the <u>tiny holes</u> in the filter paper — so it <u>collects on the filter paper</u>.
5) The <u>salt</u> is dissolved in <u>solution</u>, so it does go through — and when the water's <u>evaporated</u>, the salt forms as <u>crystals</u> in the <u>evaporating dish</u>.

Separating rock salt requires filtration and evaporation

In the exam, you may be asked how to separate <u>another type of mixture</u> containing <u>insoluble</u> and <u>soluble solids</u> — just apply the <u>same method</u> and <u>think through</u> what is happening in each stage.

Chromatography

Chromatography is another method used by chemists to separate out mixtures. You can use paper chromatography to separate out dyes — e.g. in inks, paints, food colourings etc. It's, er, fascinating stuff.

You Need to Know How to Do **Paper Chromatography**

1) Draw a line near the bottom of a sheet of filter paper — this is the baseline. (Use a pencil to do this — pencil marks are insoluble so won't dissolve in the solvent.)

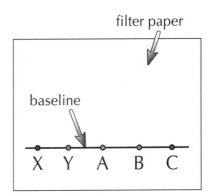

2) Add spots of different inks to the line at regular intervals.

3) Loosely roll the sheet up and put it in a beaker of solvent, e.g. water.

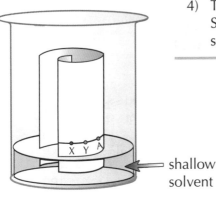

4) The solvent used depends on what's being tested. Some compounds dissolve well in water, but sometimes other solvents, like ethanol, are needed.

5) Make sure the level of solvent is below the baseline — you don't want the inks to dissolve into the solvent.

shallow solvent

6) Place a lid on top of the container to stop the solvent evaporating.

7) The solvent seeps up the paper, carrying the inks with it.

spots of dye move up the paper

8) Each different dye in the inks will move up the paper at a different rate and form a spot in a different place.

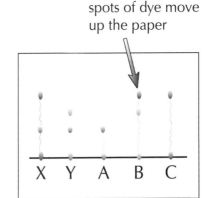

9) When the solvent has nearly reached the top of the paper, take the paper out of the beaker and leave it to dry.

10) The end result is a pattern of spots called a chromatogram.

Chromatography separates the different dyes in inks

Make sure you use a pencil to draw your baseline on the sheet of paper for your chromatogram. If you use a pen, all the components of the ink in the pen will get separated, along with the substance you're analysing, which will make your results very confusing.

Chromatography

Now that you know how to do chromatography, it's time to find out <u>how it works</u>.

How Chromatography Separates Mixtures...

1) Chromatography works because <u>different dyes</u> will move up the paper at <u>different rates</u>.

2) Some will <u>stick</u> to the <u>paper</u> and others will <u>dissolve</u> more readily in the solvent and travel more <u>quickly</u>.

3) The <u>distance</u> the dyes travel up the paper depends on the <u>solvent</u> and the <u>paper</u> you use.

You can Calculate an R_f Value for Each Chemical

1) An R_f value is the <u>ratio</u> between the distance travelled by the dissolved substance (the solute) and the distance travelled by the solvent. You can find R_f values using the formula:

$$R_f = \frac{\text{distance travelled by solute}}{\text{distance travelled by solvent}}$$

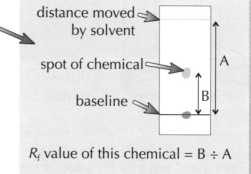

R_f value of this chemical = B ÷ A

2) To find the distance travelled by the solute, measure from the <u>baseline</u> to the <u>centre of the spot</u>.

3) Chromatography is often carried out to see if a certain substance is present in a mixture. You run a <u>pure sample</u> of a substance that you think might be in your mixture alongside a sample of the mixture itself. If the sample has the same R_f values as one of the spots, they're likely to be the <u>same</u>.

4) Chemists sometimes run samples of pure substances called <u>standard reference materials</u> (SRMs) next to a mixture to check the identities of its components. SRMs have controlled <u>concentrations and purities</u>.

You need to learn the formula for R_f

Sometimes, when you're doing paper chromatography, you'll end up with a <u>spot</u> left sitting on the <u>baseline</u>, even after your solvent has run all the way up the paper. Any substance that remains on the baseline is <u>insoluble in that solvent</u> — you could <u>rerun</u> the experiment using a <u>different solvent</u> to try and identify it.

Simple Distillation

Distillation is used to separate mixtures which contain liquids. This first page looks at simple distillation.

Simple Distillation is Used to Separate Out Solutions

1) Simple distillation is used for separating out a liquid from a solution.
2) The solution is heated. The part of the solution that has the lowest boiling point evaporates.
3) The vapour is then cooled, condenses (turns back into a liquid) and is collected.
4) The rest of the solution is left behind in the flask.

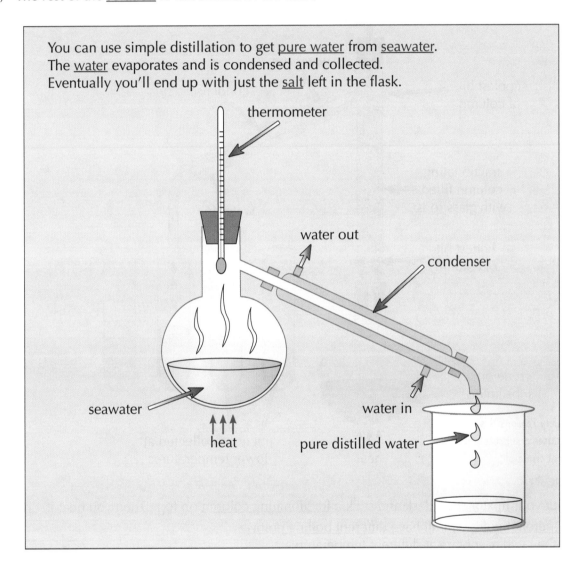

You can use simple distillation to get pure water from seawater.
The water evaporates and is condensed and collected.
Eventually you'll end up with just the salt left in the flask.

thermometer

water out

condenser

seawater

heat

water in

pure distilled water

5) The problem with simple distillation is that you can only
use it to separate things with very different boiling points.
6) If you have a mixture of liquids with similar boiling points, you need another
method to separate them out — like fractional distillation (see next page).

Heating ⟶ Evaporating ⟶ Cooling ⟶ Condensing

You might have used distilled water in Chemistry lessons. Because it's been distilled, there aren't any impurities in it (like ions, see page 29) that might interfere with experimental results. Clever stuff.

Fractional Distillation

Another type of distillation is <u>fractional distillation</u>. This is more complicated to carry out than simple distillation but it can <u>separate</u> out <u>mixtures of liquids</u> even if their <u>boiling points</u> are <u>close together</u>.

Fractional Distillation is Used to Separate a Mixture of Liquids

If you've got a <u>mixture of liquids</u> you can separate it using <u>fractional distillation</u>.
Here is a lab demonstration that can be used to model <u>fractional distillation of crude oil</u> at a <u>refinery</u>.

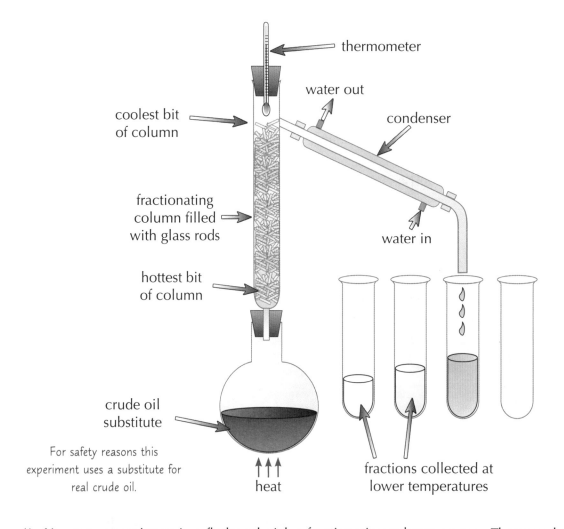

thermometer

water out

coolest bit
of column

condenser

fractionating
column filled
with glass rods

water in

hottest bit
of column

crude oil
substitute

For safety reasons this
experiment uses a substitute for
real crude oil.

heat

fractions collected at
lower temperatures

1) You put your <u>mixture</u> in a flask and stick a <u>fractionating column</u> on top. Then you heat it.
2) The <u>different liquids</u> will all have <u>different boiling points</u>
   — so they will evaporate at <u>different temperatures</u>.
3) The liquid with the <u>lowest boiling point</u> evaporates first. When the temperature on the thermometer matches the boiling point of this liquid, it will reach the <u>top</u> of the column.
4) Liquids with <u>higher boiling points</u> might also start to evaporate. But the column is <u>cooler</u> towards the <u>top</u>. So they will only get part of the way up before <u>condensing</u> and running back down towards the flask.
5) When the first liquid has been collected, you <u>raise the temperature</u> until the <u>next one</u> reaches the top.

Fractional distillation is used in the lab and industry

You've made it to the end of the pages on <u>separation techniques</u>, so make sure you understand what each of the methods can be used to separate and the <u>apparatus</u> set up for each technique.

Warm-Up & Exam Questions

So the last few pages have all been about mixtures and how to separate them.
Here are some questions to test whether you know your filtration from your distillation...

Warm-Up Questions

1) Which separation technique could you use to separate a soluble solid from a solution?
2) Which technique could you use to separate a mixture of liquids with similar boiling points?

Exam Questions

1   Different groups of seaweed contain different types of a pigment called chlorophyll.

The table below shows which types of chlorophyll each group of seaweed contains.

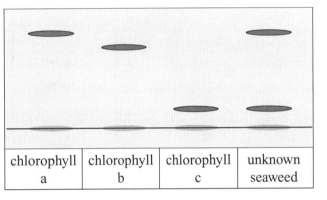

Group of seaweed	Type of chlorophyll		
	a	b	c
Red	✓		
Brown	✓		✓
Green	✓	✓	

Use the chromatogram on the right to identify which group the unknown seaweed belongs to.

[1 mark]

2   The diagram below shows a set of equipment you could use for separating a mixture in the lab.

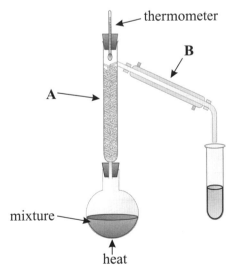

(a)   Name the pieces of equipment labelled **A** and **B**.

[2 marks]

(b)   Explain how fractional distillation works to separate a mixture of liquids.

[4 marks]

Exam Questions

3 Lawn sand is a mixture of insoluble sharp sand and soluble ammonium sulfate fertiliser.

(a) Describe how you would obtain pure, dry samples of the two components in the lab.

[4 marks]

(b) A student separated 51.4 g of lawn sand into sharp sand and ammonium sulfate.
After separation, the total mass of the two products was 52.6 g.
Suggest **one** reason for this error.

[1 mark]

PRACTICAL

4 A forensic scientist is using paper chromatography to analyse the ink used on a document.
The chromatogram she produced is shown in the diagram below.

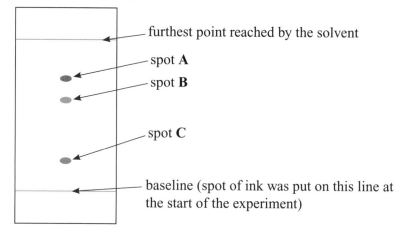

furthest point reached by the solvent

spot **A**

spot **B**

spot **C**

baseline (spot of ink was put on this line at the start of the experiment)

(a) Calculate the R_f value of spot **B**. Use a ruler to help you.

[3 marks]

(b) (i) The scientist wants to compare the ink on the document with the ink in three different printers.
Describe how she could set up a paper chromatography experiment to compare the inks.

[3 marks]

(ii) Explain how her results could be used to identify the printer that produced the document.

[1 mark]

5 The table below lists the boiling points of three compounds.

Name	Formula	Boiling point / °C
cyclopentane	C_5H_{10}	49
ethanol	C_2H_6O	78
ethyl ethanoate	$C_4H_8O_2$	77

Suggest why a mixture of ethanol and ethyl ethanoate might be more difficult to separate than a mixture of ethanol and cyclopentane.

[2 marks]

Revision Summary for Section 1

That wraps up <u>Section 1</u> — time to put yourself to the test and find out <u>how much you really know</u>.
- Try these questions and <u>tick off each one</u> when you <u>get it right</u>.
- When you've done <u>all the questions</u> under a heading and are <u>completely happy</u> with it, tick it off.

States of Matter (p.1-2) ☑

1) A substance keeps the same volume, but changes its shape according to the container it's in.
   Is it a solid, a liquid or a gas? ☑
2) Are the forces of attraction between the particles in a liquid stronger or weaker than those in a gas? ☑
3) Describe what happens when a substance changes from a liquid to a gas. ☑

Diffusion and Solutions (p.3-7) ☐

4) What is diffusion? ☐
5) Describe an experiment that you can do to demonstrate diffusion. ☐
6) Define the term 'saturated solution'. ☐
7) What are the units for solubility of a substance? ☐
8) What three measurements do you need to calculate the solubility of a substance
   at a particular temperature from an experiment? ☐

Atoms, Compounds and Mixtures (p.10-13) ☐

9) Draw a table showing the relative masses and charges of the three types of particle in an atom. ☑
10) Sketch the nuclear model of an atom.
    Give three details about the nucleus and three details about the electrons. ☐
11) What do the mass number and atomic number of an element tell you? ☐
12) What is an isotope? ☐
13) Describe the difference between a mixture and a compound. ☑

Separation Techniques (p.15-20) ☐

14) Describe how to carry out filtration. ☐
15) Describe how you could separate the dyes in some inks using paper chromatography. ☑
16) Give the formula for calculating R_f values. ☑
17) Name the physical method you could use to separate
    a mixture of liquids with different boiling points. ☑

The Periodic Table

In 1869, Dmitri Mendeleev arranged 50 known elements in order of atomic mass to make a Table of Elements. Mendeleev's table placed elements with similar chemical properties in the same vertical groups — but he found that he had to leave gaps in his table to make this work. The gaps in Mendeleev's table of elements were really clever because they predicted the properties of undiscovered elements. Since then new elements have been found which fit into the gaps left in Mendeleev's table.

The **Periodic Table** is a Table of All Known **Elements**

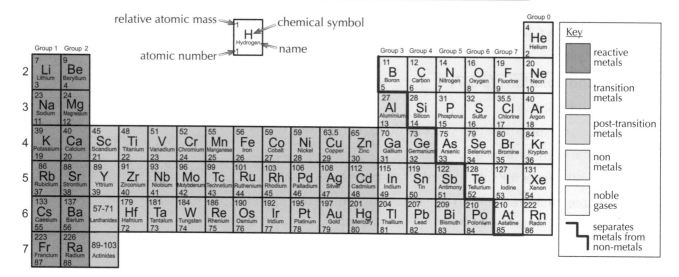

1) There are 100ish elements that all materials are made of, with more still being 'discovered'.
2) The modern periodic table shows the elements in order of increasing atomic number.
3) The periodic table is laid out so that elements with similar properties form columns.
4) These vertical columns are called groups.
5) The group to which an element belongs corresponds to the number of electrons in its outer shell. (Group 1 elements have 1 outer shell electron, Group 2 elements have 2 outer shell electrons, etc.)
6) Some of the groups have special names. Group 1 elements are called alkali metals. Group 7 elements are called halogens, and Group 0 are called the noble gases.
7) The rows are called periods. The properties of elements change as you go along a period (sometimes quite dramatically).

Elements in a **Group** Have the **Same Number** of **Outer Electrons**

1) The elements in any one group all have the same number of electrons in their outer shell.
2) That's why they have similar properties. And that's why we arrange them in this way.
3) When only a small number of elements were known, the periodic table was made by looking at the properties of the elements and arranging them in groups — the same groups that they are in today.
4) This idea is extremely important to chemistry — so make sure you understand it.

> The properties of the elements depend on the number of electrons they have.
> Atomic number is therefore very significant because it is equal to the
> number of electrons each atom has (one for each proton). But it's the
> number of electrons in the outer shell which is the really important thing.

The modern periodic table is vital for understanding chemistry

The position of an element in the periodic table gives you information about its properties. Clever stuff.

Electron Shells

The fact that electrons occupy 'shells' around the nucleus is what causes the whole of chemistry.

Electron Shell **Rules:**

1) Electrons always occupy shells (sometimes called energy levels).

2) The lowest energy levels are always filled first.   ← *The lowest energy levels are the ones that are closest to the nucleus.*

3) Only a certain number of electrons are allowed in each shell:

   1st shell: 2   2nd shell: 8   3rd shell: 8

Electron Shells can be Shown as **Diagrams** or **Numbers**

1) Electron configurations can be shown as diagrams like this:

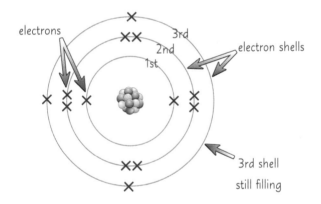

2) They can also be shown as numbers like this: 2.8.3.

3) Both of the electron configurations shown above are for aluminium.

Electron shells — probably the most important thing in chemistry

It's really important to learn the rules for filling electron shells, so here's a quick recap. The energy of the shells increases with increasing number (so shell 1 is the lowest energy level). You always fill the shell with the lowest energy first. The 1st shell can only hold a maximum of 2 electrons, but the 2nd and 3rd shells can both hold a maximum of 8 electrons. Practise following these rules on the next page.

Electron Shells

You can easily work out the <u>electronic configurations</u> for the first <u>20</u> elements of the periodic table (things get a bit more complicated after that). This page will show you how to do just that.

Working Out **Electronic Configurations**

1) The <u>electronic configurations</u> of the first <u>20</u> elements are shown in the diagram below. They're not hard to work out. Here are a couple of examples:

> <u>Example:</u> Finding the electronic configuration of <u>nitrogen</u>
> - The periodic table tells you that the atomic number of nitrogen is <u>seven</u>. That means nitrogen has seven protons, so it must have <u>seven electrons</u>.
> - Follow the '<u>Electron Shell Rules</u>' on the previous page. The <u>first</u> shell can only take 2 electrons and the <u>second</u> shell can take a <u>maximum</u> of 8 electrons.
> - So the electronic configuration of nitrogen must be <u>2.5</u>.

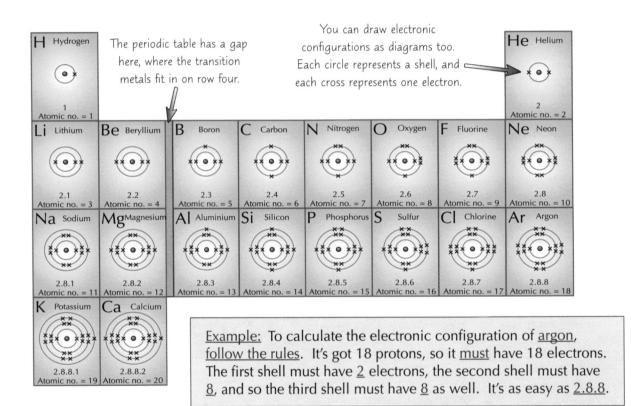

> <u>Example:</u> To calculate the electronic configuration of <u>argon</u>, follow the rules. It's got 18 protons, so it <u>must</u> have 18 electrons. The first shell must have <u>2</u> electrons, the second shell must have <u>8</u>, and so the third shell must have <u>8</u> as well. It's as easy as <u>2.8.8</u>.

2) You can also work out the electronic configuration of an element from its <u>period</u> and <u>group</u>.
   - The <u>number of shells</u> which contain electrons is the same as the <u>period</u> of the element.
   - The <u>group number</u> tells you <u>how many electrons</u> occupy the <u>outer shell</u> of the element.

> <u>Example:</u> Sodium is in <u>period 3</u>, so it has <u>3</u> shells occupied. The first two shells must be full (2.8). It's in <u>Group 1</u>, so it has <u>1</u> electron in its outer shell. So its electronic configuration is <u>2.8.1</u>.

For a neutral atom, atomic number = total number of electrons

<u>Electronic configurations</u> may seem complicated, but once you know how to do them, they're not too bad.

More on the Periodic Table

Remember the periodic table back on page 24? Well there's more about it on this page here. It has all the elements in a nice logical order, which makes it great for <u>spotting trends</u>.

The Elements can be Classified as **Metals** or **Non-Metals**

The periodic table can be <u>split</u> into two parts — the <u>metals</u> are on one side and the <u>non-metals</u> are on the other.

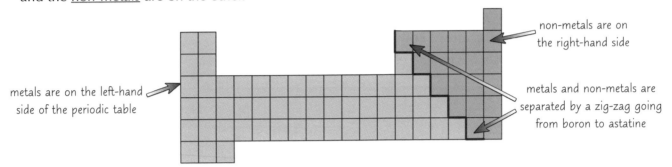

non-metals are on the right-hand side

metals are on the left-hand side of the periodic table

metals and non-metals are separated by a zig-zag going from boron to astatine

Metals

1) The elements on the <u>left</u> of the zigzag are all classified as <u>metals</u>.
2) Metals <u>conduct electricity</u> because they allow charge to pass through them easily.
3) <u>Metal oxides</u> are <u>basic</u>. This means they will neutralise acids. Metal oxides that dissolve will form solutions with a <u>pH</u> of <u>more than 7</u>.

Non-metals

1) The elements on the <u>right</u> of the zigzag are all classified as <u>non-metals</u>.
2) Non-metals are <u>poor conductors</u> of <u>electricity</u>.
3) <u>Non-metal oxides</u> are <u>acidic</u>. This means that they will neutralise bases. They dissolve in water to form solutions with a <u>pH</u> of <u>less than 7</u>.

You can read all about pH on page 82.

Group 0 Elements are All **Inert, Colourless Gases**

1) Group 0 elements are called the <u>noble gases</u> and include the elements <u>helium</u>, <u>neon</u> and <u>argon</u> (plus a few others).

2) They are <u>inert</u> — this means they <u>don't react</u> with much at all.

3) The reason for this is that it takes a lot of <u>energy</u> to <u>add</u> or <u>remove electrons</u> from a noble gas atom.

Because they are inert, noble gases exist as single atoms. They don't go around in pairs like in oxygen (O_2) or hydrogen (H_2).

Group 6	Group 7	Group 0
		4 He Helium 2
O	F	20 Ne Neon 10
S	Cl	40 Ar Argon 18
Se	Br	84 Kr Krypton 36
Te	I	131 Xe Xenon 54
Po	At	222 Rn Radon 86

Metals have quite different properties from non-metals

If you're staring at the <u>periodic table</u> and trying to remember where the line dividing <u>metals</u> from <u>non-metals</u> should go, just remember: <u>BAt stairs</u>. Imagine you're standing inside square <u>B</u> (<u>boron</u>). Draw a staircase that will take you down to inside square <u>At</u> (<u>astatine</u>). That's your dividing line.

Warm-Up & Exam Questions

The last few pages have been tough, with lots of information to learn. Luckily, here are some questions to get your head around to help you test your understanding.

Warm-Up Questions

1) Based on its position in the periodic table, would you expect the chemical properties of potassium to be more similar to those of sodium or calcium?
2) How many electrons can be held in: a) the first electron shell? b) the second electron shell?
3) Give the electronic structure of boron.
4) Describe the reactivity of Group 0 elements.

Exam Questions

1 Elements can be classified as metals or non-metals based on the acid-base nature of their oxide. *(Grade 4-6)*

(a) Which of these oxides will dissolve to form a solution with a pH of less than 7?

☐ **A** calcium oxide   ☐ **C** copper oxide

☐ **B** sulfur dioxide   ☐ **D** iron oxide

[1 mark]

(b) The diagram below shows the position of the element bismuth in the periodic table.

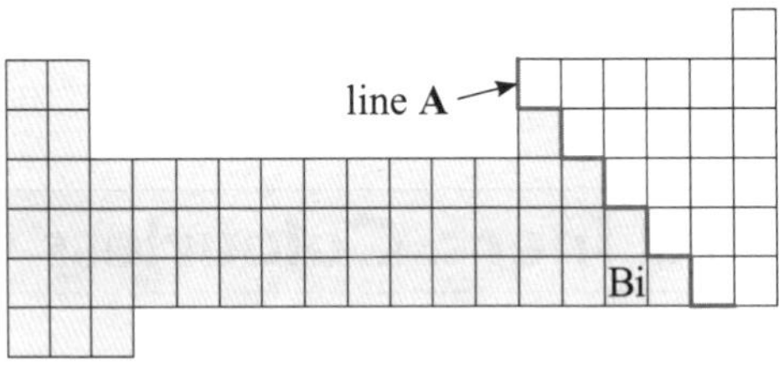

Element **X** is found in the same group of the periodic table as bismuth.
Element **X** does not conduct electricity. Predict whether element **X** will be found to the left or the right of line **A** in the diagram. Explain your answer.

[2 marks]

2 The atomic number of sulfur is 16. *(Grade 6-7)*

(a) Write down the electronic structure of sulfur.

[1 mark]

(b) Draw a diagram to show how the electrons are arranged in a single sulfur atom.

[1 mark]

3 Magnesium is found in group 2 and period 3 of the periodic table. *(Grade 6-7)*

(a) Explain how you could use this information to deduce the electronic structure of magnesium.

[3 marks]

(b) Give the electronic structure of magnesium.

[1 mark]

Ions

Ions crop up all over the place in chemistry. You have to be able to explain <u>how</u> they form and predict the <u>charges</u> of simple ions formed by elements in <u>Groups 1-3</u> and <u>Groups 5-7</u>.

Simple Ions Form When Atoms Lose or Gain Electrons

1) <u>Ions</u> are <u>charged</u> particles — they can be <u>single atoms</u> (e.g. Na^+) or <u>groups of atoms</u> (e.g. NO_3^-).

2) <u>Negative ions</u> (anions) form when atoms <u>gain electrons</u> — they have more electrons than protons. <u>Positive ions</u> (cations) form when atoms <u>lose electrons</u> — they have more protons than electrons.

3) The <u>number</u> of electrons lost or gained is the same as the <u>charge</u> on the ion. E.g. If 2 electrons are <u>lost</u> the charge is 2+. If 3 electrons are <u>gained</u> the charge is 3−.

You calculate the number of protons and neutrons in an ion in the same way as for an atom (see page 10).

You Can Predict the Ions Formed From the Group Number

1) <u>Group 1, 2 and 3 elements</u> are <u>metals</u>. They <u>lose</u> electrons to form <u>positive ions</u>.

2) <u>Group 5, 6 and 7 elements</u> are <u>non-metals</u>. They <u>gain</u> electrons to form <u>negative ions</u>.

3) Elements in the same <u>group</u> all have the same number of <u>electrons</u> in their <u>outer shell</u>. So they can all <u>lose or gain</u> the same number of outer electrons. And this means that they form ions with the <u>same charge</u>.

4) You <u>don't</u> have to <u>remember</u> what ions <u>most elements</u> form — you just look at the periodic table.

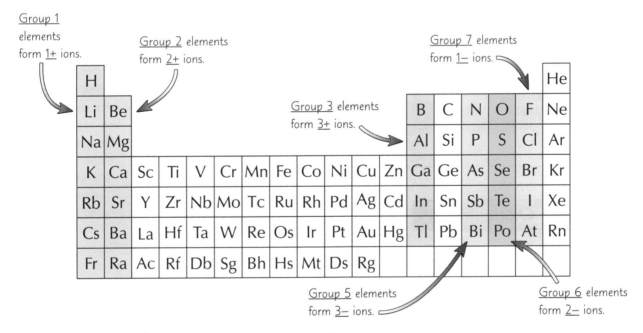

5) Here are some trickier ions that you just have to <u>learn</u>:

Ag^+	Fe^{2+}	Pb^{2+}	Hydrogen: H^+	Ammonium: NH_4^+	Nitrate: NO_3^-
Cu^{2+}	Fe^{3+}	Zn^{2+}	Hydroxide: OH^-	Carbonate: CO_3^{2-}	Sulfate: SO_4^{2-}

You can usually use the periodic table to predict ion charges...

...but not always. For the ions shown in the box above, you'll just have to learn them, or use your knowledge of an ionic compound that they form to work them out — see page 32 for more.

Ionic Bonding

Time to find out how particles bond together to form compounds. There are a few types of <u>bonding</u> that you need to know about — they're covered in the rest of this section. First up, <u>ionic bonding</u>...

Transfer of Electrons Produces an Ionic Compound

1) Most of the time, when a <u>metal</u> reacts with a <u>non-metal</u> (such as when a Group 1 metal reacts with a Group 7 element), the <u>metal atom loses</u> electrons to form a <u>positive ion</u> (cation) and the <u>non-metal gains these electrons</u> to form a <u>negative ion</u> (anion).

2) These oppositely charged ions are <u>strongly attracted</u> to one another by <u>electrostatic attractions</u>.

3) This attraction is called an <u>ionic bond</u>.

Ionic Compounds All Form in a Similar Way

You can use '<u>dot and cross</u>' diagrams to show what happens to the electrons when <u>ionic bonding</u> happens:

Sodium Chloride (NaCl)

1) The <u>sodium</u> atom gives up its outer electron, becoming an Na^+ ion.

2) The <u>chlorine</u> atom picks up the electron, becoming a Cl^- (<u>chloride</u>) ion.

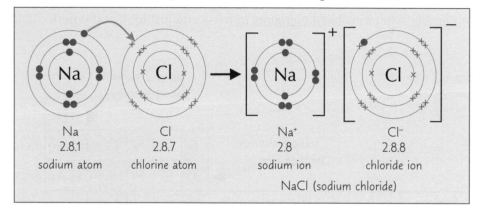

| Na
2.8.1
sodium atom | Cl
2.8.7
chlorine atom | Na⁺
2.8
sodium ion | Cl⁻
2.8.8
chloride ion |

NaCl (sodium chloride)

In these examples, the dots represent the electrons from one of the atoms and the crosses represent the electrons from the other. (All electrons are really identical, but this is a good way of following their movement.)

Magnesium Oxide (MgO)

1) The <u>magnesium</u> atom gives up its <u>two</u> outer electrons, becoming an Mg^{2+} ion.

2) The <u>oxygen</u> atom picks up the electrons, becoming an O^{2-} (<u>oxide</u>) ion.

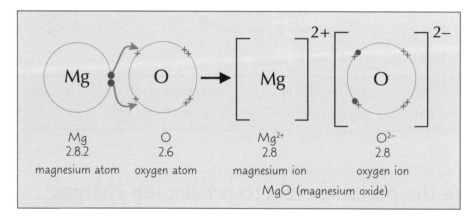

| Mg
2.8.2
magnesium atom | O
2.6
oxygen atom | Mg²⁺
2.8
magnesium ion | O²⁻
2.8
oxygen ion |

MgO (magnesium oxide)

Ionic Bonding

Aluminium Chloride ($AlCl_3$)

1) The <u>aluminium</u> atom gives up its <u>three</u> outer electrons, becoming an $\underline{Al^{3+}}$ ion.
2) The <u>chlorine</u> atoms pick up the three electrons, becoming <u>three Cl^-</u> ions.

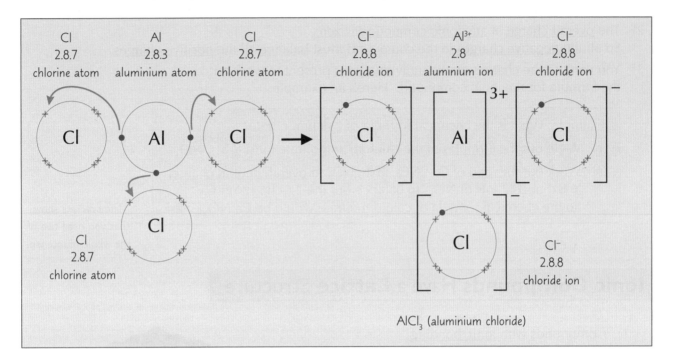

You only need to draw the outer shells of electrons in dot and cross diagrams.

Sodium Oxide (Na_2O)

1) Two <u>sodium</u> atoms each give up their outer electrons, becoming <u>two Na^+</u> ions.
2) The <u>oxygen</u> atom picks up the <u>two</u> electrons, becoming an $\underline{O^{2-}}$ ion.

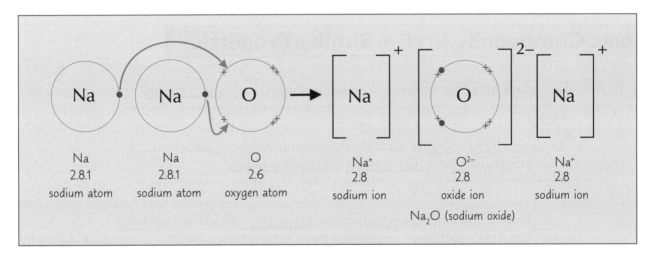

Transferring electrons from one atom to another creates ions

<u>Metals</u> tend to <u>lose electrons</u> to form <u>positively charged ions</u>, and <u>non-metals</u> tend to <u>gain these electrons</u> to form <u>negatively charged ions</u>. Make sure you can describe how different ionic compounds are formed using both <u>words</u> and <u>dot and cross diagrams</u>. It does get much easier with <u>practice</u>, I promise...

Ionic Compounds

An ionic compound is any compound that only contains ionic bonds. You need to know how to work out the formula of an ionic compound — handily, there's some information on how to do that coming up...

You Can Work Out the Formula of an Ionic Compound

1) Ionic compounds are made up of a positively charged part and a negatively charged part.

2) The overall charge of any ionic compound is zero.
So all the negative charges in the compound must balance all the positive charges.

3) You can use the charges on the individual ions present to work out the formula for the ionic compound. Here's an example:

> Example: What is the chemical formula of calcium nitrate?
>
> 1) Write out the formulas of the calcium and nitrate ions: Ca^{2+}, NO_3^-
>
> 2) Work out the ratio of Ca : NO_3 that gives an overall neutral charge.
> You'd need 2 lots of NO_3^- to balance out the 2+ charge on Ca^{2+}.
> So the chemical formula of calcium nitrate would be $Ca(NO_3)_2$.

The brackets show that you need two of the whole nitrate ion.

Ionic Compounds Have a Lattice Structure

1) Compounds with ionic bonding always have giant ionic structures.

2) The ions are held together in a closely packed 3D lattice arrangement by the attraction between oppositely charged ions.

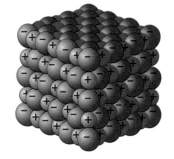

Ionic Compounds All Have Similar Properties

1) The electrostatic attraction between oppositely charged ions is very strong.

2) Because a lot of energy is needed to overcome the strong attraction, ionic compounds have high melting and boiling points.

3) Ionic compounds are not electrical conductors when they are solid.
But if you melt them, or dissolve them in water, they are able to conduct electricity.

Ionic compounds form a giant lattice structure

As long as you can find the charge of the ions in an ionic compound, you can work out the formula of the compound. Try thinking of a few different positive and negative ions and how they might combine together to make ionic compounds using the method shown in the example above.

Warm-Up & Exam Questions

That's all things ionic wrapped up (for now at least). Try your hand at these questions to make sure you've understood everything that's been covered over the previous few pages.

Warm-Up Questions

1) An ion is formed from a Group 2 element. What charge will the ion have?
2) An ion is formed from a Group 6 element. What charge will the ion have?
3) Give the chemical formula of the ionic compound sodium sulfate.

Exam Questions

1   Potassium chloride (KCl) is an ionic compound
    containing potassium ions bonded to chloride ions.

(a)   Describe the bonding between the potassium ions and chloride ions in potassium chloride.

[2 marks]

(b)   (i) Potassium is in Group 1. Deduce the formula of a potassium ion.

[1 mark]

      (ii) Chlorine is in Group 7. Deduce the formula of a chloride ion.

[1 mark]

2   The diagram below shows the ions in an ionic compound. All of the electrons are shown.

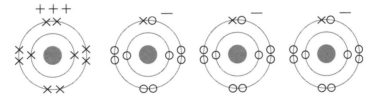

    Identify the positive and negative ions in this compound.

[2 marks]

3   A student reacts magnesium nitrate with potassium hydroxide.
    The products of the reaction are magnesium hydroxide and potassium nitrate.

    Write the chemical formulae of magnesium hydroxide and potassium nitrate.

[2 marks]

4   Sodium chloride is an ionic compound.

(a)   Describe the structure of a crystal of sodium chloride. You should state:
      • What particles are present in the crystal.
      • How these particles are arranged.
      • What holds the particles together.

[4 marks]

(b)   Explain why sodium chloride has a high melting point.

[2 marks]

Covalent Bonding

Ionic bonding (see p.30-31) isn't the only type you need to know about — there's <u>covalent bonding</u> too.

Covalent Substances Contain Shared Pairs of Electrons

1) Sometimes atoms make <u>covalent bonds</u> by <u>sharing</u> pairs of electrons with other atoms.

2) Each <u>covalent bond</u> provides one <u>extra</u> shared electron for each atom.

3) In covalent bonding, there's a strong <u>electrostatic attraction</u> between the negatively charged <u>shared electrons</u> (the bonding pair) and the positively charged <u>nuclei</u> of the atoms involved.

An electrostatic attraction is when two (or more) oppositely charged particles are attracted to each other.

Learn These Important Examples:

Hydrogen, H_2

A hydrogen atom has <u>one electron</u> in its outer shell. It can only fit <u>one more</u> electron in that shell...

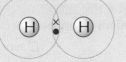   OR   H—H   OR   H $\overset{\times}{\underset{\bullet}{}}$ H

...so hydrogen atoms can form <u>one covalent bond</u>.

Chlorine, Cl_2

A chlorine atom has <u>seven electrons</u> in its outer shell. It can only fit <u>one more</u> electron in that shell...

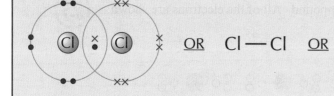   OR   Cl—Cl   OR

...so chlorine atoms also form <u>one covalent bond</u>.

Hydrogen chloride, HCl

This is very <u>similar</u> to H_2 and Cl_2.

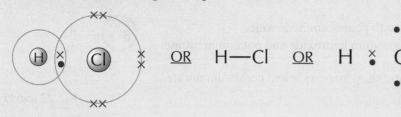   OR   H—Cl   OR

Each atom can only fit <u>one more electron</u> in its outer shell — so they form <u>one covalent bond</u>.

Ammonia, NH_3

A nitrogen atom has <u>five electrons</u> in its outer shell. It can only fit <u>three more</u> electrons in that shell...

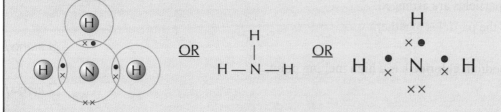

OR

```
    H
    |
H — N — H
```

OR

...so in ammonia, it forms <u>three covalent bonds</u> — one each with three hydrogen atoms.

Covalent Bonding

Nitrogen, N₂

Again, a nitrogen atom can only fit <u>three more electrons</u> in its outer shell...

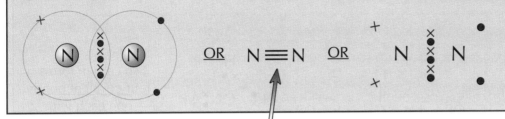

...so <u>two nitrogen atoms</u> can share <u>three pairs of electrons</u>. This creates a <u>triple covalent bond</u>.

This is the <u>displayed formula</u> of a molecule of nitrogen (see page 118 for more).

Oxygen, O₂

An oxygen atom has <u>six electrons</u> in its outer shell. It can fit <u>two more</u> electrons in that shell...

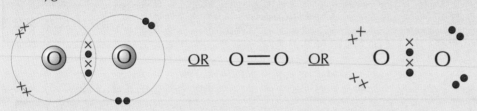

...so in <u>oxygen gas</u>, two oxygen atoms share <u>two pairs</u> of electrons to form a <u>double covalent bond</u>.

Water, H₂O

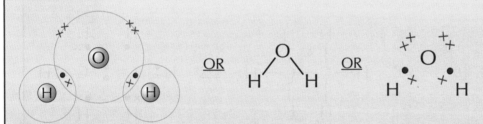

In <u>water molecules</u>, two hydrogen atoms each share a pair of electrons with an oxygen atom to form <u>two covalent bonds</u>.

Methane, CH₄

A carbon atom has <u>four electrons</u> in its outer shell. It can fit <u>four more</u> electrons in that shell...

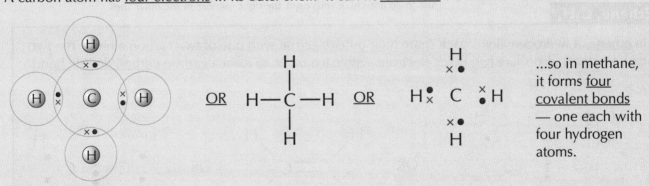

...so in methane, it forms <u>four covalent bonds</u> — one each with four hydrogen atoms.

Carbon dioxide, CO₂

In <u>carbon dioxide</u>, two oxygen atoms each share two pairs of electrons with a carbon atom.

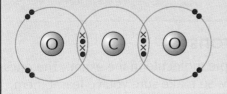 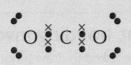

This forms two <u>double covalent bonds</u>.

Covalent Bonding

Chloromethane, CH₃Cl

This is very similar to CH₄. Like an H atom, a <u>Cl atom</u> can only fit <u>one more electron</u> in its <u>outer shell</u>...

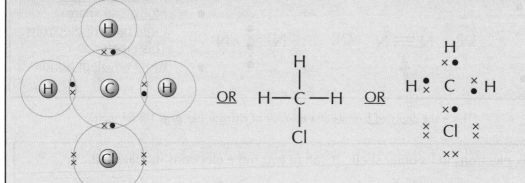

...so carbon forms <u>four covalent bonds</u> — one each with <u>three hydrogen</u> atoms and <u>one</u> with a <u>chlorine</u> atom.

Ethane, C₂H₆

In <u>ethane</u>, 6 <u>hydrogen</u> atoms each share their outer electron with one of two carbon atoms. The two carbon atoms also share <u>one</u> outer electron with <u>each other</u>, to form a <u>single covalent bond</u>.

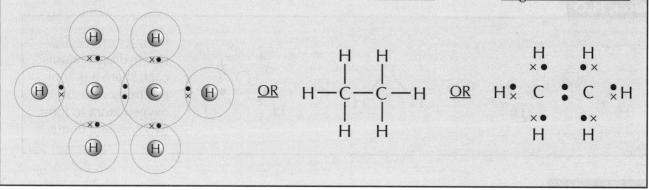

When you've drawn a dot and cross diagram, it's a good idea to count up the number of electrons, just to double-check you've got the right number in the outer shell.

Ethene, C₂H₄

In <u>ethene</u>, 4 hydrogen atoms each share their outer electron with one of two carbon atoms. The two carbon atoms also share <u>two</u> outer electrons with each other, to form a <u>carbon-carbon double bond</u>.

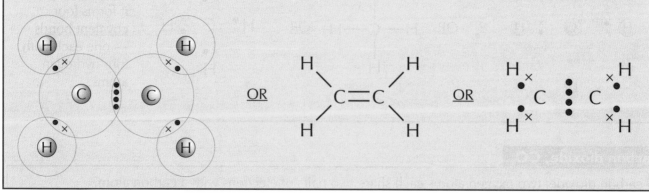

Covalent bonding involves sharing electrons

EXAM TIP You could be asked to draw a dot and cross diagram for a simple molecule in the exam. The ones on pages 34-36 are important examples that you need to know, so make sure you've learnt them.

Simple Molecular Substances

When a few atoms are joined together by covalent bonds, you get a molecule. Substances that are made up of molecules are called simple molecular substances. Which seems sensible...

The Forces of Attraction Between Simple Molecules are Weak

1) The atoms within a molecule are held together by very strong covalent bonds.

2) By contrast, the forces of attraction between the molecules are very weak.

Weak intermolecular forces

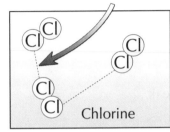
Chlorine

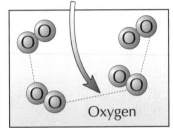
Oxygen

3) The result of these feeble intermolecular forces is that the melting and boiling points are very low, because the molecules are easily separated.

4) In general, intermolecular forces are stronger between molecules with a high relative molecular mass (M_r) than between smaller molecules. This is because there are more points along the larger molecules for intermolecular forces to act between them, so more energy is needed to break the forces.

The M_r of a molecule is a measure of how big it is.

5) Due to the increasing strength of the forces, the melting and boiling points of simple molecular substances increase as the relative molecular mass increases.

6) Most molecular substances are gases or liquids at room temperature. You can usually spot one just by its physical state — it'll either be a liquid or gas or an easily melted solid.

Simple molecular substance = low melting and boiling point...

The examiners might give you information about the properties of a substance and ask you to work out what kind of substance it is. Make sure you know the typical properties of different types of substances and you'll be able to answer these questions with ease — for starters, if a substance has a low melting or boiling point, you can be pretty sure it is simple molecular.

Giant Covalent Structures and Fullerenes

Simple molecular substances aren't the only compounds held together by covalent bonds. <u>Giant covalent structures</u> and <u>fullerenes</u> are too. This page covers some examples you need to know about for the <u>exam</u>.

Most **Giant Covalent** Structures Have Certain Properties

1) Giant covalent structures are similar to giant ionic structures (p.32) except there are <u>no charged ions</u>.
2) <u>All</u> the atoms are <u>bonded</u> to <u>each other</u> by <u>strong</u> covalent bonds.
3) There are <u>lots</u> of these bonds which means it takes a <u>lot of energy</u> to break them, so giant covalent structures are solids with <u>very high melting</u> and <u>boiling points</u>.
4) They <u>don't conduct electricity</u> — not even when <u>molten</u> (except for graphite that is — see below).
5) They're usually <u>insoluble</u> in water.
6) Important examples are <u>diamond</u> and <u>graphite</u>, which are made only from <u>carbon atoms</u>.

Diamond is Very **Hard**

1) Diamond is made up of a network of carbon atoms that each form <u>four covalent bonds</u>.
2) The <u>strong covalent bonds</u> take lots of energy to break, so diamond has a <u>high melting point</u>.
3) The strong covalent bonds also hold the atoms in a very <u>rigid lattice structure</u>, making diamond <u>really hard</u>.
4) It <u>doesn't conduct electricity</u> because it has <u>no free electrons</u> or <u>ions</u>.

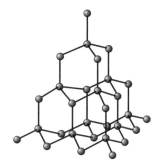

Graphite Contains **Sheets** of **Hexagons**

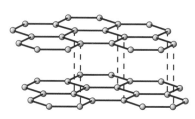

1) In graphite, each carbon atom only forms <u>three covalent bonds</u>, creating <u>layers</u> of <u>carbon atoms</u>.
2) The layers are only held together <u>weakly</u> by <u>intermolecular forces</u>, so are free to slide over each other. This makes graphite <u>soft</u> and <u>slippery</u>.
3) Graphite's got a <u>high melting point</u> — the covalent bonds in the layers need <u>loads of energy</u> to break.
4) Only <u>three</u> out of each carbon's four outer electrons are used in bonds, so each carbon atom has <u>one</u> electron that's <u>delocalised</u> (free) and can move. So graphite is a non-metal that <u>conducts electricity</u>.

C_{60} **Fullerene** is a **Simple Molecular Substance**

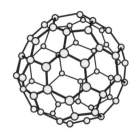

1) C_{60} <u>fullerene</u> molecules are <u>hollow spheres</u> made up of <u>60 carbon atoms</u>.
2) Unlike diamond and graphite, C_{60} <u>isn't</u> a giant covalent structure — it's just made up of <u>large covalent molecules</u>.
3) The C_{60} molecules are only held together by <u>intermolecular forces</u> and so they can <u>slide</u> over each other. This means the material is <u>soft</u>.
4) Like graphite, each carbon in C_{60} fullerene has <u>one delocalised electron</u>. However, the electrons can't move <u>between</u> the molecules, so C_{60} fullerene is a <u>poor conductor</u> of <u>electricity</u>.

C_{60} molecules are large, so the intermolecular forces between the molecules are relatively strong. This means C_{60} fullerene is a solid at room temperature.

Diamond, graphite and C_{60} fullerene contain exactly the same atoms

The different substances on this page are made <u>purely</u> from carbon — there's no difference at all in their atoms. The difference in their properties is all down to the way that the atoms are <u>held together</u>.

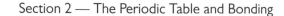

Electrical Conductivity and Metals

Metals are pretty good conductors of electricity — it's all about the <u>movement</u> of electrons or ions.

Electric Current is a Flow of Electrons or Ions

1) <u>Electrons</u> have a <u>negative</u> charge. <u>Ions</u> can have either a <u>negative</u> or a <u>positive</u> charge.
2) When electrons or ions <u>move</u>, they can cause the material they're in to <u>conduct electricity</u>.
3) The electric current is the <u>flow</u> of the electrons or ions.

Molten and Dissolved Ionic Compounds Conduct Electricity

1) Ionic compounds are made of a <u>lattice</u> of <u>positive and negative ions</u> (more on this on pages 29-32).
2) <u>Solid</u> ionic compounds <u>don't</u> conduct electricity because the ions <u>aren't</u> able to move around.
3) When an ionic compound is <u>dissolved</u> the ions separate and are <u>able to move</u> in the <u>solution</u>. This means that the compound will <u>conduct electricity</u>.
4) When an ionic compound <u>melts</u>, the ions are also <u>able to move</u> so the compound can <u>conduct electricity</u>.

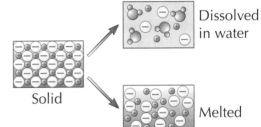

Dissolved in water

Solid

Melted

Covalent compounds don't have any charged particles that are able to move, so they can't conduct electricity (except for graphite — see previous page.)

Metals are Held Together by Metallic Bonding

1) Metals have a <u>giant structure</u> of <u>positive ions</u> surrounded by a <u>sea of delocalised electrons</u>.
2) The <u>electrostatic attraction</u> between the nuclei of the positive ions and the electrons is called <u>metallic bonding</u>.
3) It's this metallic bonding which gives metals their <u>properties</u>.

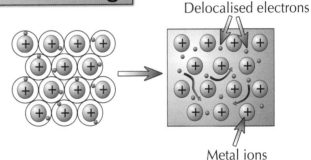

Delocalised electrons

Metal ions

Metals are Good Conductors of Electricity and Heat

1) The <u>delocalised electrons</u> are able to <u>move</u> through the structure. This means metals can conduct <u>electricity</u>.
2) The movement of electrons also means <u>energy</u> can be transferred quickly through the material, so metals are good conductors of <u>heat</u>.

Delocalised electrons are also known as free electrons.

Most Metals are Malleable

1) The layers of ions in a metal can <u>slide</u> over each other, making metals <u>malleable</u>.
2) This means that they can be <u>hammered</u> or <u>rolled</u> into <u>flat sheets</u>.

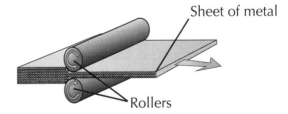

Sheet of metal

Rollers

Metallic bonding is what makes metals, well... metals

<u>Delocalised electrons</u> allow metals to be <u>good conductors</u> of <u>electricity</u> and <u>heat</u>, and be <u>malleable</u> as well. As with all these properties, you'll need to be able to explain why this is the case too...

Paper 2

Warm-Up & Exam Questions

Covalent bonding is a mega-important topic. Test your understanding by doing these questions.

Warm-Up Questions

1) How many double covalent bonds are there in one molecule of carbon dioxide?

2) Why does chlorine have a very low melting point?

Exam Questions

1 The table on the right shows the properties of four substances.

Which substance could be silicon dioxide, a giant covalent substance? Explain your answer.

[2 marks]

Substance	Melting Point (°C)	Conducts electricity when liquid?
A	−102	no
B	1085	yes
C	993	yes
D	1650	no

PAPER 2

2 Metals are held together by metallic bonding.

(a) Draw a labelled diagram to show how the metal ions and the electrons that take part in bonding are arranged in a metal.

[3 marks]

(b) Metals are good conductors of electricity and most are malleable. Explain how the structure you drew in part a) gives metals these properties.

[2 marks]

3 Dot and cross diagrams show the position of electrons in covalent molecules.

(a) Draw dot and cross diagrams for hydrogen chloride (HCl), oxygen (O_2) and ammonia (NH_3). Only show the outer electrons.

[3 marks]

(b) Explain how the atoms are held together in a molecule of hydrogen chloride.

[2 marks]

4 Three different carbon structures, **A**, **B** and **C**, are shown below.

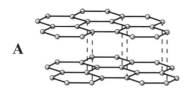 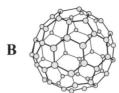 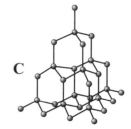

(a) Name each of the structures labelled **A - C**.

[3 marks]

(b) Explain how the bonding in structures **A** and **C** affects their electrical conductivity and hardness.

[4 marks]

(c) When a substance sublimes, it turns directly from a solid into a gas. If a sample of **A** and a sample of **B** were both sublimed, explain why **B** would sublime at a lower temperature than **A**.

[3 marks]

Revision Summary for Section 2

And that's it for Section 2 — time to put yourself to the test and find out how much you really know.
- Try these questions and tick off each one when you get it right.
- When you've done all the questions under a heading and are completely happy with it, tick it off.

The Periodic Table and Electron Shells (p.24-27) ☑
1) What feature of atoms determines the order of the modern periodic table?
2) How many electrons are in the outer shell of an atom of a Group 7 element?
3) How you would work out the electronic configuration of an atom, given its atomic number?
4) Are the elements in Group 1 metals or non-metals?

Ionic Bonding and Compounds (p.29-32) ☑
5) What type of ion do elements from each of the following groups form?
   a) Group 1
   b) Group 7
6) Describe the process of ionic bonding.
7) Draw a dot and cross diagram to show the bonding in:
   a) sodium chloride (NaCl),
   b) magnesium oxide (MgO).
8) State three properties of ionic compounds.

Covalent Bonding and Compounds (p.34-38) ☑
9) What is covalent bonding?
10) Sketch dot and cross diagrams showing the bonding in molecules of:
   a) hydrogen,
   b) water,
   c) carbon dioxide,
   d) ethene.
11) a) Describe one property of simple molecular substances.
   b) Explain how the bonding in simple molecular substances causes this property.
12) Explain why C_{60} fullerene is a poor conductor of electricity.

Electrical Conductivity and Metals (p.39) ☑
13) Explain why ionic compounds only conduct electricity when molten or in solution.
14) What is metallic bonding?
15) List two properties of metals.

Balancing Equations

Equations crop up <u>everywhere</u> in chemistry — you can't hide from them. They show you just what's happening in a chemical reaction — what <u>reacts together</u> and what's <u>formed</u>.

Equations Show the Reactants and Products of a Reaction

1) A chemical reaction can be described as the process of going from <u>reactants</u> to <u>products</u>.

2) You can write <u>word equations</u> or <u>symbol equations</u> to show any chemical reaction.

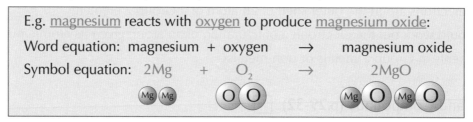

E.g. <u>magnesium</u> reacts with <u>oxygen</u> to produce <u>magnesium oxide</u>:

Word equation:　magnesium　+　oxygen　　→　　magnesium oxide

Symbol equation:　　$2Mg$　　+　　O_2　　→　　$2MgO$

3) <u>Look out for state symbols</u> in equations — they tell you what <u>physical state</u> the reactants and products are in:

See page 1 for more on states.

(s) — Solid　　　(l) — Liquid　　　(g) — Gas　　　(aq) — Aqueous (dissolved in water)

Here's the example including state symbols: $2Mg(s) + O_2(g) \rightarrow 2MgO(s)$

So, this is solid magnesium reacting with oxygen gas to make solid magnesium oxide.

Symbol Equations Need to be Balanced

1) There must always be the <u>same</u> number of atoms of each element on <u>both sides</u> of the equation — atoms can't just <u>disappear</u>.

2) You <u>balance</u> the equation by putting numbers <u>in front</u> of the formulas where needed. Take this equation for reacting sulfuric acid with sodium hydroxide:

$$H_2SO_4 + NaOH \rightarrow Na_2SO_4 + H_2O$$

3) The <u>formulas</u> are all correct but the numbers of some atoms <u>don't match up</u> on both sides.

4) You <u>can't change formulas</u> like H_2SO_4 to H_2SO_5. You can only put numbers <u>in front of them</u>.

5) The more you <u>practise</u>, the <u>quicker</u> you get, but all you do is this:

- Find an element that <u>doesn't balance</u> and <u>pencil in a number</u> to try and sort it out.
- <u>See where it gets you</u>. It may create <u>another imbalance</u>, but if so, pencil in <u>another number</u> and see where that gets you.
- Carry on chasing <u>unbalanced</u> elements and it'll <u>sort itself out</u> pretty quickly.

In the equation above you soon notice we're short of H atoms on the RHS (right-hand side).

1) The only thing you can do about that is make it $2H_2O$ instead of just H_2O:

$$H_2SO_4 + NaOH \rightarrow Na_2SO_4 + 2H_2O$$

2) But that now gives too many H atoms and O atoms on the RHS, so to balance that up you could try putting a 2 in front of the NaOH on the LHS (left-hand side):

$$H_2SO_4 + 2NaOH \rightarrow Na_2SO_4 + 2H_2O$$

Putting a 2 in front of the NaOH has sorted out the Na atoms too.

3) And suddenly there it is. <u>Everything balances</u>.

Balancing equations is all about practice

Remember, you can't balance equations by changing the formulas, only by putting numbers in front of them.

Relative Formula Mass

When it comes to chemistry, you've sometimes got to do a little bit of <u>maths</u>.

You can Calculate the **Relative Formula Mass** of a Compound

1) If you have a compound like MgCl$_2$ then it has a <u>relative formula mass</u>, M_r, which is just all the relative atomic masses (A_r) of the atoms it contains <u>added together</u>.

Look back at page 12 for more about relative atomic masses.

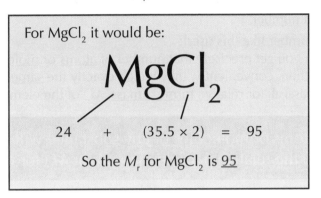

For MgCl$_2$ it would be:

$$MgCl_2$$

$$24 + (35.5 \times 2) = 95$$

So the M_r for MgCl$_2$ is <u>95</u>

2) You can easily get the A_r for any element from the <u>periodic table</u>. In the exam you'll be given a periodic table so you can look them up.

3) Here are a couple more examples for you:

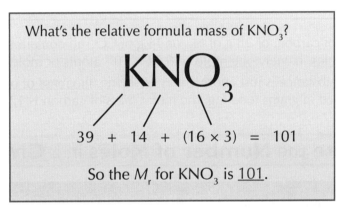

What's the relative formula mass of KNO$_3$?

$$KNO_3$$

$$39 + 14 + (16 \times 3) = 101$$

So the M_r for KNO$_3$ is <u>101</u>.

If you're asked to work out the relative molecular mass (RMM) of a compound, just use the same method as for relative formula mass.

Find the relative formula mass for the alcohol C$_2$H$_4$(OH)$_2$, using the given data:

A_r for C = 12 A_r for H = 1 A_r for O = 16

$$C_2H_4(OH)_2$$

The brackets and the little 2 around the OH just means that there are two lots of OH.

$$(12 \times 2) + (1 \times 4) + [(16 + 1) \times 2] = 62$$

So the relative formula mass for C$_2$H$_4$(OH)$_2$ is <u>62</u>.

Relative formula mass is the sum of the relative atomic masses

That's <u>all there is to it</u>. It might have a fancy name and symbol, but all it really means is "add up all the relative atomic masses". If you want some <u>extra practice</u>, flick through this book and pick out some <u>compounds</u>. Then grab a periodic table and calculate the <u>relative formula masses</u> for each.

Moles

The mole might seem a bit confusing. But don't be put off by the funny word, it's not that hard really...

"The Mole" is Simply the Unit for the Amount of a Substance

1) Just like "a million" is this many: 1 000 000; or "a billion" is this many: 1 000 000 000, so "a mole" is this many: <u>602 000 000 000 000 000 000 000</u> or <u>6.02×10^{23}</u>. And that's <u>all</u> it is. Just a <u>number</u>.

2) So why is such a long number like this used?
   The answer is that when you get precisely that number of <u>atoms</u> or <u>molecules</u>, of any element or compound, then, conveniently, they weigh exactly the <u>same</u> number of grams as the <u>relative atomic mass</u>, A_r (or <u>relative formula mass</u>, M_r) of the element or compound.

> One mole of atoms or molecules of any substance will have a mass in grams equal to the relative particle mass (A_r or M_r) for that substance.

Examples:

- Carbon has an A_r of 12.   So one mole of carbon weighs exactly 12 g.
- Nitrogen gas, N_2, has an M_r of 28 (2×14).   So one mole of N_2 weighs exactly 28 g.
- Carbon dioxide, CO_2, has an M_r of 44.   So one mole of CO_2 weighs exactly 44 g.

3) This means that 12 g of carbon, or 28 g of N_2, or 44 g of CO_2, all contain the <u>same number of particles</u>, namely <u>one mole</u> or 6.02×10^{23} atoms or molecules.

4) The <u>molar mass</u> of a substance is just another way of saying '<u>the mass of one mole</u>'. Molar mass is measured in <u>grams</u> too. E.g. the molar mass of carbon is <u>12 g</u>.

You can Calculate the Number of Moles in a Given Mass:

$$\text{Number of Moles} = \frac{\text{Mass in g (of element or compound)}}{M_r \text{ (of element or compound)}}$$

> E.g. how many moles are there in 66 g of carbon dioxide?
> <u>Method:</u> M_r of CO_2 = 12 + (16 × 2) = 44
>   No. of moles = Mass (g) ÷ M_r = 66 ÷ 44 = 1.5 moles.

1) You may need to <u>rearrange</u> the equation to find the mass of a certain number of moles.

2) Putting an equation into a <u>formula triangle</u> makes rearranging equations straightforward. Here's the formula triangle that links moles, mass and relative formula mass.

3) To use a formula triangle, just cover the thing you want to find, and you're left with the expression you need to calculate it. The <u>line</u> through the triangle stands for <u>division</u>.

You need to be able to convert between moles and grams

Take some time to get your head round all of this. Write out the formula and the formula triangle on this page until you know them by heart. Then do it again later, to make sure it's really sunk in.

Calculating Masses in Reactions

This page covers a few more calculations. First up — how to use moles to work out <u>reacting masses</u>.

You can Calculate the Amount of **Product** from a **Mass** of **Reactant**

You can use a <u>balanced chemical equation</u> to work out the <u>mass of product formed</u> from a given <u>mass of a reactant</u>. Here's how...

1) Write out the <u>balanced equation</u>.
2) <u>Work out relative formula masses</u> (M_r) of the reactant and product you're interested in.
3) Find out <u>how many moles</u> there are of the substance you <u>know</u> the mass of.
4) Use the balanced equation to work out <u>how many moles</u> there'll be of the <u>other</u> substance (i.e. how many moles of product will be made by this many moles of reactant).
5) Use the number of moles to calculate the <u>mass</u>.

Don't worry — these steps should all make sense when you look at the example below.

<u>Example:</u> What mass of magnesium oxide is produced when 60 g of magnesium is burnt in air?

1) Write out the <u>balanced equation</u>: $2Mg + O_2 \rightarrow 2MgO$

2) Work out the <u>relative formula masses</u> of the reactants and products you're interested in:
Mg: 24   MgO: 24 + 16 = 40

3) <u>Calculate the number of moles</u> of magnesium in 60 g:
moles = mass ÷ M_r = 60 ÷ 24 = 2.5

In this reaction, O_2 is in excess. This means that there is more O_2 available to react than there is Mg. So, it's the amount of Mg that determines how much MgO is made.

4) Look at the <u>ratio</u> of moles in the equation —
2 moles of Mg react to produce 2 moles of MgO.
So 2.5 moles of Mg will react to produce 2.5 moles of MgO.

5) <u>Calculate the mass</u> of 2.5 moles of magnesium oxide: mass = moles × M_r = 2.5 × 40 = 100

This tells you that <u>60 g of magnesium</u> will produce <u>100 g of magnesium oxide</u>. If the question had said, "<u>find how much magnesium</u> gives 500 g of magnesium oxide", you'd calculate the number of moles of magnesium oxide first, because that's the one you'd have the information about.

The mass of product (in this case magnesium oxide) is called the <u>yield</u> of a reaction.
Masses you calculate in this way are called <u>theoretical yields</u>. In practice you never get
100% of the yield, so the amount of product you get will be <u>less</u> than you calculated.

Percentage Yield Compares **Actual** and **Theoretical** Yield

The more reactant you start with, the higher the <u>yield</u> will be — that's pretty obvious.
But the <u>percentage yield</u> doesn't depend on the <u>amount</u> of reactants you started with — it's a <u>percentage</u>.

1) The <u>theoretical yield</u> of a reaction can be calculated from the <u>balanced equation</u> (see above).
2) Percentage yield is given by the formula:

$$\text{percentage yield} = \frac{\text{actual yield (grams)}}{\text{theoretical yield (grams)}} \times 100$$

3) Percentage yield is <u>always</u> somewhere between 0 and 100%.
4) A 100% yield means that you got <u>all</u> the product you expected to get.
5) A 0% yield means that <u>no</u> reactants were converted into product, i.e. no product at all was <u>made</u>.

Warm-Up & Exam Questions

There's been a lot of equations and numbers over last few pages. It's easy to get in a muddle with these kind of things, so use this handy page of questions to get some practice in.

Warm-Up Questions

1) Which state symbol is used to show that a species in a reaction equation is a solid?
2) Balance the following equation: $Zn(OH)_2 + 2HCl \rightarrow ZnCl_2 + H_2O$
3) Calculate the relative formula mass of sodium hydrogen carbonate ($NaHCO_3$).
4) What is the mass of one mole of sodium?
5) The M_r of H_2O is 18. Calculate the number of moles in 54 g of H_2O.
6) Give the formula for calculating percentage yield.

Exam Questions

1   Methane (CH_4) burns in oxygen (O_2) to make carbon dioxide (CO_2) and water (H_2O).

    (a)   Write a word equation for this reaction.

[1 mark]

    (b)   Write a **balanced** chemical equation for this reaction.

[2 marks]

2   A pharmacist is synthesising aspirin ($C_9H_8O_4$) as part of a drugs trial.
After the experiment, the pharmacist calculates that she has made 12.4 moles of aspirin.

What mass of aspirin has the pharmacist made? Give your answer in grams.
The relative atomic mass, A_r, of C = 12, of H = 1 and of O = 16.

[2 marks]

3   In a reaction between magnesium and oxygen, 3.52 kg of magnesium oxide is formed.
The equation for the reaction is: $2Mg + O_2 \rightarrow 2MgO$

Calculate the number of moles of magnesium oxide formed in this reaction.

[3 marks]

4   Aluminium and iron oxide (Fe_2O_3) react to produce aluminium oxide (Al_2O_3) and iron.
The equation for the reaction is: $2Al + Fe_2O_3 \rightarrow Al_2O_3 + 2Fe$

    (a)   What is the maximum mass of iron, in g, that can be produced from 20 g of iron oxide?

[3 marks]

    (b)   What is the maximum mass of aluminium, in kg, that will react with 32.0 kg of iron oxide?

[2 marks]

5   When heated, calcium carbonate decomposes to form calcium oxide and carbon dioxide.
The equation for the reaction is: $CaCO_3 \rightarrow CaO + CO_2$

In an industrial reaction, 68.00 kg of calcium carbonate decomposed to form
28.56 kg of calcium oxide, CaO. Calculate the percentage yield of calcium oxide.

[5 marks]

Empirical and Molecular Formulae

This isn't as complicated as it sounds. Just follow the same <u>method</u> every time and you'll be laughing.

Finding the **Empirical Formula** (from Masses or Percentages)

1) The empirical formula gives you the <u>smallest whole number ratio</u> of atoms in a compound.
2) Here's a <u>stepwise method</u> for calculating an empirical formula:

> 1) <u>List all the elements</u> in the compound.
> 2) <u>Underneath them</u>, write their <u>experimental masses</u>.
> 3) Find the number of <u>moles</u> of each element by <u>dividing</u> each mass by the <u>relative atomic mass</u> (A_r) for that particular element.
> 4) Turn the numbers you get into <u>a nice simple ratio</u> by dividing by the <u>smallest</u> number of moles.
> 5) Get the ratio in its <u>simplest whole number form</u> — that's the empirical formula of the compound.

If the amounts of each element are in percentages, just divide each one by the A_r for that element. Then carry on with the method as normal.

> <u>Example:</u> In an experiment, some <u>iron oxide</u> powder is reduced to <u>pure metallic iron</u>.
> Use the following <u>experimental data</u> to find the <u>empirical formula</u> of the iron oxide used.
>
> | Mass of empty container | 32.0 g |
> |---|---|
> | Mass of container + mass of iron oxide | 96.0 g |
> | Mass of container + iron | 76.8 g |
>
> (A_r for iron = 56, A_r for oxygen = 16)
>
> <u>Method</u>:
> During the experiment <u>oxygen</u> is <u>lost</u>. The <u>mass of oxygen lost</u> is the difference between the mass of the container and iron oxide and the mass of the container and iron: 96.0 g – 76.8 g = 19.2 g.
> The <u>mass of iron made</u> is the difference between the mass of the container with the iron and the mass of the empty container: 76.8 g – 32.0 g = 44.8 g.
>
> | | | Fe | O |
> |---|---|---|---|
> | 1) | List the two elements: | | |
> | 2) | Write in the experimental masses: | 44.8 | 19.2 |
> | 3) | Find the number of moles of each element: | 44.8 ÷ 56 = 0.8 | 19.2 ÷ 16 = 1.2 |
> | 4) | Divide by the smallest number of moles: | 0.8 ÷ 0.8 = 1 | 1.2 ÷ 0.8 = 1.5 |
> | 5) | Multiply to get whole numbers: | 1 × 2 = 2 | 1.5 × 2 = 3 |
>
> *You don't have to multiply if you get whole numbers in step 4.*
>
> So the simplest formula is 2 atoms of Fe to 3 atoms of O, i.e. Fe_2O_3. And that's it done.

The **Empirical** and **Molecular Formulae** Won't Always **Match**

1) The <u>empirical formula</u> of a compound is the <u>simplest</u> formula that tells you the <u>ratio</u> of different elements in the compound.
2) This is different to the <u>molecular formula</u> of a compound, which tells you the <u>actual number</u> of atoms of each element in a single molecule.
3) <u>Molecular formulae</u> are <u>whole-number multiples</u> of empirical formulae.

> <u>Example</u>: A molecule has an empirical formula of $C_4H_3O_2$, and a relative molecular mass of 166. Work out its <u>molecular formula</u>.
>
> <u>Method</u>:
> 1) Find the <u>mass</u> of the <u>empirical formula</u>: $(4 \times 12) + (3 \times 1) + (2 \times 16) = 48 + 3 + 32 = 83$ g
> 2) The relative molecular mass is 166, so there are 166 ÷ 83 = <u>2 empirical units</u> in the molecule.
> 3) The molecular formula must be the empirical formula × 2, so the molecular formula must be $C_4H_3O_2 \times 2 = C_8H_6O_4$. So there you go.

PRACTICAL Finding Formulae Using Experiments

These next two pages are all about how to carry out <u>experiments</u> to determine the <u>empirical formula</u> of a compound. Firstly, here's how to do it using <u>combustion</u>...

You can Find Empirical Formulae Using Combustion

<u>Combustion</u> happens when a substance <u>reacts</u> with <u>oxygen</u> when it's burned in air.

Here's how you could use <u>combustion</u> to calculate the <u>empirical formula</u> of a metal oxide, e.g. magnesium oxide:

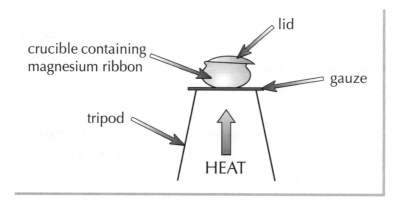

1) Get a <u>crucible</u> and heat it until it's red hot. (This will make sure it's <u>clean</u> and there are no traces of <u>oil or water</u> lying around from a previous experiment.)

2) Leave the crucible to <u>cool</u>, then <u>weigh</u> it, along with its lid.

3) Add some clean <u>magnesium ribbon</u> to the crucible. <u>Reweigh</u> the crucible, lid and magnesium ribbon. The <u>mass of magnesium</u> you're using is this reading minus the initial reading for the mass of the crucible and lid.

4) <u>Heat</u> the crucible containing the magnesium. Put the lid on the crucible so as to <u>stop</u> any bits of solid from <u>escaping</u>, but leave a <u>small gap</u> to allow <u>oxygen</u> to enter the crucible.

5) Heat the crucible strongly for around <u>10 minutes</u>, or until all the magnesium ribbon has turned <u>white</u>.

6) Allow the crucible to <u>cool</u> and <u>reweigh</u> the crucible with the lid and its contents. The <u>mass</u> of <u>magnesium oxide</u> you have is this reading, minus the initial reading for the mass of the crucible and lid.

The <u>mass of oxygen</u> in the magnesium oxide is the <u>difference</u> between the mass of <u>magnesium</u> and the mass of <u>magnesium oxide</u>. You can then use the method on the previous page to calculate the <u>empirical formula</u>.

Always pay close attention to your measurements

It won't matter how perfectly you've carried out the reaction if you write something down wrong. Make sure you use your <u>common sense</u> — for example, in the experiment above, magnesium is <u>gaining oxygen</u> to form magnesium oxide. The mass you measure for magnesium oxide should be <u>larger</u> than the mass you measured for magnesium. If it's not, something has gone wrong.

Finding Formulae Using Experiments

Sometimes you won't be able to use a combustion reaction to find the <u>empirical formula</u> of a compound.
Here's <u>another</u> experiment that you could use instead.

You can also Find **Empirical Formulae** Using **Reduction**

<u>Reduction</u> is the <u>loss</u> of <u>oxygen</u> from a substance (see page 76 for more on reduction).
You can reduce a <u>metal oxide</u> to find out its <u>empirical formula</u>. Here's how you'd do it for copper(II) oxide:

1) Place a rubber <u>bung</u> (with a hole through the middle) into a <u>test tube</u> with a small hole in the end, and <u>weigh</u> them using a mass balance.

2) Take the bung out of the test tube and spread out a small amount of <u>copper(II) oxide</u> in the <u>middle</u> of the tube.

3) Re-insert the bung and <u>weigh</u> the test tube again. Set up the equipment as shown in the diagram.

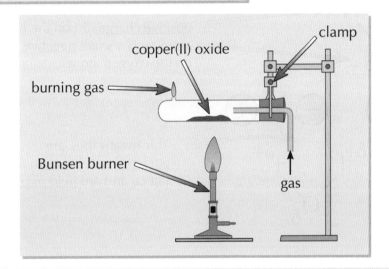

4) Expel the air from the test tube by gently turning on the <u>gas</u>. After about <u>5 seconds</u>, light the gas by holding a burning splint next to the hole in the end of the test tube. You can control the size of the flame by changing the <u>amount of gas</u> that's flowing through the test tube.

5) Use a Bunsen burner to heat the copper(II) oxide for about <u>10 minutes</u> (or until the solid changes colour from <u>black</u> to a <u>brownish-pink colour</u>).

6) Turn off the Bunsen burner and leave the test tube to <u>cool</u>.

7) Once the tube has cooled, <u>turn off</u> the gas and <u>weigh</u> the test tube with the bung and its contents.

Once you've finished the experiment, you should have all the <u>data</u> you need to work out the <u>empirical formula</u> of the <u>copper(II) oxide</u> using the method on page 47.

 Remember to turn off the gas once you've finished with it
The gas in this experiment is flammable and could cause an explosion. Take care when using it.

Water of Crystallisation

Some salts are <u>hydrated</u>. This means their lattices contain <u>water molecules</u> as well as positive and negative ions. Others don't — these salts are <u>anhydrous</u>.

Salts Can be **Anhydrous** or **Hydrated**

1) All solid salts consist of a <u>lattice</u> of positive and negative <u>ions</u> (see page 32).

2) In some salts, <u>water molecules</u> are incorporated in the lattice too.

Here's a tiny part of the lattice in a <u>hydrated salt</u>:

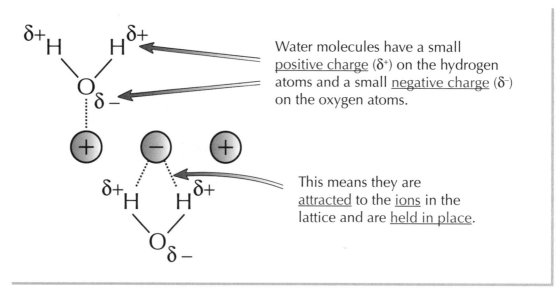

Water molecules have a small <u>positive charge</u> (δ^+) on the hydrogen atoms and a small <u>negative charge</u> (δ^-) on the oxygen atoms.

This means they are <u>attracted</u> to the <u>ions</u> in the lattice and are <u>held in place</u>.

3) The water in a lattice is called <u>water of crystallisation</u>.

4) A solid salt containing water of crystallisation is <u>hydrated</u>.

5) If a salt <u>doesn't</u> contain any water of crystallisation, it's called <u>anhydrous</u>.

Some salts contain water molecules

The little δ symbol is called <u>delta</u>. It tells you that the hydrogen and oxygen atoms in the water molecules in the lattice are only <u>slightly</u> positive or negative. Don't mistake it for a <u>full +1 or –1 charge</u> — they're not actually ions. Make sure you understand this page before moving on to some hydrated salt-related maths...

Water of Crystallisation

Now you know a bit about <u>hydrated salts</u>, it's time to have a look at how a simple experiment and a few calculations can allow you to work out <u>how many</u> moles of <u>water</u> a salt contains.

Calculating How Much **Water of Crystallisation** a Salt Contains

1) One mole of a <u>hydrated salt</u> always has a <u>particular number of moles</u> of <u>water of crystallisation</u> — its <u>formula</u> shows <u>how many</u> (it's always a whole number).

2) For example, hydrated copper sulfate has <u>five moles of water</u> for every <u>one mole</u> of the salt. So its formula is $CuSO_4.5H_2O$. (Notice that there's a <u>dot</u> between the $CuSO_4$ and the $5H_2O$.)

3) Many hydrated salts <u>lose</u> their water of crystallisation when <u>heated</u>, to become <u>anhydrous</u>. If you know the mass of the salt when it's hydrated <u>and</u> when it's anhydrous, you can work its <u>formula</u> out like this:

<u>Example:</u> Heating hydrated magnesium sulfate, $MgSO_4.XH_2O$, in a crucible forms <u>anhydrous</u> magnesium sulfate, $MgSO_4$.

Use the experimental data below to find the <u>value of X</u> and write the <u>formula</u> of the <u>hydrated salt</u>.

Mass of empty crucible	42.000 g
Mass of crucible + MgSO₄.XH₂O	45.210 g
Mass of crucible + MgSO₄	43.567 g

<u>Method:</u>

1) First, work out what <u>mass</u> of $MgSO_4.XH_2O$ and $MgSO_4$ you have.
Mass of $MgSO_4.XH_2O$ = 45.210 − 42.000 = 3.210 g
Mass of $MgSO_4$ = 43.567 − 42.000 = 1.567 g

2) Calculate the <u>number of moles</u> of <u>water lost</u>. $M_r H_2O = (2 \times 1) + 16 = 18$
Mass of water lost: 3.210 − 1.567 = 1.643 g
Number of moles of water lost: mass ÷ M_r = 1.643 g ÷ 18 = 0.0913 moles

3) Calculate the <u>number of moles</u> of <u>anhydrous salt</u> made.
Molar mass of $MgSO_4$: 24 + 32 + (4 × 16) = 120 g
Number of moles $MgSO_4$: mass ÷ M_r = 1.567 ÷ 120 = 0.0131 moles

4) Work out the <u>ratio of moles</u> of <u>anhydrous salt</u> to <u>moles of water</u>.
From the experiment, 0.0131 moles of salt : 0.0913 moles of water,
So, 1 mole of salt : (0.0913 ÷ 0.0131) = 6.97 moles of water

5) <u>X</u> must be a <u>whole number</u>, and some errors are to be expected in any experiment, so you can <u>round off</u> your result — X = 7 and the formula of the hydrated salt is $MgSO_4.7H_2O$.

Don't forget the dot — it's very important

There are a few steps to calculations like the one in the example above. If you have to do a similar calculation in an exam, make sure you write out every step. That way, you might still get some marks even if you don't get the right answer. You're also a lot less likely to make mistakes.

Moles and Concentration

Concentration is all about "how much" stuff you have in a solution.

Concentration is the 'Amount of Stuff' per Unit Volume

1) The concentration of a solution is usually measured in moles per dm³ (i.e. moles per litre). So 1 mole of stuff in 1 dm³ of solution has a concentration of 1 mole per dm³ (or 1 mol/dm³).

   1 dm³ = 1000 cm³ = 1 litre

2) You might also sometimes see concentration being measured in grams per dm³. So 56 grams of stuff dissolved in 1 dm³ of solution has a concentration of 56 g per dm³ (or 56 g/dm³).

Concentration = No. of Moles ÷ Volume

1) If you ever have to find the concentration of a solution, here's the formula you'll need:

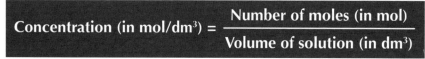

$$\text{Concentration (in mol/dm}^3\text{)} = \frac{\text{Number of moles (in mol)}}{\text{Volume of solution (in dm}^3\text{)}}$$

Here it is in a handy formula triangle.

Number of moles — n

Volume — V

Concentration — c

c × V

Example: What's the concentration of a solution with 2 moles of potassium iodide in 500 cm³?

Answer: Easy — you've got 2 moles of potassium iodide and 500 cm³ = 0.5 dm³.
So just stick these numbers in the formula: Concentration = 2 ÷ 0.5 = 4 mol/dm³

2) You can use the same formula triangle to find the number of moles that are in a solution:

Example: How many moles of sodium chloride are in 250 cm³ of a 3 mol/dm³ solution?

Answer: 250 cm³ = 0.25 dm³. So, using the formula from the triangle...
Number of moles = concentration × volume = 3 × 0.25 = 0.75 moles

Converting Moles per dm³ to Grams per dm³

1) Calculating concentrations in grams per dm³ is easy. You just divide the mass of the chemical in grams by the volume of solvent you used to dissolve it in dm³.

   Mass (in grams) — m

   Number of moles — n

   n × M_r

   Relative formula mass

   Example: Give the concentration in g/dm³ of a solution made by dissolving 3 g of NaCl in 100 cm³ of water.

   Answer: Concentration = mass (g) ÷ volume (dm³) = 3 ÷ 0.1 = 30 g/dm³

2) Changing a concentration from mol/dm³ to g/dm³ isn't too tricky. All you need to do is use the formula you met on page 44 to convert the moles per dm³ into mass per dm³.

   Example: You have a 0.04 mol/dm³ solution of sulfuric acid. What is the concentration in grams per dm³?

   Step 1: Work out the relative formula mass of the chemical.
   So, H_2SO_4 = (1 × 2) + 32 + (16 × 4) = 98

   Step 2: Convert the concentration in moles into concentration in grams.
   So, in 1 dm³: mass in grams = moles × relative formula mass = 0.04 × 98 = 3.92 g
   So the concentration in g/dm³ = 3.92 g/dm³

Calculating Volume

<u>Another formula</u> to learn on this page — this time about the <u>volume</u> of <u>gases</u>.

Avogadro's Law — One Mole of Any Gas Occupies 24 dm³

1) The space that <u>one mole</u> of a gas takes up is called its <u>molar volume</u>.
Here's a handy fact about molar volume that you definitely <u>need to learn</u>:

> One mole of any gas always occupies 24 dm³ (= 24 000 cm³) at room temperature and pressure (RTP: 20 °C and 1 atmosphere)

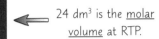 24 dm³ is the <u>molar volume</u> at RTP.

2) This means you can use the formula below to convert the number of moles of <u>any</u> gas at RTP to a <u>volume</u>:

Volume (dm³) = moles of gas × 24

If you need to work out the moles of gas from its mass, use the formula moles = mass ÷ M_r (see page 44).

Example 1: What's the volume of 4.5 moles of chlorine at RTP?

Answer: volume of 1 mole = 24 dm³, so volume of 4.5 moles = 4.5 × 24 dm³ = <u>108 dm³</u>

Example 2: How many moles are there in 8280 cm³ of hydrogen gas at RTP?

Answer: Number of moles = $\dfrac{\text{Volume of gas}}{\text{Volume of 1 mole}}$ = $\dfrac{8.28}{24}$ = <u>0.345 moles</u>

Don't forget to convert from cm³ to dm³.

You Can Calculate Volumes in Reactions If You Know the Masses

For this type of question there are <u>three stages</u>:

1) Calculate the <u>moles</u> of the <u>substance</u> you know the <u>mass</u> of.
2) <u>Find the moles of gas</u> using the balanced equation.
3) Then <u>convert the moles into a volume</u> using the formula above.

Example: Find the volume of carbon dioxide produced at RTP when 2.4 g of carbon is completely burned in oxygen. (A_r of carbon = 12, A_r of oxygen = 16)

1) Write out the <u>balanced equation</u>: C + O_2 → CO_2
2) Work out the <u>relative formula mass</u> of the substance you know the mass of: M_r of C = 12
3) <u>Calculate the number of moles</u> of carbon in 2.4 g: moles = mass ÷ M_r = 2.4 ÷ 12 = 0.2
4) Look at the <u>ratio</u> of moles in the equation — 1 mole of C reacts to produce 1 mole of CO_2. So <u>0.2 moles</u> of <u>C</u> will react to produce <u>0.2 moles</u> of <u>CO_2</u>.
5) Use the formula above to work out the <u>volume</u>: volume = moles × 24 = 0.2 × 24 = <u>4.8 dm³</u>

Use the formula to work out the volume of any gas at RTP

All this stuff ties in with what you saw on page 45 — if you're not comfortable working out reacting masses, have a look there to refresh your memory. The only new thing here is this molar volume business: 1 mole of gas = 24 dm³. This is the same for all gases at RTP, so you've only got one new formula to learn.

Warm-Up & Exam Questions

There's been a lot to remember over the last few pages. Check that it's all sunk in by tackling the following questions. And if there's any you can't do, don't panic — have a look back at the pages and try again.

Warm-Up Questions

1) Glucose has the molecular formula $C_6H_{12}O_6$. What is its empirical formula?
2) What word is used to describe a solid salt that does not contain any water of crystallisation?
3) 6.25 moles of sodium chloride are dissolved in 25.0 dm³ of water.
   What is the concentration of the sodium chloride solution in mol/dm³?
4) True or false? Only O_2, N_2 and CO_2 have a molar volume of 24 dm³ at RTP.

Exam Questions

PRACTICAL

1 A student is carrying out a reaction to find the formula of an oxide of manganese. His experimental set-up is shown on the right. **Grade 4-6**

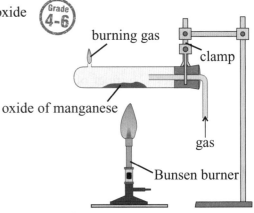

(a) What is the name given to this type of reaction?

☐ A neutralisation

☐ B combustion

☐ C reduction

☐ D polymerisation

[1 mark]

(b) During the reaction, manganese and oxygen are produced. Some of the student's results are shown in the table.

mass of test tube and bung	36.48 g
mass of test tube and bung + manganese	84.88 g

(i) Calculate the mass of manganese present in the sample. Give your answer in grams.

[1 mark]

(ii) The mass of oxygen present was 14.08 g. Calculate the empirical formula of the oxide.
$A_r(Mn) = 55$, $A_r(O) = 16$

[3 marks]

PAPER 2

2 The volume that one mole of a gas occupies is called its molar volume. **Grade 4-6**

(a) State the value of the molar volume of a gas at room temperature and pressure.

[1 mark]

(b) What volume, in dm³, does 1.5 moles of hydrogen take up at room temperature and pressure?

[1 mark]

Exam Questions

3   A molecule has an empirical formula of C_3H_7O, and a relative molecular mass of 118.
Deduce the molecular formula of the molecule.

[3 marks]

PAPER 2

4   Sodium hydroxide (NaOH) reacts with sulfuric acid
to produce sodium sulfate (Na_2SO_4) and water.

  (a)   How many moles of sodium hydroxide are in 125 cm^3 of a 2.5 mol/dm^3 solution?

[1 mark]

  (b)   What is the concentration, in mol/dm^3, of a solution with 3 moles of sodium sulfate in 750 cm^3?

[1 mark]

  (c)   Give your answer for part (b) in g/dm^3.

[2 marks]

5 $Na_2CO_3.xH_2O$ is a hydrated salt, which means that water molecules are
present in the lattice structure. This water is called water of crystallisation.

By heating a sample of a hydrated salt you can gradually remove the
water of crystallisation. This can be done by placing a sample of the
hydrated salt into a crucible and gently heating it using a Bunsen burner.

A student used this method to remove the water of crystallisation from $Na_2CO_3.xH_2O$
to produce the salt Na_2CO_3. The student put a sample of $Na_2CO_3.xH_2O$ into a crucible,
weighed both together, and recorded the mass. The student then heated the sample for
2 minutes, left it to cool and recorded the mass of the sample and crucible again.
The student repeated this until two separate masses that had the same value were recorded.
The student made a note of this mass.

The student recorded the following masses:

starting mass of crucible + $Na_2CO_3.xH_2O$	61.224 g
final mass of crucible + Na_2CO_3	56.364 g

  (a)   Suggest the purpose of heating the hydrated salt until the mass remains constant.

[1 mark]

  (b)   The mass of the crucible was 53.500 g.
Use this to calculate the masses of the following samples.
   (i) $Na_2CO_3.xH_2O$

[1 mark]

   (ii) Na_2CO_3

[1 mark]

  (c)   The relative formula mass of water is 18.
Calculate the relative formula mass of Na_2CO_3 and use this along with
your answers to part (b) to work out the value of x in $Na_2CO_3.xH_2O$.

[4 marks]

Electrolysis

And now for something completely different... We're about to embark on some <u>electrolysis</u>.

Electrolysis Involves Oxidation and Reduction

1) <u>Electrolysis</u> is the <u>breaking down</u> of a substance using <u>electricity</u>.
   An electric current is passed through an <u>electrolyte</u>
   (a <u>molten</u> or <u>dissolved</u> ionic compound), causing it to <u>decompose</u>.

2) In electrolysis, <u>oxidation</u> (<u>loss of electrons</u>) and <u>reduction</u> (<u>gain of electrons</u>) occur.

See page 65 for more on oxidation and reduction.

3) The <u>positive ions</u> (<u>cations</u>) in the electrolyte move towards
   the <u>cathode</u> (negative electrode) and are reduced (<u>gain</u> electrons).

This creates a flow of charge through the electrolyte.

4) The <u>negative ions</u> (<u>anions</u>) in the electrolyte move towards
   the <u>anode</u> (positive electrode) and are oxidised (<u>lose</u> electrons).

5) As ions gain or lose electrons they form the uncharged substances and are <u>discharged</u> from the electrolyte.

Half Equations Show the Transfer of Electrons

<u>Ionic half equations</u> show how electrons are transferred during reactions. They're really useful for showing what happens at <u>each electrode</u> during electrolysis. To write a half equation:

1) Put <u>one</u> of the things <u>being oxidised or reduced</u> on one side of an arrow,
   and the thing it gets <u>oxidised or reduced to</u> on the other.

2) Balance up the <u>numbers of atoms</u> just like in a normal equation.

3) Then add <u>electrons</u> (written e⁻) on to one side to balance up the charges.

The charges on each side of the equation should balance.

<u>Examples</u>: Sodium is losing one electron to become a sodium ion: $Na \rightarrow Na^+ + e^-$
Hydrogen ions are gaining electrons to become hydrogen: $2H^+ + 2e^- \rightarrow H_2$

Here's How to Set Up an Electrochemical Cell

1) An <u>electrochemical cell</u> is a <u>circuit</u>, made up of the anode, cathode,
   electrolyte, a power source and the wires that connect the two electrodes.

You can use this type of cell to electrolyse aqueous solutions — see page 58.

2) You need to know how to <u>set up</u> an electrochemical cell
   for an <u>aqueous solution</u>. Here's how you'd do it:

    1) Get <u>two inert electrodes</u>, e.g.
   graphite or platinum electrodes.

    2) Clean the surfaces of the electrodes
   using some <u>emery paper</u> (or sandpaper).

    3) From this point on, be careful <u>not to touch</u>
   the surfaces of the electrodes with your hands
   — you could transfer grease back onto the strips.

    4) Place both electrodes into a <u>beaker</u>
   filled with your <u>electrolyte</u>.

    5) Connect the electrodes to a power supply using <u>crocodile clips</u> and <u>wires</u>.
   When you turn the power supply on, a <u>current</u> will flow through the cell.

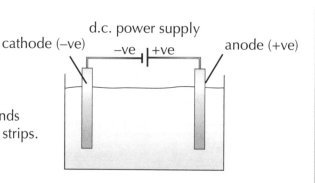

You could put an ammeter or bulb in series with your circuit to check you've set it up correctly.

Paper 2

Electrolysis of Molten Substances

Time to cover what's <u>going on</u> at the <u>electrodes</u> themselves. First up, it's <u>molten ionic substances</u>.

In **Molten** Ionic Compounds, There's Only **One** Source of **Ions**

1) <u>Molten</u> ionic compounds can be electrolysed because the ions can <u>move freely</u>.
2) They're usually broken up into their <u>elements</u>.
3) Have a look at the following example:

Example: Electrolysis of **Molten Lead (II) Bromide** (PbBr$_2$)

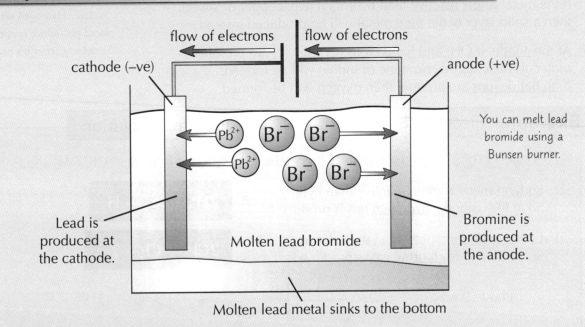

flow of electrons   flow of electrons

cathode (−ve)   anode (+ve)

You can melt lead bromide using a Bunsen burner.

Lead is produced at the cathode.

Molten lead bromide

Bromine is produced at the anode.

Molten lead metal sinks to the bottom

You can write <u>half-equations</u> to show what's happening at each <u>electrode</u>.

At the **Cathode**:

- The <u>positive</u> Pb^{2+} ions are attracted to the <u>negative cathode</u>.
- A lead ion <u>accepts two electrons</u> and is reduced to a <u>lead atom</u>.

$$Pb^{2+} + 2e^- \rightarrow Pb$$

At the **Anode**:

- The <u>negative</u> Br$^-$ ions are attracted to the <u>positive anode</u>.
- Two bromide ions <u>lose one electron</u> each and are oxidised to a <u>bromine molecule</u>.

$$2Br^- \rightarrow Br_2 + 2e^-$$

4) The <u>electrodes</u> are made from an <u>inert</u> (unreactive) material so they <u>don't</u> take part in the reaction.
5) It's easy to predict what products you get when you electrolyse <u>molten</u> substances — but you need to get the <u>half equations</u> right too. Here are some examples:

Molten Electrolyte	Product at Cathode	Half equation at Cathode	Product at Anode	Half equation at Anode
potassium chloride, KCl	potassium	$K^+ + e^- \rightarrow K$	chlorine	$2Cl^- \rightarrow Cl_2 + 2e^-$
aluminium oxide, Al$_2$O$_3$	aluminium	$Al^{3+} + 3e^- \rightarrow Al$	oxygen	$2O^{2-} \rightarrow O_2 + 4e^-$

58

PRACTICAL | Electrolysis of Aqueous Solutions

You saw how to set up an <u>electrochemical cell</u> for an aqueous solution on page 56.
This page covers what actually happens when you use the cell the <u>electrolyse</u> the solution.

Electrolysis of Aqueous Solutions Involves the Ions From Water

1) In <u>aqueous solutions</u>, as well as the <u>ions</u> from the ionic compound,
there will be <u>hydrogen ions</u> (H^+) and <u>hydroxide ions</u> (OH^-) from the <u>water</u>.

2) At the <u>cathode</u>, if <u>H^+ ions and metal ions</u> are present, <u>hydrogen gas</u> will
be produced if the metal is <u>more reactive</u> than hydrogen (e.g. sodium).
If the metal is <u>less reactive</u> than hydrogen (e.g. copper or silver),
then a solid layer of the <u>pure metal</u> will be produced instead.

You can use reactivity series to compare the reactivity of metals. Hydrogen would be placed just above copper in the reactivity series on page 74.

3) At the <u>anode</u>, if <u>OH^- and halide ions</u> (Cl^-, Br^-, I^-) are present,
molecules of chlorine, bromine or iodine will be formed.
If <u>no halide ions</u> are present, then <u>oxygen</u> will be formed.

Example: Electrolysis of Sodium Chloride (NaCl) Solution

1) A solution of <u>sodium chloride</u> (NaCl) contains <u>four different ions</u>: Na^+, Cl^-, OH^- and H^+.

2) <u>Sodium</u> metal is more reactive than hydrogen.
So at the cathode, <u>hydrogen gas</u> is produced.

$$2H^+ + 2e^- \rightarrow H_2$$

3) <u>Chloride ions</u> are present in the solution.
So at the anode <u>chlorine gas</u> is produced.

$$2Cl^- \rightarrow Cl_2 + 2e^-$$

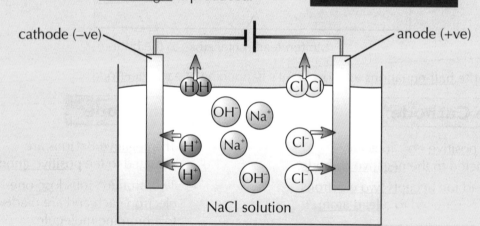

4) You need to be able to <u>predict</u> the <u>products</u> when an aqueous solution is <u>electrolysed</u>.
Here are some examples:

Aqueous Electrolyte	Product at Cathode	Half equation at Cathode	Product at Anode	Half equation at Anode
copper(II) sulfate, $CuSO_4$	copper	$Cu^{2+} + 2e^- \rightarrow Cu$	oxygen	$4OH^- \rightarrow O_2 + 2H_2O + 4e^-$
dilute sulfuric acid, H_2O/H_2SO_4	hydrogen	$2H^+ + 2e^- \rightarrow H_2$	oxygen	$4OH^- \rightarrow O_2 + 2H_2O + 4e^-$

You might see the half equation for this reaction at the anode written like this: $2H_2O \rightarrow 4H^+ + O_2 + 4e^-$

Remember — all aqueous solutions contain OH^- and H^+ ions

The main points to remember about the <u>electrolysis</u> of <u>aqueous solutions</u> are: 1) At the <u>cathode</u>, <u>hydrogen</u> gas is made, <u>unless</u> metal ions are present which are <u>less reactive</u> than hydrogen — then you get a coating of the <u>metal</u>. 2) At the <u>anode</u>, <u>oxygen</u> is made, <u>unless halide ions</u> are present — then the <u>halogen</u> is made.

Section 3 — Equations, Calculations and Electrolysis

Warm-Up & Exam Questions

I bet you think you know everything there is to know about electrolysis after those last few pages.
Here's your chance to prove it. Get started with the warm-up questions, then it's exam practice time.

Warm-Up Questions

1) Name the process in which an electric current is passed through
   an ionic compound to make a new substance.

2) What state must an ionic compound be in if it's to be used as an electrolyte?

3) Which electrode are positive ions attracted to during electrolysis?

Exam Questions

PAPER 2

1   Write a balanced half-equation for the reaction occurring in the electrolysis of lead bromide at:

   (a)   the negative electrode,

[2 marks]

   (b)   the positive electrode

[2 marks]

PAPER 2

2   A student carries out the electrolysis of molten potassium iodide.

   (a)   (i) Name the substance that will form at the negative electrode.

[1 mark]

       (ii) Name the substance that will form at the positive electrode.

[1 mark]

   (b)   Is the reaction at the positive electrode an example of oxidation or reduction? Explain your answer.

[1 mark]

PAPER 2   PRACTICAL

3   A student investigated the products of electrolysis of
    a variety of aqueous solutions using inert electrodes.

   (a)   Draw a **labelled** diagram of suitable apparatus that could be used for these experiments.

[3 marks]

   (b)   An aqueous solution of copper sulfate ($CuSO_4$) can undergo electrolysis.
      (i) State the **four** ions that this solution contains.

[4 marks]

      (ii) Copper is produced in a reaction at one of the electrodes during the electrolysis of this solution.
         Write the half-equation for this reaction.

[2 marks]

   (c)   When potassium nitrate solution is electrolysed neither potassium nor nitrogen are discharged.
      Explain why and state what is produced instead.

[4 marks]

Revision Summary for Section 3

That's the end of <u>Section 3</u>. Give yourself a pat on the back — and then...
* ...try these questions and <u>tick off each one</u> when you <u>get it right</u>.
* When you've done <u>all the questions</u> under a heading and are <u>completely happy</u> with it, tick it off.

Equations, Calculating Masses and Moles (p.42-45) ☐
1) What do the following state symbols stand for?
   a) (l)   b) (aq)   c) (g) ☑
2) Give a definition for the relative formula mass of a compound. ☑
3) What equation links the number of moles with the mass and M_r of a substance? ☑
4) What is the percentage yield of a reaction where no products are made? ☐

Calculating Empirical and Molecular Formulae (p.47-51) ☑
5) What is the empirical formula of a compound? ☑
6) How does the molecular formula of a compound relate to its empirical formula? ☐
7) Outline an experiment involving combustion that you could
   use to work out the empirical formula of magnesium oxide. ☐
8) In hydrated copper sulfate, for every one mole of salt, there are five moles of water.
   Write the formula of hydrated copper sulfate ($CuSO_4$). ☐

Concentration and Volume (p.52-53) ☑
9) What equation links the concentration of a solution
   with its volume and the number of moles present? ☐
10) Describe how to convert a concentration from moles/dm³ to g/dm³. ☑
11) Describe what is meant by the 'molar volume' of a gas? ☐

Electrolysis (p.56-58) ☐
12) What is electrolysis? ☐
13) What is a cation? ☑
14) Towards which electrode do the anions in an electrolyte move? ☐
15) At which electrode does the metal form during the electrolysis of a molten ionic compound? ☑
16) Name the components of an electrochemical cell. ☐
17) Write a half equation to show what happens at the cathode
    in the electrolysis of sodium chloride solution, NaCl. ☑
18) Name the products formed when a solution of copper sulfate is electrolysed. ☑

Group 1 — The Alkali Metals

Group 1 elements are known as the <u>alkali metals</u>. As metals go, they're pretty <u>reactive</u>.

Group 1 Elements All **React** in a **Similar Way** with **Water**

1) <u>Simple reactions</u> can be used to work out if an element is part of the same <u>family</u> as other elements. Elements of the same family will react in a similar way.

2) For example, when <u>lithium</u>, <u>sodium</u> and <u>potassium</u> are put in <u>water</u>, they all react <u>vigorously</u>.

3) The <u>reaction</u> produces a <u>metal hydroxide</u> solution. This solution is <u>alkaline</u> — this is why Group 1 elements are known as the <u>alkali metals</u>.

4) The <u>reaction</u> of the alkali metals with water also produces <u>hydrogen</u> — this is why you can see <u>fizzing</u>.

5) These reactions can be written as <u>chemical equations</u> — e.g. for <u>sodium</u> the equation is...

STATE SYMBOLS:
(s) = <u>solid</u>, (l) = <u>liquid</u>, (g) = <u>gas</u>, (aq) = <u>aqueous</u> (dissolved in water)

Word equation: **sodium + water → sodium hydroxide + hydrogen**

Symbol equation: $\mathbf{2Na_{(s)} + 2H_2O_{(l)} \rightarrow 2NaOH_{(aq)} + H_{2(g)}}$

Oxides are Formed when **Alkali Metals** React with **Oxygen**

1) The Group 1 metals can also react with <u>oxygen</u> in the air to form <u>metal oxides</u>.

This is why they tarnish when left in air, leaving a dull metal oxide layer.

2) Different <u>types of oxide</u> will form depending on the Group 1 metal:

- Lithium reacts to form <u>lithium oxide</u> (Li_2O).
- Sodium reacts to form a mixture of <u>sodium oxide</u> (Na_2O) and <u>sodium peroxide</u> (Na_2O_2).
- Potassium reacts to form a mixture of <u>potassium peroxide</u> (K_2O_2) and <u>potassium superoxide</u> (KO_2).

Alkali metals react vigorously with water

The reaction equations follow the same <u>structure</u>: metal + water → metal hydroxide + hydrogen. Make sure you know it and you'll be able to write the equation for <u>any alkali metal</u> and <u>water</u>.

Group 1 — The Alkali Metals

You're not quite done with the <u>alkali metals</u> yet — this page is all about their <u>reactivity</u>.

Group 1 Elements Become More Reactive Down the Group

1) As you go <u>down</u> Group 1 the elements become <u>more reactive</u>.

2) You can see this in the <u>rate of reaction</u> with water (i.e. the time taken for a lump of the same size of each element to <u>react completely</u> with the water and disappear).

3) <u>Lithium</u> takes longer than sodium or potassium to react, so it's the <u>least reactive</u>.

4) <u>Potassium</u> takes the shortest time to react of these three elements, so it's the <u>most reactive</u>.

5) The <u>trend in reactivity</u> can also be seen in the reaction between the alkali metals and <u>oxygen</u>. Potassium reacts to form its oxide <u>quicker</u> than sodium and lithium when left in <u>air</u>.

6) You can use the trend in reactivity to <u>predict</u> how other group 1 metals will react.

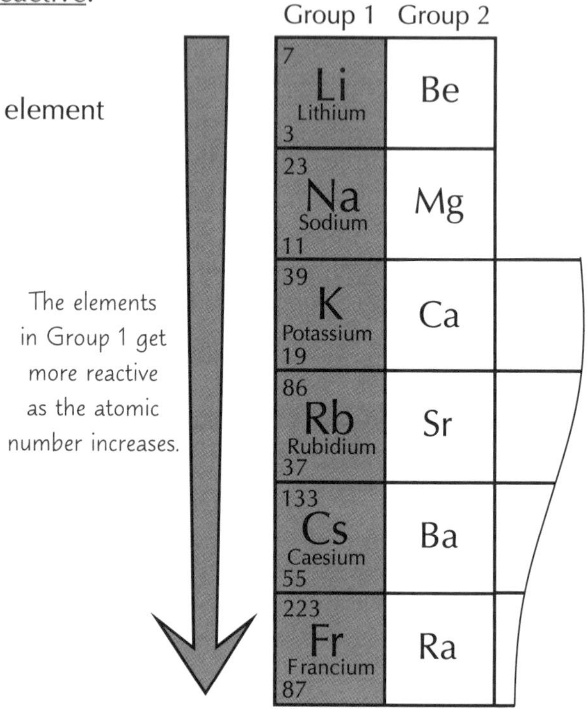

The elements in Group 1 get more reactive as the atomic number increases.

Group 1	Group 2
7 **Li** Lithium 3	Be
23 **Na** Sodium 11	Mg
39 **K** Potassium 19	Ca
86 **Rb** Rubidium 37	Sr
133 **Cs** Caesium 55	Ba
223 **Fr** Francium 87	Ra

E.g. you could predict that <u>caesium</u> will react <u>more vigorously</u> than potassium with <u>water</u> (in fact, it <u>explodes</u>).

Atoms Lose Electrons More Easily Down the Group

1) All <u>Group 1</u> metals have <u>1 electron</u> in their outer shell.

2) As you go <u>down</u> Group 1, the <u>outermost electron</u> is in a shell that's <u>further from the nucleus</u>.

3) This means the <u>attraction</u> between the <u>outermost electron</u> and the <u>nucleus</u> becomes <u>less</u>.

4) So as you go down Group 1 the atoms get <u>bigger</u>, the outer electron is <u>more easily lost</u>, and the metals are <u>more reactive</u>.

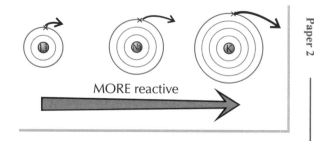

MORE reactive

Paper 2 (left margin)

Paper 2 (right margin)

Alkali metals at the bottom of Group 1 are more reactive...

... so they react more <u>quickly</u> and <u>violently</u>. Remember, an alkali metal's reactivity comes from its ability to easily <u>give up</u> its <u>outer shell electron</u> — the more <u>easily</u> it does this, the more <u>reactive</u> it is.

Group 7 — The Halogens

Here's a page on another periodic table group that you need to be familiar with — <u>the halogens</u>.

HALOGEN — Seven Letters — Group 7

1) The elements in <u>Group 7</u> of the periodic table are called the <u>halogens</u>.

2) As the <u>atomic number</u> of the halogens <u>increases</u>, the elements have a <u>darker colour</u> and a <u>higher boiling point</u>. This means at <u>room temperature</u>:

<u>Chlorine</u> (Cl_2) is a fairly reactive, poisonous, <u>green gas</u>.

<u>Bromine</u> (Br_2) is a poisonous, <u>red-brown liquid</u> which gives off an <u>orange vapour</u>.

<u>Iodine</u> (I_2) is a <u>dark grey crystalline solid</u> which gives off a <u>purple vapour</u> when heated.

3) This table shows how the <u>properties</u> of the elements in Group 7 gradually change as you go <u>down the group</u>:

Group VII Elements	Properties			
	Atomic number	Colour	Physical state at room temperature	Boiling point
Chlorine	17	green	gas	−34 ºC
Bromine	35	red-brown	liquid	59 ºC
Iodine	53	dark grey	solid	185 ºC

4) The <u>higher up</u> Group 7 an element is, the <u>more reactive</u> it is.

5) You might need to use these trends to <u>predict</u> the properties of <u>other halogens</u>.

E.g. You can see that boiling point <u>increases</u> down the group, and the colours of the halogens get <u>darker</u>, so you could predict that astatine (which comes below iodine) would be a <u>dark-coloured solid</u> at room temperature. Sure enough, astatine is a <u>black solid</u> with a melting point of around <u>300 ºC</u>.

Reactivity Decreases Going Down Group 7

1) Halogen atoms have seven electrons in their <u>outer shell</u>. They can gain <u>one</u> electron to form a <u>1− ion</u>.

2) The <u>easier</u> it is for a halogen atom to <u>attract</u> an electron, the <u>more reactive</u> the halogen will be.

3) As you go <u>down</u> Group 7, the halogens become <u>less reactive</u> — it gets <u>harder</u> to attract the <u>extra electron</u> to fill the outer shell when it's <u>further away</u> from the nucleus (the <u>atomic radius</u> is <u>larger</u>).

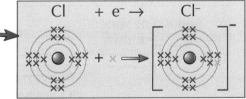

Halogens get less reactive as you go down the group

Learn the trends given on this page — you may be asked to use them to predict the properties of a halogen.

Halogen Displacement Reactions

The halogens are competitive — the <u>more reactive</u> ones will push the <u>less reactive</u> ones out of a compound.

More Reactive Halogens will Displace Less Reactive Ones

1) The elements in Group 7 take part in <u>displacement reactions</u>.

2) A <u>displacement reaction</u> is where a <u>more reactive</u> element "<u>pushes out</u>" (displaces) a <u>less reactive</u> element from a compound.

3) For example, <u>chlorine</u> is more reactive than <u>iodine</u> (it's higher up Group 7).

4) So, if you add <u>chlorine water</u> to <u>potassium iodide</u> solution the chlorine will react with the potassium in the potassium iodide to form <u>potassium chloride</u>.

5) The <u>iodine</u> is <u>displaced from the salt</u> and gets left in the solution, turning it <u>brown</u>.

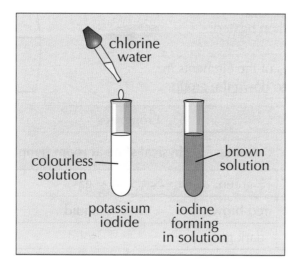

6) The table below shows what happens when you mix different combinations of <u>chlorine</u>, <u>bromine</u> and <u>iodine</u> with the salts <u>potassium chloride</u>, <u>potassium bromide</u> and <u>potassium iodide</u>.

Start with:	Potassium chloride solution $KCl_{(aq)}$ — colourless	Potassium bromide solution $KBr_{(aq)}$ — colourless	Potassium iodide solution $KI_{(aq)}$ — colourless
Add chlorine water $Cl_{2\,(aq)}$ — colourless	no reaction	orange solution (Br_2) formed	brown solution (I_2) formed
Add bromine water $Br_{2\,(aq)}$ — orange	no reaction	no reaction	brown solution (I_2) formed
Add iodine water $I_{2\,(aq)}$ — brown	no reaction	no reaction	no reaction

These experiments are dead easy. All you need to do is add a few drops of the halogen solution to the salt solution. Then look for a colour change.

Halogens higher up the group will displace the ones lower down

Once you know that halogens get <u>less reactive</u> down the group, you can work out what will happen when you mix <u>any halogen</u> with <u>any halide salt</u>. Learn the <u>colour changes</u> that go with the reactions too.

Halogen Displacement Reactions

Here goes a little bit more on halogen displacement reactions — it's all about movement of <u>electrons</u>...

Halogen Displacement Reactions Involve **Transfer of Electrons**

1) You can show the <u>displacement reactions</u> between halogens and salt solutions as <u>equations</u>. For example:

$$Cl_2 \text{(aq)} + 2KI \text{(aq)} \rightarrow I_2 \text{(aq)} + 2KCl \text{(aq)}$$

This is the equation for chlorine displacing iodine from potassium iodide. They might give you a different example in the exam, but the principle is always the same.

2) When this reaction happens <u>electrons</u> are <u>passed</u> from the iodine to the chlorine.

Each chlorine atom in the Cl_2 molecule <u>gains</u> an electron to form <u>two negative</u> Cl^- ions.

$$Cl_2 \text{(aq)} + 2I^- \text{(aq)} \rightarrow 2Cl^- \text{(aq)} + I_2 \text{(aq)}$$

Two iodide ions <u>lose</u> an electron each and then form a <u>neutral</u> I_2 molecule.

You can remember which is which by using OIL RIG. Oxidation Is Loss, Reduction Is Gain (of electrons).

3) A <u>loss of electrons</u> is called <u>oxidation</u>. A <u>gain in electrons</u> is called <u>reduction</u>. *Oxidation and reduction can also describe the gain and loss of oxygen — see p.76.*

4) In displacement reactions, reduction and oxidation happen <u>simultaneously</u>. For example, in this reaction the <u>chlorine is reduced</u> and the <u>iodine is oxidised</u>.

5) An <u>oxidising agent</u> accepts electrons and <u>gets reduced</u>. So, here <u>chlorine</u> is an oxidising agent.

6) A <u>reducing agent</u> donates electrons and <u>gets oxidised</u>. So <u>iodine</u> is a reducing agent.

7) Reactions where reduction and oxidation happen at the same time are called <u>redox reactions</u>.

OIL RIG — Oxidation Is Loss, Reduction Is Gain...

<u>OIL RIG</u> is a pretty handy way to remind yourself what goes on during a <u>redox reaction</u>. Make sure that you don't forget that redox reactions are all about the <u>transfer of electrons</u>.

Warm-Up & Exam Questions

These questions are all about Groups 1 and 7 of the periodic table.

Warm-Up Questions

1) Name the product formed when lithium reacts with oxygen.

2) How do the boiling points of the halogens change as you go down the group?

3) A student added a few drops of a halogen solution to a solution of potassium bromide. The solution did not change colour. Suggest which halogen the student's solution contained.

4) Do halide ions have a positive or a negative charge?

Exam Questions

1 A teacher dropped small, similar sized pieces of three different alkali metals, **A**, **B** and **C**, into water. The students recorded the time taken for each piece to react completely.

Metal	Time taken to react (s)
A	27
B	8
C	42

(a) State which of these metals, **A**, **B** or **C**, is the most reactive. Explain how you know.

[2 marks]

(b) The three metals used were lithium, sodium and potassium. Use the results shown in the table to match them up to the correct letters **A**, **B** and **C**.

[2 marks]

(c) What products would be formed in a reaction between sodium and water?

[2 marks]

(d) One of the students said, "The amount of time taken for rubidium to react with water would be shorter than for metal **A**, but longer than for metal **B**". Why is the student incorrect?

[2 marks]

2 When chlorine water is added to a solution of potassium iodide, a chemical reaction occurs.

(a) State the colour of the solution before and after the reaction.

[2 marks]

(b) Astatine is below iodine in Group 7. Predict whether chlorine water would react with sodium astatide solution. Explain your answer.

[2 marks]

PAPER 2

3 The reactivity of halogens is dependent on their electronic configuration.

(a) Describe the electronic configuration of the halogens and how it changes down Group 7.

[2 marks]

(b) Sodium reacts violently with fluorine, at room temperature, to form sodium fluoride. Predict how astatine might react with sodium at room temperature. Explain your answer.

[4 marks]

Gases in the Atmosphere

This page is all about the gases in our <u>atmosphere</u> — what a breath of fresh air...

The **Atmosphere** is Mostly **Nitrogen** and **Oxygen**

For <u>200 million years</u> or so, the atmosphere has been about how it is now:

- 78% <u>nitrogen</u>
- 21% <u>oxygen</u>
- nearly 1% <u>argon</u>
- only 0.04% <u>carbon dioxide</u>

There can be a lot of water vapour too.

Make sure you know the <u>proportions</u> of each <u>gas</u>.

You can Investigate the **Proportion** of Oxygen in the **Air** ⬚ PRACTICAL

1) <u>Iron</u> can be used to determine the percentage of oxygen in the atmosphere.

2) This is because <u>iron</u> reacts with oxygen in the air to form <u>rust</u> (see page 75) — so iron will <u>remove oxygen</u> from the air.

You can also use a non-metal to investigate the percentage of oxygen in the air — see the next page.

Here's how you'd do this experiment:

- First soak some <u>iron wool</u> in <u>acetic acid</u> (the acid will catalyse the reaction). Then push the wool into a <u>measuring cylinder</u> and invert the measuring cylinder into a beaker of water.

- Record the <u>starting position</u> of the water using the scale on the measuring cylinder — this is the starting volume of air.

- Over time, the level of the water in the measuring cylinder will <u>rise</u>.

- This is because the iron <u>reacts</u> with the <u>oxygen</u> in the air to make iron oxide. The water rises to fill the space the oxygen took up.

- Leave the measuring cylinder for <u>around a week</u> or until the water level <u>stops changing</u>.

- Record the <u>finishing</u> position of the water — this is the final volume of air.

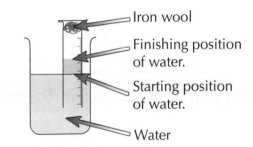

Iron wool
Finishing position of water.
Starting position of water.
Water

You can then use the results of this experiment to calculate the percentage of oxygen in the atmosphere using the formula on the next page.

The atmosphere is 78% N_2, 21% O_2, nearly 1% Ar and 0.04% CO_2

You need to know how you could use a metal to investigate the <u>proportion of oxygen</u> in the atmosphere, so learn the <u>set-up</u> of this experiment. <u>Read</u> over the page again, then <u>cover</u> it and see if you can <u>draw</u> the diagram showing the equipment you'll need. Don't forget to <u>label</u> it to show how the experiment works.

 # Gases in the Atmosphere

Don't panic — if you don't like rusting iron (see previous page) there's another way you can investigate the proportion of <u>oxygen</u> in the atmosphere. It doesn't take a week either.

Phosphorus Reacts with Oxygen in the Atmosphere

You can also use <u>phosphorus</u> to determine the percentage of oxygen in the air. Here's how:

- Place the <u>phosphorus</u> in a tube and attach a glass <u>syringe</u> at <u>either end</u>. Make sure one of the syringes is <u>filled</u> with air and the other is <u>empty</u>.

- <u>Heat</u> the phosphorus and use the syringes to pass the air over it — the phosphorus will react with oxygen in the air to make <u>phosphorus oxide</u>.

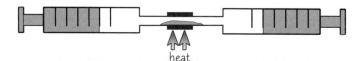

heat

- As it reacts, the amount of air in the syringes will <u>decrease</u>.

Push all the air into one syringe to measure the final volume.

- Measure the <u>starting</u> and <u>final volumes</u> of air using the <u>scale</u> on one of the syringes.

- You can then calculate the <u>percentage</u> of oxygen in the air using the <u>formula below</u>.

You Can Calculate the Percentage of Oxygen in the Atmosphere

1) If you have found the <u>volume</u> of oxygen in an experiment such as the one above or the one on the previous page, you can use your results to calculate the <u>percentage</u> of oxygen in the atmosphere.

2) To calculate the percentage of oxygen just put the volumes you recorded into this <u>formula</u>:

$$\frac{\text{Start volume} - \text{Final volume}}{\text{Start volume}} \times 100$$

3) The answer you get should be about <u>20%</u>.

 ## Find the proportion of oxygen by measuring change in volume

Don't be put off by the formula, it's just like finding <u>percentage change</u> in maths — work out the difference in volumes and then divide by the volume you started with. Learn the formula now.

Gases in Reactions

Lots of reactions involve <u>gases</u>, sometimes as <u>reactants</u>, sometimes as <u>products</u>.

When you **Burn** Something it **Reacts** with **Oxygen** in Air

When an element is burnt in air it <u>reacts</u> with the oxygen to form an <u>oxide</u>.
These oxides can have either <u>acidic</u> or <u>basic</u> character (see page 82).
Here are some examples you need to <u>know</u>:

Magnesium

<u>Magnesium</u> burns with a <u>bright white flame</u> in air and
the <u>white powder</u> that is formed is <u>magnesium oxide</u>.
Magnesium oxide is slightly <u>alkaline</u> when it's dissolved in water.

$$2Mg_{(s)} + O_{2(g)} \rightarrow 2MgO_{(s)}$$

Hydrogen

$$2H_{2(g)} + O_{2(g)} \rightarrow 2H_2O_{(g)}$$

<u>Hydrogen</u> burns <u>very easily</u> in oxygen, in fact it can be <u>explosive</u>.
It has an <u>orangey/yellow flame</u> and the only product is <u>water</u> (as water vapour).

The combustion of hydrogen is often used as a <u>test</u> for hydrogen gas.
In small amounts, the resulting explosion gives the characteristic '<u>squeaky pop</u>' (see p.93).

Sulfur

<u>Sulfur</u> burns in air or oxygen with a <u>pale blue flame</u> and produces <u>sulfur dioxide</u>.
Sulfur dioxide is <u>acidic</u> when it's dissolved in water.

$$S_{(s)} + O_{2(g)} \rightarrow SO_{2(g)}$$

The **Thermal Decomposition** of Metal Carbonates Produces **CO$_2$**

1) If you <u>heat</u> a <u>metal carbonate</u>, you get <u>carbon dioxide</u> and a <u>metal oxide</u>.
2) This is an example of <u>thermal decomposition</u>, which is when a substance <u>breaks down</u> into simpler substances <u>when heated</u>.
3) <u>Copper(II) carbonate</u> is a <u>green powder</u> that will easily decompose to form <u>carbon dioxide</u> and <u>copper(II) oxide</u> when you heat it.
4) <u>Here's the equation</u> for the thermal decomposition of copper(II) carbonate:

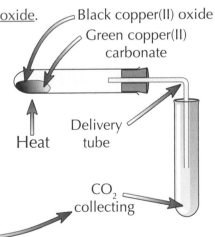

$$CuCO_{3(s)} \rightarrow CuO_{(s)} + CO_{2(g)}$$

copper(II) carbonate → copper oxide + carbon dioxide

5) To do the experiment, heat <u>copper(II) carbonate</u> then collect the gas that's given off in a <u>test tube</u>.
6) The gas that is collected can then be <u>tested</u> to see if it is CO$_2$ using the method on page 93.

As carbon dioxide is denser than air, it sinks to the bottom of the tube and can be collected.

An oxide is produced when an element is burnt in air

Thermal decomposition sounds scary, but 'thermal' is just 'heat' and 'decomposition' is breaking stuff down.

Carbon Dioxide

You've probably heard of <u>carbon dioxide</u> — it's always in the news. This page will tell you why.

Carbon Dioxide is a Greenhouse Gas

1) The <u>temperature</u> of the Earth is a <u>balance</u> between the heat it gets from the Sun and the heat it radiates back out into space.

2) Gases in the <u>atmosphere</u> like <u>carbon dioxide</u>, <u>methane</u> and <u>water vapour</u> naturally act like an <u>insulating layer</u>. They are often called '<u>greenhouse gases</u>'. They absorb most of the heat that would normally be radiated out into space, and re-radiate it in all directions — including back towards the Earth.

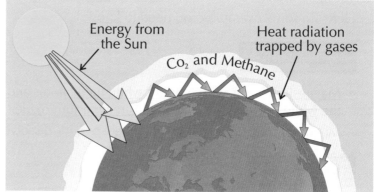

3) <u>Human activity</u> affects the <u>amount of carbon dioxide</u> in the atmosphere — examples include:

   <u>Deforestation</u>: fewer trees means less CO_2 is removed from the atmosphere via photosynthesis.
   <u>Burning fossil fuels</u>: carbon that was 'locked up' in these fuels is being released as CO_2.

4) It is because of this human activity that over the last 200 years or so, the concentration of carbon dioxide in the atmosphere has been increasing. For this to have happened, CO_2 must be being <u>released</u> into the air <u>faster</u> than it's being <u>removed</u> — this is linked to climate change (see below).

Increasing Carbon Dioxide is Linked to Climate Change

1) There's a <u>correlation</u> between increasing levels of carbon dioxide and the gradual <u>heating up</u> of the Earth's atmosphere (<u>global warming</u>). Although the Earth's temperature varies naturally, there's a <u>scientific consensus</u> that the extra carbon dioxide has <u>caused</u> the average <u>temperature</u> of the Earth to <u>increase</u>.

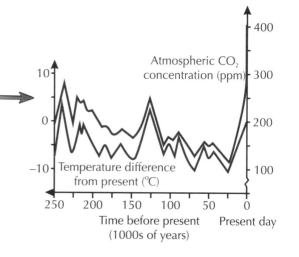

2) Global warming is a type of <u>climate change</u> and causes other types of climate change, e.g. changing rainfall patterns. It could also cause severe <u>flooding</u> due to the polar ice caps melting and <u>sea level rise</u>.

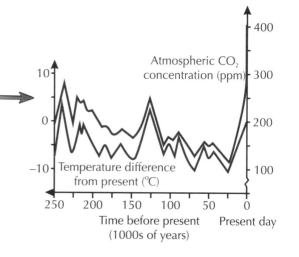

(EXAM TIP) ## Human activity has increased the concentration of CO_2
Be careful to use the right phrases in the exam — <u>global warming</u> is just the <u>heating up</u> of the Earth's <u>atmosphere</u> over the last 200 years, but the <u>climate</u> has changed in <u>other ways</u> too.

Warm-Up & Exam Questions

Time to see how much you remember from the previous few pages. This page is full of questions on gases and the atmosphere — have a go at them and then take a well-earned break.

Warm-Up Questions

1) Give the approximate percentages of the following gases in the air:
   a) nitrogen   b) carbon dioxide
2) Give the equation for the thermal decomposition of $CuCO_3$.
3) Give one example of a human activity that is leading to an increase in the concentration of carbon dioxide in the atmosphere.

Exam Questions

1   Carbon dioxide is a greenhouse gas.

(a)   This experiment was used to compare the effects of nitrogen and carbon dioxide on heat radiation.

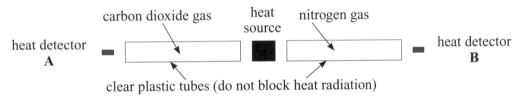

carbon dioxide gas   heat source   nitrogen gas

heat detector **A**   heat detector **B**

clear plastic tubes (do not block heat radiation)

Suggest which detector, **A** or **B**, will detect more heat from the heat source. Explain your choice.

[2 marks]

(b)   Explain the effect of atmospheric carbon dioxide on heat radiated from the Earth's surface.

[2 marks]

2   Some elements burn in air to produce oxides.

(a)   State the colour of the flame from the combustion reaction of sulfur.

[1 mark]

(b)   Magnesium can also be burnt to form an oxide.
      Describe what you would see when magnesium is burnt in air.

[2 marks]

(c)   Give the balanced symbol equation for the combustion of hydrogen in air.

[2 marks]

PRACTICAL

3   The proportion of oxygen in the atmosphere can be found by heating an excess of phosphorus so that it reacts with oxygen in the air to form phosphorus oxide.

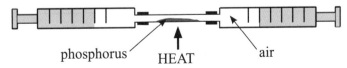

phosphorus   HEAT   air

There was 50.0 cm³ of dry air in the apparatus at the start of the experiment.
How much air would be in the apparatus at the end of the experiment?

[2 marks]

Section 4 — Inorganic Chemistry

 **Reactions of Metals**

Reactive metals tend to do exciting, fizzy things when you drop them into acid or water...

How **Metals** React With **Acids** Tells You About Their **Reactivity**

1) Some metals react with acids to produce a <u>salt</u> and <u>hydrogen gas</u>.

$$\textbf{Acid + Metal} \rightarrow \textbf{Salt + Hydrogen}$$

2) You can use the reactions of different metals with <u>dilute acids</u> to work out how <u>reactive</u> they are. The more <u>reactive</u> the metal, the <u>faster</u> the reaction will go — very reactive metals (e.g. sodium) react <u>explosively</u>.

3) You can carry out a practical to investigate the <u>differences in reactivity</u> of a variety of metals by using their reaction with acids.

4) First, set up <u>three boiling tubes</u> and fill them with <u>equal volumes</u> of <u>dilute hydrochloric acid</u> or <u>dilute sulfuric acid</u>.

The type of salt produced depends on the acid used — see page 83.

5) Then, place pieces of <u>magnesium</u>, <u>zinc</u> and <u>iron</u> in separate test tubes — make sure that the size and shape of the metal pieces is the same.

6) The <u>speed</u> of reaction is indicated by the <u>rate</u> at which the <u>bubbles</u> of hydrogen are given off.

7) The <u>hydrogen</u> is confirmed by the <u>burning splint test</u> (see page 93). The magnesium should give the loudest 'squeaky pop' as it has the most vigorous reaction producing the most hydrogen gas.

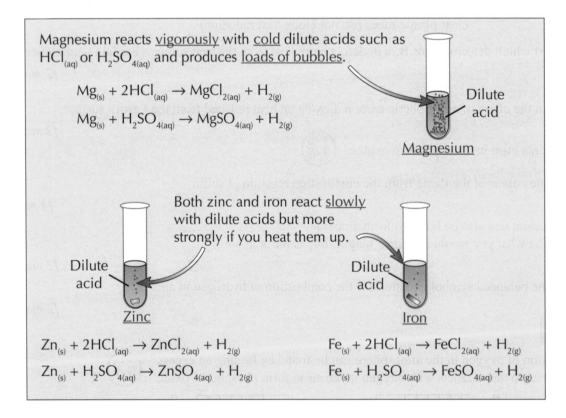

Magnesium reacts <u>vigorously</u> with <u>cold</u> dilute acids such as $HCl_{(aq)}$ or $H_2SO_{4(aq)}$ and produces <u>loads of bubbles</u>.

$$Mg_{(s)} + 2HCl_{(aq)} \rightarrow MgCl_{2(aq)} + H_{2(g)}$$
$$Mg_{(s)} + H_2SO_{4(aq)} \rightarrow MgSO_{4(aq)} + H_{2(g)}$$

Both zinc and iron react <u>slowly</u> with dilute acids but more strongly if you heat them up.

$$Zn_{(s)} + 2HCl_{(aq)} \rightarrow ZnCl_{2(aq)} + H_{2(g)}$$
$$Zn_{(s)} + H_2SO_{4(aq)} \rightarrow ZnSO_{4(aq)} + H_{2(g)}$$

$$Fe_{(s)} + 2HCl_{(aq)} \rightarrow FeCl_{2(aq)} + H_{2(g)}$$
$$Fe_{(s)} + H_2SO_{4(aq)} \rightarrow FeSO_{4(aq)} + H_{2(g)}$$

 ## Always take care when carrying out experiments

You should always think about how you could <u>minimise</u> the possible <u>risks</u> before doing any practical work. For example, when carrying out the reactions above, you should wear <u>goggles</u> to protect yourself from any acid that might spit out of the test tube when you add the metal.

Reactions of Metals

The <u>reactions of metals</u> with <u>water</u> and <u>steam</u> aren't quite as exciting as those with acids (see previous page). Still, they might just come up in your exam, so read on...

Some Metals React With Water

1) In a similar way to their reactions with acids, the reactions of metals with <u>water</u> also show the reactivity of metals.

2) This is the basic reaction:

metal + water → metal hydroxide + hydrogen

3) Very reactive metals like <u>potassium</u>, <u>sodium</u>, <u>lithium</u> and <u>calcium</u> will all react <u>vigorously</u> with water.

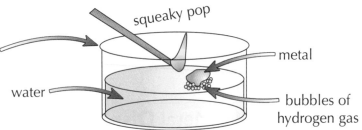

squeaky pop

metal

water

bubbles of hydrogen gas

Less Reactive Metals Only React With Steam

1) Less reactive metals like <u>magnesium</u>, <u>zinc</u> and <u>iron</u> won't react much with cold water, but they will react with <u>steam</u>.

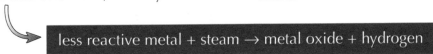

less reactive metal + steam → metal oxide + hydrogen

2) You could show this in the lab using this <u>experiment</u>:

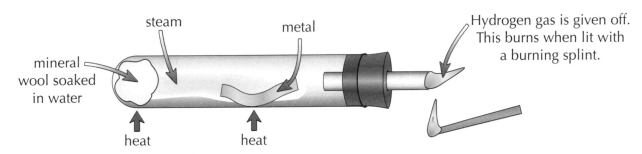

steam

metal

Hydrogen gas is given off. This burns when lit with a burning splint.

mineral wool soaked in water

heat

heat

3) <u>Copper</u> is so unreactive that it won't react with either water or steam.

Less reactive metals need a bit of encouragement to react with H_2O

Some metals lower down the reactivity series aren't reactive enough to react with liquid water — they'll only react if you give the water a bit more <u>energy</u> by heating it to form <u>steam</u>. Splendid.

The Reactivity Series

Once you know how reactive metals are, you can put them in order of their reactivity...

The **Reactivity Series** — How Well a **Metal** Reacts

The reactivity series lists metals in order of their reactivity towards other substances.

Make sure you learn this list:

The Reactivity Series

Potassium	K	Very Reactive
Sodium	Na	
Lithium	Li	
Calcium	Ca	
Magnesium	Mg	Fairly Reactive
Aluminium	Al	
Zinc	Zn	
Iron	Fe	Not very Reactive
Copper	Cu	
Silver	Ag	
Gold	Au	Not at all Reactive

A **More Reactive** Metal **Displaces** a **Less Reactive** Metal

1) More reactive metals react more strongly than less reactive metals.

2) This means that a more reactive metal will displace a less reactive metal from its oxide because it will bond more strongly to the oxygen.

> Example: iron would be displaced from iron oxide by the more reactive aluminium.
>
> iron oxide + aluminium → aluminium oxide + iron
>
> Fe_2O_3 + 2Al → Al_2O_3 + 2Fe

Oxidation and reduction can refer to the gain and loss of electrons (see p.65) or oxygen (see p.76).

3) Displacement reactions like the ones above are redox reactions (see p.65) — the metal is oxidised and the displaced metal ion is reduced.

4) Metal compounds like copper sulfate, zinc chloride and sodium chloride are metal salts.

5) If you put a reactive metal into a solution of a less reactive metal salt the reactive metal will replace the less reactive metal in the salt.

> Example: put an iron nail in a solution of copper sulfate and the more reactive iron will "kick out" the less reactive copper from the salt. You end up with iron sulfate solution and copper metal.
>
> copper sulfate + iron → iron sulfate + copper
>
> $CuSO_4$ + Fe → $FeSO_4$ + Cu
>
> Cu^{2+} + Fe → Fe^{2+} + Cu

In this reaction, copper is reduced and iron is oxidised.

6) If a piece of silver metal is put into a solution of copper sulfate, nothing happens. The more reactive metal (copper) is already in the salt.

7) If a reaction occurs, there will be a change in temperature. A more reactive metal will give a greater change in temperature than a less reactive metal.

8) You can use displacement reactions to work out where in the reactivity series a metal is supposed to go. E.g. if you were given a lump of a mystery metal, you could try reacting it with different metal oxides and salts. If it reacted with copper oxide you'd know it was higher in the series than copper. If it didn't react with magnesium sulfate you'd know it was lower than magnesium in the reactivity series.

 Displacement reactions are redox reactions...

Learn the reactivity series — penguins so love cold mackerel and zebras ironically cut some grass.

Iron

Iron's <u>strength</u> has made it a very important metal that's used throughout the world for <u>building construction</u>, <u>car manufacture</u> and wrought iron <u>garden furniture</u>. But the problem is — it rusts...

Iron and Steel **Corrode** to Make **Rust**

1) Iron corrodes easily. In other words, it <u>rusts</u>.

2) Rusting only happens when the iron's in contact with both <u>oxygen</u> (from the air) and <u>water</u>.

The word "rust" is only used for the corrosion of iron, not other metals.

3) The chemical reaction that takes place when iron corrodes is an <u>oxidation</u> reaction — see next page. The iron <u>gains oxygen</u> to form <u>iron(III) oxide</u>.

4) Water then becomes loosely bonded to the iron(III) oxide and the result is <u>hydrated iron(III) oxide</u> — which we call rust.

5) Learn the <u>word equation</u> for the reaction:

> **iron + oxygen + water → hydrated iron(III) oxide (rust)**

6) Unfortunately, rust is a soft crumbly solid that soon <u>flakes off</u> to leave more iron available to <u>rust again</u>.

There are **Two** Main Ways to **Prevent Rusting**

1) The obvious way to prevent rusting is to <u>coat the iron</u> with a <u>barrier</u> to keep out the water and oxygen.

Barrier Methods

- <u>Painting/Coating with plastic</u> — ideal for big and small structures alike. It can be decorative too.
- <u>Oiling/Greasing</u> — this has to be used when moving parts are involved, like on bike chains.

2) The other way is the <u>sacrificial method</u>. This involves placing a <u>more reactive metal</u> with the iron. The water and oxygen then react with this sacrificial metal <u>instead</u> of with the iron.

Sacrificial Method

- <u>Zinc</u> is often used as a sacrificial metal.
- The zinc is <u>more reactive</u> than iron — it's further up the reactivity series.
- So, the zinc will be oxidised <u>instead</u> of the iron.
- A <u>coating of zinc</u> can be sprayed onto the object — this is known as <u>galvanising</u>.
- Or big <u>blocks of zinc</u> can be bolted to the iron. This is used on ships' hulls, or on underground iron pipes.

Rust is hydrated iron(III) oxide...

Remember that rust is the product of iron coming into contact with both oxygen <u>and</u> water. Paint, oil and grease have to be regularly re-applied to iron to stop it from rusting, which can get <u>expensive</u>.

Metals and Redox

Most metals can't be found as pure lumps. You have to extract them from a compound. This involves reduction. Don't panic though, this page will tell you all about it.

Oxidation is the Addition of Oxygen, Reduction is its Removal

1) Oxidation can mean the reaction with, or addition of oxygen.
   Reduction can be the removal of oxygen.

OXIDATION — GAIN OF OXYGEN
Magnesium is oxidised to magnesium oxide.

$$2Mg + O_2 \rightarrow 2MgO$$

REDUCTION — LOSS OF OXYGEN
Copper oxide is reduced to copper using carbon.

$$2CuO + C \rightarrow 2Cu + CO_2$$

---

2) In an oxidation reaction, the substance that oxidises the metal (and is reduced) is the oxidising agent.

3) In a reduction reaction, the substance that reduces the metal (and is oxidised) is called the reducing agent.

Most Metals are Found in Ores and have to be Separated

1) Metals that are unreactive don't tend to form compounds with other elements. Unreactive metals such as gold are found uncombined — so you just have to find them and dig them up.

2) However, most metals do react with other elements to form compounds, which can be found naturally in the Earth's crust. If a compound contains enough of the metal to make it worthwhile extracting, the compound is called a metal ore. There are limited amounts of metal ores — they're "finite resources".

3) The more reactive a metal is, the harder it is to extract it from a compound.

4) Lots of common metals like iron and aluminium form metal oxide ores.
   The metal can be separated from its oxide by a reduction reaction.

5) The most common type of reduction reaction uses carbon as a reducing agent to separate the oxygen from the metal.

$$2Fe_2O_3 + 3C \rightarrow 4Fe + 3CO_2$$

iron oxide + carbon → iron + carbon dioxide

6) But carbon can't be used for all metals. There's more on this on the next page.

Paper 2   *Paper 2*

Some metals are extracted from their ores using reduction reactions

Learn the definitions for oxidation and reduction. Then remember that extracting metals from their ores involves the removal of oxygen from the metal. Lots to learn here — look, cover, write, check.

Extracting Metals

If you're happy with the previous page and the reactivity series (see p.74), this one shouldn't be too tricky — it's just about which <u>method</u> of <u>extraction</u> is needed for different metal ores.

Methods of **Extraction** are Linked to the **Order of Reactivity**

Extraction by Reduction with Carbon

1) Only metals that are <u>less reactive</u> than <u>carbon</u> can be extracted by a reduction reaction with carbon — this is done by <u>heating</u> the ore with <u>carbon monoxide</u>. E.g. <u>iron oxide</u> is reduced in an blast furnace to make <u>iron</u>.

2) This is because <u>more reactive elements</u> form compounds more <u>readily</u>. Carbon's more reactive than iron, so carbon 'steals' oxygen from iron oxide (see page 74).

3) In other words, carbon <u>can only take the oxygen</u> away from metals which are <u>less reactive</u> than carbon <u>itself</u> is.

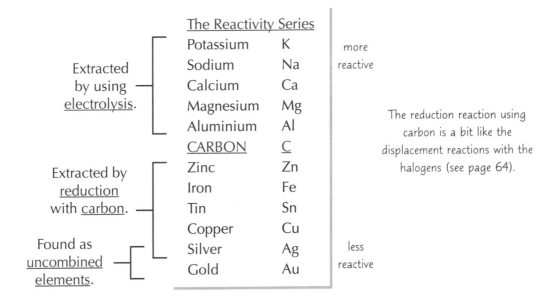

The Reactivity Series

Extracted by using <u>electrolysis</u>.
Potassium	K
Sodium	Na
Calcium	Ca
Magnesium	Mg
Aluminium	Al

<u>CARBON</u> <u>C</u>

Extracted by <u>reduction</u> with <u>carbon</u>.
Zinc	Zn
Iron	Fe
Tin	Sn
Copper	Cu

Found as <u>uncombined</u> <u>elements</u>.
| Silver | Ag |
| Gold | Au |

more reactive

less reactive

The reduction reaction using carbon is a bit like the displacement reactions with the halogens (see page 64).

Extraction by Electrolysis

1) Very reactive metals form very <u>stable</u> ores — i.e. it's difficult to get the metal out of its compound.

2) So metals that are <u>more reactive</u> than carbon (they come <u>higher</u> in the <u>reactivity series</u>) have to be extracted using <u>electrolysis</u>.

3) Electrolysis uses <u>electricity</u> to <u>separate the metal</u> from the other elements in the compound (see p.56). For example, aluminium is extracted from <u>aluminium oxide</u> using electrolysis.

Paper 2

Paper 2

Carbon can't reduce things that are above it in the reactivity series

Make sure you've got that reactivity series sorted in your head. If a metal's <u>below</u> carbon in the reactivity series, then it's <u>less reactive</u> than carbon and can be extracted from its ore by <u>reduction</u> using carbon.

78

Uses of Metals

Copper, iron and aluminium are the most produced metals in the whole wide world. Time to learn why.

Copper, Iron and Aluminium have some Properties in Common

Copper, iron and aluminium have the same basic properties — they are all metals after all.

1) They are dense and lustrous (i.e. shiny) and have high melting points —
   iron melts at 1538 °C, aluminium melts at 660 °C and copper melts at 1085 °C.

2) They have high tensile strength — they're strong and hard to break.

There's more on the properties
of metals on page 39.

3) But they can also be hammered into a different shape (they're malleable).

4) They are good conductors of electricity and of heat energy too.

The Uses of Metals Depend on their Properties

Copper

- Copper is an especially good conductor of heat and electricity.

- It is used in electrical components and wiring as it has low
  resistance and so is efficient at transferring electricity.

- It is also used in heating systems, such as underfloor heating,
  as it allows speedy transfer of heat to the surroundings.

Iron

- Iron has all the properties you'd expect a metal to have.
  Adding other materials to the iron can change its properties
  though (see next page).

- Wrought iron is almost completely pure iron.
  It's malleable, so it's used to make gates and railings.

- The main problem with iron is that it corrodes easily
  (i.e. it rusts).

Paper 2

Paper 2

Uses of Metals

Aluminium

- Aluminium is also a typical metal. However, unlike iron, it doesn't corrode easily.

- The aluminium reacts very quickly with oxygen in the air to form aluminium oxide. A nice protective layer of aluminium oxide sticks firmly to the aluminium below and stops any further reaction taking place.

- Because aluminium doesn't corrode it's useful for products that come in contact with water, e.g. drinks cans — you wouldn't want rust in your fizzy pop.

- Aluminium is also much less dense than iron, which makes it lighter.

- This makes it useful when the weight of the metal is important, e.g. in bicycle frames and aeroplanes.

Pure Metals Don't Always Have the Properties Needed

1) The regular structure of pure metals makes them soft — often too soft for use in everyday life.

2) Alloys are made by adding other elements to the metal (usually other metals and/or carbon).

3) Different elements have different sized atoms. So when another element is mixed with a pure metal, the new atoms will distort the layers of metal atoms, making it more difficult for them to slide over each other. This makes alloys harder than pure metals.

4) Alloys of iron called steels are often used instead of pure iron. Steels are made by adding small amounts of carbon and sometimes other metals to iron.

TYPE OF STEEL	PROPERTIES	USE
Low carbon steel (0.1–0.3% carbon)	easily shaped	car bodies
High carbon steel (0.22–2.5% carbon)	very strong, inflexible, brittle	bridges
Stainless steel (chromium added, and sometimes nickel)	corrosion-resistant, hard	cutlery

Low carbon steel is also known as mild steel.

5) Many other alloys are used in everyday life, e.g. brass (copper + zinc) and bronze (copper + tin).

How a metal is used will depend on its properties

A property that is good for one application may be a disadvantage in another, e.g. some metals are used for pans as they conduct heat well, but they're rarely used for mugs — hot drinks would cool too quickly.

Warm-Up & Exam Questions

Lots of information to learn on the previous few pages. Here are some questions on metals, their reactions and their uses to test yourself with.

Warm-Up Questions

1) Magnesium is reacted with dilute hydrochloric acid. Give the name of the salt formed.
2) Explain why a more reactive metal will displace a less reactive metal from its oxide.
3) What two things are needed for iron to rust?
4) How would you extract tin from its metal ore. Explain your answer.
5) Give one use of steel.

Exam Questions

PRACTICAL

1   A student performed some experiments to investigate the reactivity of metals.

(a)   First, the student placed pieces of four different metals into dilute hydrochloric acid. The diagram below shows what the four experiments looked like after 1 minute.

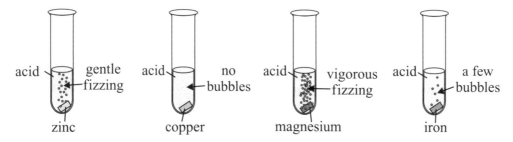

Use the information in the diagram to put these metals in order of decreasing reactivity.

[2 marks]

(b)   Next, the student was given samples of three mystery metals, marked **X**, **Y** and **Z**. She put small pieces of each of the metals in cold water. If there was no reaction with cold water, she tested the metal to see if it would react with steam. Her results are shown in the table below.

Metal	Any reaction with cold water?	Any reaction with steam?
X	Reacts vigorously. Hydrogen gas is produced.	
Y	no reaction	Reacts vigorously. Metal is coated with a white solid. Hydrogen gas is produced.
Z	no reaction	no reaction

(i)   Metal **Y** was zinc. It reacted with the steam to produce hydrogen gas and a white solid. Name the white solid that was produced by this reaction.

[1 mark]

(ii)   One of the other metals the student was given was sodium. Suggest whether sodium was metal **X** or metal **Z**. Give a reason for your answer.

[1 mark]

Exam Questions

2   Not all metals can be extracted using carbon.
    Some need to be extracted using a different method.

    (a)   Give the name of the process used to extract these metals.

                                                                        [1 mark]

    (b)   Explain why not all metals can be extracted using carbon.

                                                                        [1 mark]

3   There are several methods that can be used to prevent the corrosion of metals and alloys.

    (a)   A ship manufacturer wants to prevent the corrosion of a steel ship using sacrificial protection.
          Describe what is meant by sacrificial protection and explain how it protects the ship.

                                                                        [3 marks]

    (b)   A roofing company coats an iron roof with a layer of zinc to protect it from rusting.
          After a while, the zinc layer becomes scratched.
          Would you expect the iron roofing to begin to rust? Explain your answer.

                                                                        [2 marks]

4   The different properties of iron and aluminium lead to differences in their uses.

    Metals can be used in the construction of racing yachts.
    Suggest which metal out of iron and aluminium would be most suitable for this use.
    Explain your answer.

                                                                        [3 marks]

5   A student carries out a displacement reaction by reacting magnesium with
    an aqueous solution of iron(II) chloride ($FeCl_2$) to produce magnesium chloride and iron.

    (a)   Write the balanced symbol equation for this reaction, including state symbols.

                                                                        [2 marks]

    (b)   Explain why this displacement reaction is an example of a redox reaction.

                                                                        [2 marks]

    (c)   Copper is a brown metal and copper(II) sulfate is blue in solution.
          Aluminium is a shiny grey metal and aluminium sulfate is colourless in solution.

          Predict the student's observations when aluminium is added to copper(II) sulfate.

                                                                        [2 marks]

82

Acids and Alkalis

To test the pH of a solution, you can use an <u>indicator</u> — and that means pretty <u>colours</u>...

The **pH Scale** Goes from **0 to 14**

1) The <u>strongest acid</u> has <u>pH 0</u>. The <u>strongest alkali</u> has <u>pH 14</u>.
2) A <u>neutral</u> substance has <u>pH 7</u> (e.g. pure water).

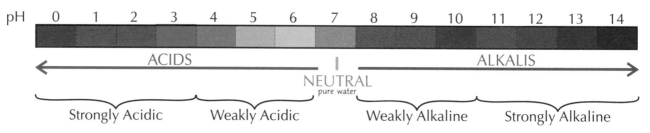

An **Indicator** is Just a **Dye** That Changes **Colour**

The dye in the indicator <u>changes colour</u> depending on whether it's <u>above</u> or <u>below</u> a <u>certain pH</u>.
Indicators are very useful for <u>estimating</u> the pH of a solution. There are several different types:

1) <u>Universal indicator</u> is a very useful <u>combination of dyes</u> which gives the colours shown above.
   To find the pH of an <u>aqueous solution</u>, add the indicator to the solution
   you are testing and compare the colour formed to a chart.
2) <u>Litmus paper</u> tests whether a solution is acidic or alkaline because
   it changes colour at about pH 7. It's <u>red</u> in <u>acidic</u> solutions,
   <u>purple</u> in <u>neutral</u> solutions and <u>blue</u> in <u>alkaline</u> solutions.
3) <u>Phenolphthalein</u> will change from <u>colourless</u> in <u>acidic</u> solutions
   to <u>bright pink</u> in <u>alkaline</u> solutions.
4) <u>Methyl orange</u> changes from <u>red</u> in <u>acidic</u> solutions to
   <u>yellow</u> in <u>alkaline</u> solutions.

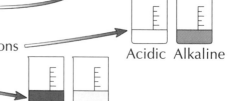

Acids can be **Neutralised** by **Bases** (or **Alkalis**)

An <u>ACID</u> is a source of <u>hydrogen ions</u> (H^+). They are <u>proton donors</u>. Acids have a pH of less than 7.

A <u>BASE</u> is a substance that can neutralise an acid. They are <u>proton acceptors</u>. <u>ALKALIS</u> are
<u>soluble bases</u>. An alkali is a source of <u>hydroxide ions</u> (<u>OH$^-$</u>) and has a pH greater than 7.

The reaction between an acid and a base (or an acid and an alkali) is called <u>neutralisation</u>.
Neutralisation can be seen in terms of <u>H$^+$</u> and <u>OH$^-$ ions</u> like this:

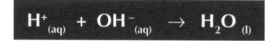

$$H^+_{(aq)} + OH^-_{(aq)} \rightarrow H_2O_{(l)}$$

These reactions are sometimes
called acid-base reactions.

The reaction can also be seen in terms of <u>proton transfer</u>.
The acid <u>donates</u> protons which are then <u>accepted</u> by the base.
When an acid neutralises a base (or vice versa), the <u>products</u> are <u>neutral</u>, i.e. they have a <u>pH of 7</u>.

Interesting fact — your skin is slightly acidic (pH 5.5)

You'll need to <u>know</u> all this stuff <u>later</u> in the section so make sure you've got it <u>nailed</u> before moving on.

Section 4 — Inorganic Chemistry

Reactions of Acids

Acids are an enthusiastic bunch — they get involved in loads of reactions.
For example, they can react with <u>metals</u> (see page 72), <u>metal oxides</u> and <u>metal carbonates</u>.

Salts Form When Acids React with Bases...

1) A <u>salt</u>, an ionic compound, is formed during a <u>neutralisation reaction</u> (a reaction between an <u>acid</u> and a <u>base</u>). This is a general equation for a neutralisation reaction:

$$acid + base \rightarrow salt + water$$

2) The <u>type of salt</u> depends on the <u>acid</u> used. In general, <u>hydrochloric acid</u> produces <u>chloride</u> salts, <u>sulfuric acid</u> produces <u>sulfate salts</u> and <u>nitric acid</u> produces <u>nitrate salts</u>.

3) You need to be able to remember what happens when you add acids to various bases...

Acid + Metal Oxide → Salt + Water

<u>Examples</u>: $2HCl + CuO \rightarrow CuCl_2 + H_2O$ (Copper chloride)
$H_2SO_4 + ZnO \rightarrow ZnSO_4 + H_2O$ (Zinc sulfate)
$2HNO_3 + MgO \rightarrow Mg(NO_3)_2 + H_2O$ (Magnesium nitrate)

Acid + Metal Hydroxide → Salt + Water

<u>Examples</u>: $HCl + NaOH \rightarrow NaCl + H_2O$ (Sodium chloride)
$H_2SO_4 + Zn(OH)_2 \rightarrow ZnSO_4 + 2H_2O$ (Zinc sulfate)
$HNO_3 + KOH \rightarrow KNO_3 + H_2O$ (Potassium nitrate)

These are the same as the acid/alkali neutralisation reaction you met on page 82.

Acid + Ammonia → Ammonium Salt

<u>Examples</u>: $HNO_{3(aq)} + NH_{3(aq)} \rightarrow NH_4NO_{3(aq)}$ (ammonium nitrate)
$H_2SO_{4(aq)} + 2NH_{3(aq)} \rightarrow (NH_4)_2SO_{4(aq)}$ (ammonium sulfate)

When ammonia dissolves in water it forms NH_4^+ and OH^- ions. So this reaction is actually:
$NH_4^+ + OH^- + HNO_3 \rightarrow NH_4NO_3 + H_2O$ as the reactant is aqueous ammonia.

...And When Acids React With Metals or Metal Carbonates

You also need to know what happens when you react an <u>acid</u> with a <u>metal</u> or a <u>metal carbonate</u>. The reaction of acids and metals is covered on page 72 in more detail.

<u>Examples</u>: $2HCl + Mg \rightarrow MgCl_2 + H_2$ (Magnesium chloride)
$H_2SO_4 + Mg \rightarrow MgSO_4 + H_2$ (Magnesium sulfate)

The reaction of nitric acid with metals can be more complicated — you get a nitrate salt, but instead of hydrogen gas, the other products are usually a mixture of water, NO and NO_2.

Acid + Metal Carbonate → Salt + Water + Carbon Dioxide

<u>Examples</u>: hydrochloric acid + sodium carbonate → sodium chloride + water + carbon dioxide
$2HCl + Na_2CO_3 \rightarrow 2NaCl + H_2O + CO_2$

sulfuric acid + calcium carbonate → calcium sulfate + water + carbon dioxide
$H_2SO_4 + CaCO_3 \rightarrow CaSO_4 + H_2O + CO_2$

nitric acid + calcium carbonate → calcium nitrate + water + carbon dioxide
$2HNO_3 + CaCO_3 \rightarrow Ca(NO_3)_2 + H_2O + CO_2$

Quite a few reactions to learn here...

...but learning the <u>general equations</u> for each reaction can help, e.g. <u>acid</u> + <u>base</u> → <u>salt</u> + <u>water</u>.

Titrations

Titrations have a bad reputation — but they're not as bad as they're made out to be.

Titrations are Used to Find Out Concentrations

1) Titrations allow you to find out exactly how much acid is needed to neutralise a quantity of alkali (or vice versa). Here's how you do a titration...

2) Using a pipette and pipette filler, add some alkali (usually about 25 cm³) to a conical flask, along with two or three drops of indicator. (The pipette filler stops you getting a mouthful of alkali.)

   You can also do titrations the other way round — adding alkali to acid.

3) Fill a burette with the acid. Make sure you do this BELOW EYE LEVEL — you don't want to be looking up if some acid spills over.

4) Using the burette, add the acid to the alkali a bit at a time — giving the conical flask a regular swirl. Go especially slowly when you think the end-point (colour change) is about to be reached.

5) The indicator changes colour when all the alkali has been neutralised, e.g. phenolphthalein is pink in alkalis, but colourless in acids.

6) Record the volume of acid used to neutralise the alkali. It's best to repeat this process a few times, making sure you get (pretty much) the same answer each time — this makes for more reliable results.

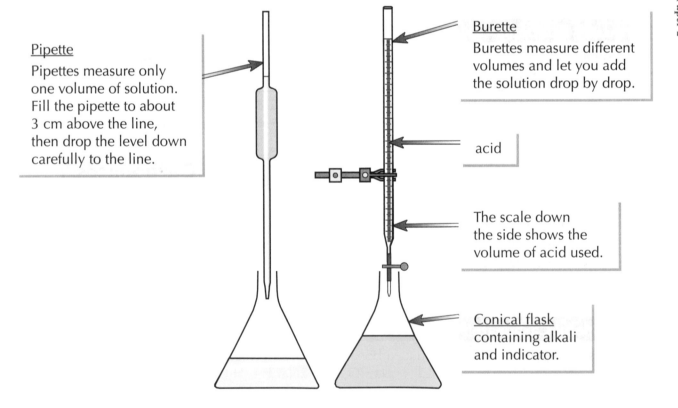

Paper 2

Pipette
Pipettes measure only one volume of solution. Fill the pipette to about 3 cm above the line, then drop the level down carefully to the line.

Burette
Burettes measure different volumes and let you add the solution drop by drop.

acid

The scale down the side shows the volume of acid used.

Conical flask
containing alkali and indicator.

Paper 2

Phenolphthalein is a handy indicator — learn how to spell it
The indicator tells you when the reaction is finished. Phenolphthalein is good for acids and alkalis, but you could use others. However, don't use universal indicator — it's too hard to tell accurately when the reaction is over. You want an indicator that gives a sudden colour change.

Titration Calculations

Once you've done a titration, you can carry out some <u>calculations</u> with your results.

The **Calculation** — Work Out the **Numbers of Moles**

Basically, you're trying to find the <u>number of moles</u> of each substance (see p.44).
A <u>formula triangle</u> is pretty handy here, I reckon. (And it's the same one as on page 52, conveniently.)

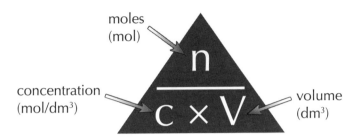

moles (mol)

concentration (mol/dm³)

volume (dm³)

Example:

Suppose you start off with <u>25 cm³</u> of sodium hydroxide solution in your flask, and you know that its concentration is <u>0.1 moles per dm³</u>.
You then find from your titration that it takes <u>30 cm³</u> of sulfuric acid (of an unknown concentration) to neutralise the sodium hydroxide.

To find the <u>concentration</u> of the acid:

<u>Step 1</u>: Work out how many <u>moles</u> of the 'known' substance you have:
Number of moles = concentration × volume = 0.1 × (25 ÷ 1000) = <u>0.0025 moles</u>

<u>Step 2</u>: Write down the <u>equation</u> for the reaction...

$$2NaOH + H_2SO_4 \longrightarrow Na_2SO_4 + 2H_2O$$

...and work out how many <u>moles</u> of the '<u>unknown</u>' stuff you must have had.

Using the equation, you can see that for every <u>two moles</u> of sodium hydroxide you had...
...there was just <u>one mole</u> of sulfuric acid.

So if you had <u>0.0025 moles</u> of sodium hydroxide...
...you must have had 0.0025 ÷ 2 = <u>0.00125 moles</u> of sulfuric acid.

<u>Step 3</u>: Work out the concentration of the '<u>unknown</u>' stuff.
Concentration = number of moles ÷ volume
= 0.00125 ÷ (30 ÷ 1000)
= <u>0.0417 mol/dm³</u>

If you need the concentration in g/dm³, convert your answer using the method on page 52.

Titration calculations really aren't too bad

Remembering the <u>formula triangle</u> will be a huge help, because you can use that to find the missing values in <u>Step 1</u> and <u>Step 3</u>. Apart from that, you just need the <u>balanced equation</u>.

Making Insoluble Salts

Unfortunately for you, you've got to learn which salts are <u>soluble</u> and which ones <u>aren't</u>.

The **Rules** of **Solubility**

*Soluble things dissolve in water.
Insoluble things don't.*

1) How you make a salt depends on whether it's <u>soluble</u> or <u>insoluble</u>.

2) You may need to work out if, when two solutions are mixed, a salt will form as a <u>precipitate</u> (i.e. it's an insoluble salt), or whether it will just form <u>in solution</u> (i.e. it's a soluble salt).

3) This table is a pretty fail-safe way of working out whether a substance is soluble in water or not.

Substance	Soluble or Insoluble?
common salts of sodium, potassium and ammonium	soluble
nitrates	soluble
common chlorides	soluble (except silver chloride and lead (II) chloride)
common sulfates	soluble (except lead (II), barium and calcium sulfate)
common carbonates	insoluble (except for sodium, potassium and ammonium ones)
common hydroxides	insoluble (except for sodium, potassium and calcium ones)

Making **Insoluble** Salts — **Precipitation** Reactions

1) To make a pure, dry sample of an <u>insoluble</u> salt, you can use a <u>precipitation reaction</u>. You just need to pick the right two <u>soluble salts</u> and <u>react</u> them together to get your <u>insoluble salt</u>.

2) E.g. to make <u>lead sulfate</u> (insoluble), mix <u>lead nitrate</u> and <u>magnesium sulfate</u> (both soluble).

lead nitrate + magnesium sulfate → lead sulfate + magnesium nitrate

$$Pb(NO_3)_{2\ (aq)} + MgSO_{4(aq)} \rightarrow PbSO_{4\ (s)} + Mg(NO_3)_{2\ (aq)}$$

Making **Lead Sulfate**   PRACTICAL

1) Add 1 spatula of <u>lead nitrate</u> to a test tube. Add <u>water</u> to dissolve it. You should use deionised water to make sure there are no other ions about. <u>Shake it thoroughly</u> to ensure that all the lead nitrate has <u>dissolved</u>. Then, in a separate test tube, do the same with 1 spatula of <u>magnesium sulfate</u>.

precipitate

2) Tip the <u>two solutions</u> into a small beaker, and give it a good stir to make sure it's all mixed together. The <u>lead sulfate</u> should <u>precipitate</u> out.

filter paper
filter funnel

3) Put a folded piece of <u>filter paper</u> into a <u>filter funnel</u>, and stick the funnel into a <u>conical flask</u>.

4) <u>Pour</u> the contents of the beaker into the middle of the filter paper. Make sure that the solution doesn't go above the filter paper — otherwise some of the solid could dribble down the side.

5) <u>Swill out</u> the beaker with more deionised water, and tip this into the filter paper — to make sure you get <u>all the precipitate</u> from the beaker.

6) Rinse the contents of the filter paper with deionised water to make sure that <u>all the soluble magnesium nitrate</u> has been washed away.

7) Then just scrape the <u>lead sulfate</u> onto fresh filter paper and leave it to dry in an oven or a desiccator.

lead sulfate

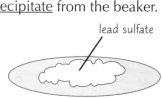

Paper 2

Making Soluble Salts   PRACTICAL

You met the technique for making <u>insoluble salts</u> on the last page. Time for <u>soluble salts</u> now...

Making **Soluble Salts** — Use an **Acid** and an **Insoluble Base**

You can make a <u>soluble salt</u> by reacting an <u>acid</u> that contains one of the ions you want in the salt with an <u>insoluble base</u> that contains the other ion you need (often a <u>metal oxide</u> or <u>metal hydroxide</u>).

For some salts, you can use a <u>metal</u> instead of the base.

Method

1) Start by <u>heating the acid</u> in a <u>water bath</u> — this speeds up the reaction between the acid and the insoluble base. Do this in a <u>fume cupboard</u> to avoid releasing acid fumes into the room.

2) Then add the <u>base</u> to the <u>acid</u> — the base and acid will react to produce a <u>soluble salt</u> (and water). You will know when the base is in excess and all the acid has been neutralised because the excess solid will just <u>sink</u> to the bottom of the flask.

It's important that the base is in excess so that you don't have any leftover acid in your product.

3) <u>Filter</u> off the <u>excess</u> solid to get a solution containing only the <u>salt</u> and <u>water</u>.

4) <u>Heat the solution gently</u>, using a Bunsen burner, to slowly <u>evaporate</u> off some of the water.

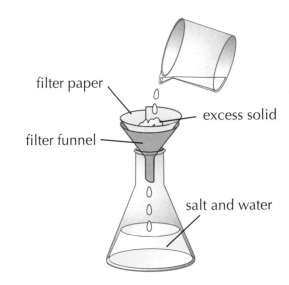

filter paper
excess solid
filter funnel
salt and water

5) Leave the solution to cool and allow the salt to <u>crystallise</u> (see p.15).

6) Filter off the <u>solid salt</u> and leave it to <u>dry</u>.

<u>Example:</u> You can add <u>copper oxide</u> to warm <u>sulfuric acid</u> to make a solution of <u>copper sulfate</u>:
$$CuO_{(s)} + H_2SO_{4\,(aq)} \rightarrow CuSO_{4\,(aq)} + H_2O_{(l)}$$
If you evaporate off some of the water and leave this solution to <u>crystallise</u>, you should get lovely <u>blue crystals</u> of <u>hydrated copper sulfate</u>, which you can <u>filter off</u> and <u>dry</u>.

Acid + insoluble base → soluble salt + water
Remember to make sure the <u>base</u> is <u>in excess</u> in this experiment, so that you <u>don't have</u> any <u>leftover acid</u> in your product. That way, the <u>final solution</u> is simply a <u>soluble salt</u> and <u>water</u>.

Making Soluble Salts

You can Make Soluble Salts Using Acid/Alkali Reactions

1) Soluble salts (salts that dissolve in water) can be made by reacting an acid with an <u>alkali</u>.

2) But you can't tell whether the reaction has <u>finished</u> — there's no signal that all the acid has been neutralised. You also can't just add an <u>excess</u> of alkali to the acid, because the salt is <u>soluble</u> and would be contaminated with the excess alkali.

3) Instead, you need to work out <u>exactly</u> the right amount of alkali to <u>neutralise</u> the acid. For this, you need to do a <u>titration</u> using an <u>indicator</u>. Here's what you do...

Method

1) Measure out a set amount of acid into a conical flask using a <u>pipette</u>.

2) Add a few drops of <u>indicator</u>. For a titration, you should use an indicator with a <u>single, clear colour change</u> (like <u>phenolphthalein</u> or <u>methyl orange</u>). Universal indicator is no good as its colour change is <u>too gradual</u>.

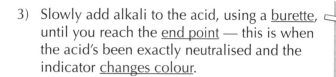

3) Slowly add alkali to the acid, using a <u>burette</u>, until you reach the <u>end point</u> — this is when the acid's been exactly neutralised and the indicator <u>changes colour</u>.

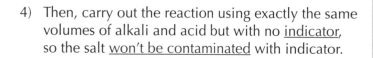

4) Then, carry out the reaction using exactly the same volumes of alkali and acid but with no <u>indicator</u>, so the salt <u>won't be contaminated</u> with indicator.

5) The <u>solution</u> that remains when the reaction is complete contains only the <u>salt</u> and <u>water</u>.

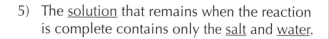

See page 84 for more on titrations.

6) Slowly <u>evaporate</u> off some of the water and then leave the solution to crystallise (see page 15 for more on crystallisation). Filter off the solid and dry it — you'll be left with a <u>pure</u>, <u>dry</u> salt.

Titrations can be used to make sure the alkali isn't in excess

Alkalis are <u>soluble</u> in water, so it's hard to stop them from <u>contaminating</u> the soluble salt produced in the reaction. Fortunately, <u>titrations</u> can help you out — they allow you to calculate the <u>exact amount</u> of acid and alkali you need to add to <u>complete the reaction</u> without either of them being in excess. Splendid.

Warm-Up & Exam Questions

Salt, glorious salt. There were a lot of experimental methods crammed into the last few pages, so make sure you can remember each of the steps and why they're important before tackling these questions.

Warm-Up Questions

1) What range of values does pH take?

2) What term is used to describe a substance with a pH of 7?

3) Caustic soda is a strong alkali. Suggest what its pH is.

4) Write the word equation for the reaction between sulfuric acid and magnesium oxide.

5) Suggest an indicator that would be suitable for use in a titration.

Exam Questions

1 Bleach has a pH of around 12.
Complete the table to show what colour it would turn the following indicators.

Indicator	Colour
Litmus paper	....
Phenolphthalein	....
Universal indicator	purple
Methyl orange	....

[3 marks]

2 A student has a test tube containing some acid.
The student adds a few drops of Universal indicator to the acid and it turns red.
The student then gradually adds some alkali to the test tube.

(a) What type of ions in the acid cause the indicator to become red?

[1 mark]

(b) What type of reaction takes place between the acid and the alkali?

[1 mark]

(c) Write the equation for the reaction that occurs between the ions in the acid and the alkali.
Include state symbols in your answer.

[2 marks]

3 When a spatula of magnesium carbonate powder ($MgCO_3$) is added to
a test tube containing nitric acid (HNO_3), bubbles of gas are given off.

(a) Name the gas evolved during the reaction.

[1 mark]

(b) Write a balanced symbol equation for the reaction.

[2 marks]

(c) Some magnesium carbonate powder is left over.
Suggest an appropriate acid that could be added to it to make magnesium chloride.

[1 mark]

Exam Questions

4   A student is making a sample of lead sulfate, an insoluble salt, by mixing two salt solutions.

   (a)   Suggest **two** salt solutions that the student could mix to make lead sulfate.

[1 mark]

   (b)   Once the student has made the salt, he pours the whole solid and salt solution into a filter funnel, as shown in the diagram below.

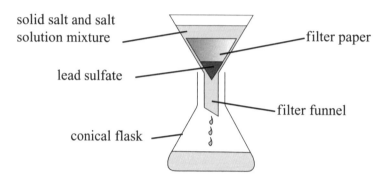

solid salt and salt solution mixture

filter paper

lead sulfate

filter funnel

conical flask

      What has the student done wrong? Explain how this could affect the mass of solid salt that he collects from the solution.

[2 marks]

   (c)   In a second reaction, the student wants to produce the insoluble salt calcium carbonate, $CaCO_3$. Suggest **two** soluble salts he could react together to make a precipitate of calcium carbonate.

[2 marks]

5   In a titration, 10.0 cm^3 of sulfuric acid was used to neutralise 30.0 cm^3 of 0.10 mol/dm^3 potassium hydroxide solution. The equation for the reaction is:

$$H_2SO_4 \ + \ 2KOH \ \rightarrow \ K_2SO_4 \ + \ 2H_2O$$

   (a)   Calculate the concentration of the sulfuric acid in mol/dm^3.

[3 marks]

   (b)   Calculate the concentration of the sulfuric acid in g/dm^3.

[2 marks]

6   Copper sulfate is a soluble salt that can be made by the reaction between sulfuric acid, H_2SO_4, and copper oxide, CuO.

   (a)   Write a balanced chemical equation, including state symbols, for the reaction between sulfuric acid and copper oxide.

[2 marks]

   (b)   Outline how you could prepare a pure, dry sample of copper sulfate in the lab from sulfuric acid and copper oxide.

[6 marks]

Tests for Cations

Cations are positively charged ions. You can identify some of them using the tests on this page.

Flame Tests Identify Metal Ions

Compounds of some metals burn with a characteristic colour (as you see every November 5th).

So you can test for various metal ions by heating your substance
and seeing whether it burns with a distinctive colour flame.

> Lithium, Li+, burns with a red flame.
> Sodium, Na+, burns with a yellow flame.
> Potassium, K+, burns with a lilac flame.
> Calcium, Ca²⁺, burns with an orange-red flame.
> Copper ions, Cu²⁺, give a blue-green flame.

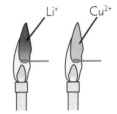

To do the test you need to clean a platinum wire loop by dipping it in some dilute HCl and then holding it in a flame. Once you hold the loop in the flame and it burns without any colour you can dip it into the sample you want to test, then put it back in the clear blue part of the Bunsen flame (the hottest bit).

Some Metals Form a Coloured Precipitate with NaOH

This is also a test for metal ions, but it's slightly more involved. Concentrate now...

1) Many metal hydroxides are insoluble and precipitate out of solution when formed. Some of these hydroxides have a characteristic colour.

2) So in this test you add a few drops of sodium hydroxide solution to a solution of your mystery compound in a test tube — all in the hope of forming an insoluble hydroxide.

3) If you get a coloured insoluble hydroxide you can then tell which metal was in the compound.

Metal Ion	Colour of Precipitate	Ionic Equation
Copper(II), Cu²⁺	Blue	$Cu^{2+}_{(aq)} + 2OH^-_{(aq)} \rightarrow Cu(OH)_{2(s)}$
Iron(II), Fe²⁺	Sludgy green	$Fe^{2+}_{(aq)} + 2OH^-_{(aq)} \rightarrow Fe(OH)_{2(s)}$
Iron(III), Fe³⁺	Reddish brown	$Fe^{3+}_{(aq)} + 3OH^-_{(aq)} \rightarrow Fe(OH)_{3(s)}$

"Ammonium Compound + NaOH" Gives Off (Stinky) Ammonia

1) Ammonia gas (NH_3) is smelly — it reeks of cat wee. You can usually tell if there's some about, but it's not a good idea to smell it deliberately as it can be really harmful to your eyes — not cool.

2) You can check for ammonia gas using a damp piece of red litmus paper. If there's ammonia present, the paper will turn blue.

3) You can use this to test whether a substance contains ammonium ions (NH_4^+). Add some sodium hydroxide to a solution of your mystery substance in a test tube. If there's ammonia given off this means there are ammonium ions in your mystery substance.

The litmus paper needs to be damp so the ammonia gas can dissolve and make the colour change.

The colour of a flame test depends on the metal ion present

Lots of ions and colours to learn here, so just take your time. It might help to come up with little ways of remembering the colours — like Little Red Riding Hood. Or Yellow BaNaNas. It's fab.

Tests for Anions

It's not just positive ions you can test for, you'll be pleased to know.
Yep, you can also test for <u>negative ions</u>. So the fun goes on...

Hydrochloric Acid Can Help Detect Carbonates

To <u>test for carbonates</u>, add dilute <u>hydrochloric acid</u> (HCl) to your test sample.
If <u>carbonates</u> (CO_3^{2-}) are present then <u>carbon dioxide</u> will be released.

Carbonates give off CO_2 with HCl

carbonate + acid → carbon dioxide + water
$$CO_3{}^{2-}{}_{(s)} + 2H^+{}_{(aq)} \rightarrow CO_{2(g)} + H_2O_{(l)}$$

You can test for carbon dioxide using <u>limewater</u> — see next page.

Test for Sulfates with HCl and Barium Chloride

Sulfate ions (SO_4^{2-}) produce a white precipitate

To test for a <u>sulfate</u> ion (SO_4^{2-}), add <u>dilute HCl</u>, followed by <u>barium chloride solution</u>, $BaCl_2$.

$$Ba^{2+}{}_{(aq)} + SO_4{}^{2-}{}_{(aq)} \rightarrow BaSO_{4(s)}$$
barium ions + sulfate ions → barium sulfate

A <u>white precipitate</u> of <u>barium sulfate</u> means the original compound was a sulfate.

(The <u>hydrochloric acid</u> is added to get rid of any traces of <u>carbonate</u> or <u>sulfite</u> ions before you do the test.
Both of these would also produce a precipitate, so they'd <u>confuse</u> the results.)

Test for Halides (Cl⁻, Br⁻, I⁻) with Nitric Acid and Silver Nitrate

To test for <u>chloride</u>, <u>bromide</u> or <u>iodide</u> ions, add dilute <u>nitric acid</u> (HNO$_3$),
followed by <u>silver nitrate solution</u> (AgNO$_3$).

$$Ag^+{}_{(aq)} + Cl^-{}_{(aq)} \longrightarrow AgCl_{(s)}$$ A <u>chloride</u> gives a <u>white precipitate</u> of <u>silver chloride</u>.

$$Ag^+{}_{(aq)} + Br^-{}_{(aq)} \longrightarrow AgBr_{(s)}$$ A <u>bromide</u> gives a <u>cream precipitate</u> of <u>silver bromide</u>.

$$Ag^+{}_{(aq)} + I^-{}_{(aq)} \longrightarrow AgI_{(s)}$$ An <u>iodide</u> gives a <u>yellow precipitate</u> of <u>silver iodide</u>.

(Again, the <u>acid</u> is added to get rid of <u>carbonate</u> or <u>sulfite</u> ions before the test.
You use <u>nitric acid</u> in this test, though, <u>not HCl</u>.)

Halide ions can form precipitates with silver nitrate

There are a few tests to learn here, along with their results. That's quite a bit of information to
take in, so don't just stare at the whole page till your eyes are swimming and you never ever want
to see the word '<u>precipitate</u>' again. Just learn the tests <u>one by one</u> and you'll be absolutely fine.

Tests for Gases

There are lots of clever ways of testing for different gases, so get learning the ones below.

There are Tests for 5 Common Gases

1) Chlorine

Chlorine bleaches damp blue litmus paper, turning it white. (It may turn red for a moment first though — that's because a solution of chlorine is acidic.)

Blue litmus paper

2) Oxygen

Oxygen relights a glowing splint.

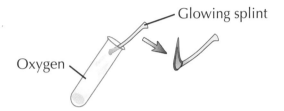
Glowing splint
Oxygen

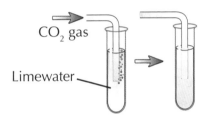
CO_2 gas
Limewater

3) Carbon Dioxide

Carbon dioxide turns limewater cloudy — just bubble the gas through a test tube of limewater and watch what happens.

4) Hydrogen

Hydrogen makes a "squeaky pop" with a lighted splint. (The noise comes from the hydrogen burning with the oxygen in the air to form H_2O.)

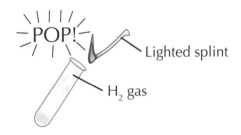
POP!
Lighted splint
H_2 gas

Red litmus paper

5) Ammonia

Ammonia turns damp red litmus paper blue. (It also has a very strong smell.)

PRACTICAL TIP

These are all really useful tests to know...

The method you use to collect a gas will depend on whether it's lighter or heavier than air. If it's heavier (like chlorine), you have the test tube the right way up and the gas will sink to the bottom. If it's lighter (like hydrogen), you have the test tube upside-down and the gas will rise to fill it.

Tests for Water

Dipping your finger in a liquid and saying "it's wet" is not the best test for water.
Don't worry though, there's a more scientific method that you can use...

Wet Copper(II) Sulfate is Blue — Dry Copper(II) Sulfate is White

Copper(II) sulfate crystals can be used as a test for water.

1) When copper(II) sulfate is bound to water (water of crystallisation, see page 50) it forms lovely blue crystals.

2) If you heat the blue hydrated copper(II) sulfate crystals it drives the water off.

Water vapour

3) This leaves a white anhydrous copper(II) sulfate powder, which doesn't have any water bound to it.

Hydrated means with water.
Anhydrous means without water.

4) If you then add a couple of drops of water to the white powder you get the blue crystals back again.

So, if you want to test for water, all you need to do is add anhydrous copper(II) sulfate and see if the white powder turns blue.
This test will tell you if water is present in a solution but it won't tell you if the water is pure.

Checking the Purity of Water

1) When a sample is pure it means it's only made up of one substance.

2) This means it has set defined physical properties like boiling point and freezing point.

3) Pure water will always:

Boil at 100 °C
Freeze at 0 °C

4) If you find the boiling point isn't 100 °C or freezing point isn't 0 °C then the sample isn't pure.

Blue copper(II) sulfate crystals contain water

Unlike with all those tests for cations and anions (pages 91 and 92) there are only two colours you need to remember here: blue and white. So, all in all, getting this lot learnt should be a pretty straightforward job.

Warm-Up & Exam Questions

Now some questions to hone your skills. There are quite a few little details to learn for all those
ion tests, plus the tests for gases and water, so make sure you've got it all before you move on.

Warm-Up Questions

1) A compound burns with a red flame. What metal ion does it contain?
2) a) Describe a test to identify ammonia gas.
   b) How does this test allow you to test for ammonium ions?
3) Describe the test for chlorine gas.
4) What colour are hydrated copper(II) sulfate crystals?

Exam Questions

1 Electrolysis of water gives hydrogen gas and oxygen gas.

 (a) Describe a simple laboratory test that you could use to identify hydrogen gas.

[2 marks]

 (b) Describe a simple laboratory test that you could use to identify oxygen gas.

[2 marks]

2 Potassium chloride is used to replace some of the sodium chloride in low-sodium table salt.
 A flame test can be used to tell the difference between potassium chloride and sodium chloride.

 (a) Describe how to carry out a flame test.

[2 marks]

 (b) Explain how you could tell from a flame test that a substance was potassium chloride
 and not sodium chloride.

[2 marks]

 (c) Some medicines contain potassium sodium tartrate. Suggest why you cannot use a
 flame test to show that these medicines contain potassium.

[2 marks]

3 A student has a sample of an ionic compound and wants to test for the presence of different ions.

 (a) Give the chemical formula and charge of the negative ion present
 in magnesium carbonate.

[1 mark]

 (b) (i) State which **two** reactants are used to test for sulfate ions.

[2 marks]

 (ii) What would be observed after adding these reactants to a solution of a sulfate compound?

[1 mark]

4 A student is given a solution and told that it contains either chloride or
 carbonate ions. Describe how the student could test for each of these ions,
 and what the student would see in each case if the ions were present.

[4 marks]

Revision Summary for Section 4

Well, that wraps up Section 4 — time to test your mettle (pun intended) on some revision questions.
- Try these questions and tick off each one when you get it right.
- When you've done all the questions under a heading and are completely happy with it, tick it off.

Alkali Metals and Halogens (p.61-65) ☐
1) Name the gas that is produced when an alkali metal reacts with water.
2) Describe how the reactivity of the halogens changes as you go up the group.
3) What is a displacement reaction?
4) If you mix chlorine water with potassium bromide solution, what colour will it go?

Atmospheric Gases (p.67-70) ☐
5) What percentage of the atmosphere is oxygen?
6) Describe the reaction that happens when magnesium is burnt in oxygen.
7) Explain the link between carbon dioxide and global warming.

Metals and their Uses (p.72-79) ☐
8) Write the word equation for the reaction of an acid with a metal.
9) Give the name of: a) a very reactive metal, b) a not-at-all reactive metal.
10) What happens when a more reactive metal is put in a solution of a less reactive metal salt?
11) Describe two ways that rusting can be prevented.
12) Are metal oxides reduced or oxidised to obtain the metal from them?
    What role does carbon play in the reduction of a metal oxide with a less reactive metal?
13) What method of extraction would you use for a) magnesium, b) iron?
14) Name an element that can be added to iron to make steel.

Acids and Alkalis (p.82-85) ☐
15) What colour will methyl orange be in alkaline solutions?
16) What two products form when a metal oxide reacts with an acid?
17) Why should you carry out a titration multiple times?

Making Salts (p.86-88) ☐
18) List three insoluble sulfates.
19) Name two soluble hydroxides.
20) Describe how you could make a pure sample of a soluble salt from an acid and an alkali.

Chemical Tests (p.91-94) ☐
21) What colour flame does copper burn with?
22) What colour precipitate do iron(II) compounds form with sodium hydroxide?
23) What colour is the precipitate formed when a bromide ion reacts with dilute nitric acid and silver nitrate?
24) How can you tell if a sample of water is pure?

Energy Transfer in Reactions

Whenever chemical reactions occur, there are changes in <u>energy</u>. This means that when chemicals get together, things either <u>heat up</u> or <u>cool down</u>. Read on to find out more...

Reactions are **Exothermic** or **Endothermic**

An <u>EXOTHERMIC reaction</u> is one which <u>gives out energy</u> to the surroundings, usually in the form of <u>heat</u> and usually shown by a <u>rise in temperature</u> of the surroundings.

Combustion reactions (where something burns in oxygen — see page 125) are always exothermic.

An <u>ENDOTHERMIC reaction</u> is one which <u>takes in energy</u> from the surroundings, usually in the form of <u>heat</u> and usually shown by a <u>fall in temperature</u> of the surroundings.

The **Change in Energy** is Called the **Enthalpy Change**

The <u>overall change</u> in energy in a reaction is called the <u>ENTHALPY change</u>. It has the symbol ΔH.

Δ is the Greek letter 'delta'. It means 'change in'. The H means enthalpy.

1) The units of ΔH are <u>kJ/mol</u> — so it's the amount of energy in kilojoules per mole.
2) Enthalpy change can have a <u>positive</u> value or a <u>negative</u> value.
   - If the reaction is <u>exothermic</u>, the value is <u>negative</u> because the reaction is <u>giving out</u> energy.
   - If the reaction is <u>endothermic</u>, the value is <u>positive</u> because the reaction <u>takes in</u> energy.

Reaction Profiles Show **Energy Changes**

<u>Reaction profiles</u> are diagrams that show the <u>relative energies</u> of the reactants and products in a reaction, and how the energy <u>changes</u> over the course of the reaction.

Reaction profiles are sometimes called energy level diagrams.

1) This shows an <u>exothermic reaction</u> — the products are at a <u>lower energy</u> than the reactants. The difference in <u>height</u> represents the <u>energy given out</u> (per mole) in the reaction. ΔH is <u>negative</u> here.

2) The <u>initial rise</u> in energy represents the energy needed to <u>start the reaction</u>. This is the <u>activation energy</u> (E_a).

3) The activation energy is the <u>minimum amount</u> of energy the reactants need to <u>collide with each other</u> and <u>react</u>.

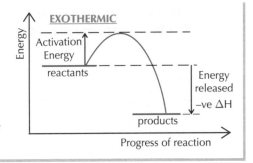

1) This shows an <u>endothermic reaction</u> because the products are at a <u>higher energy</u> than the reactants.

2) The difference in <u>height</u> represents the <u>energy taken in</u> (per mole) during the reaction. ΔH is <u>positive</u> here.

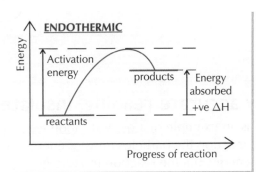

There's more on activation energy and collision theory on page 105.

Paper 2

Paper 2

PRACTICAL · Measuring Enthalpy Changes

Sometimes it's <u>not enough</u> to just know if a reaction is <u>endothermic</u> or <u>exothermic</u>. You may need to know <u>how much</u> energy is absorbed or released — you can do experiments to find this out. Fun, fun, fun...

You Can Find Out **Enthalpy Changes** Using **Calorimetry**

<u>Calorimetry</u> allows you to measure the amount of <u>energy transferred</u> in a <u>chemical reaction</u> with a pretty simple set of equipment. There are two different types of experiment you can do. Here's how you'd do the first one:

Calorimetry — **Dissolving, Displacement** and **Neutralisation** Reactions

To measure the amount of <u>energy transferred</u> in these <u>reactions</u> (in solution) you just take the <u>temperature of the reactants</u> (making sure they're the same), <u>mix</u> them and measure the <u>temperature of the solution</u> at the <u>end</u> of the reaction. Easy.

1) So if you want to investigate the enthalpy change of <u>dissolving</u>, <u>displacement</u> (see page 64) or <u>neutralisation</u> reactions (see page 82) you can do it by mixing the reactants in a <u>polystyrene cup</u>.

2) The biggest <u>problem</u> with energy measurements is the amount of energy <u>lost to the surroundings</u>.

3) You can reduce it a bit by putting the polystyrene cup into a <u>beaker of cotton wool</u> to give <u>more insulation</u>, and putting a <u>lid</u> on the cup to reduce energy lost by <u>evaporation</u>.

4) Here's how you could measure the energy transferred in a <u>neutralisation</u> reaction between hydrochloric acid (HCl) and sodium hydroxide (NaOH):

1) Put 25 cm³ of <u>hydrochloric acid</u> and <u>sodium hydroxide</u> in separate beakers.

2) Place the beakers in a <u>water bath</u> set to 25 °C until they are both at the <u>same temperature</u> (25 °C).

3) Add the HCl followed by the NaOH to a <u>polystyrene cup</u> with a lid — as in the diagram.

4) Take the <u>temperature</u> of the mixture <u>every 30 seconds</u>, and record the highest temperature.

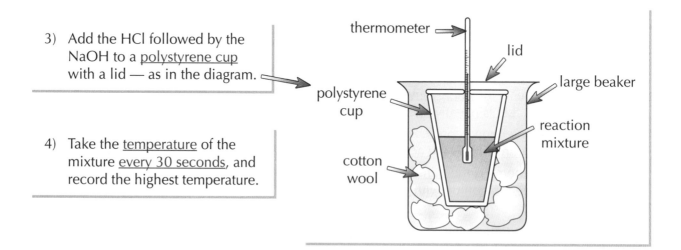

To get a reasonably accurate reading, insulate your reaction

The experiment on this page is an example of a <u>neutralisation reaction</u>, which is an <u>exothermic</u> reaction. Remember, in an exothermic reaction the particles <u>transfer</u> energy to their surroundings. This means that the particles themselves <u>lose</u> energy, but the reaction mixture gets <u>warmer</u>.

Measuring Enthalpy Changes

Here's the <u>other</u> type of calorimetry experiment you can do...

Calorimetry — **Combustion**

To measure the amount of energy transferred when a fuel is burnt, you can simply burn the fuel and use the flame to <u>heat up some water</u>. This method uses a <u>metal container</u>, usually made of <u>copper</u> because copper conducts heat so well.

1) It's dead important to make as much heat as possible go into <u>heating up</u> the water. <u>Reducing draughts</u> is the key here — use a <u>screen</u> to act as a draught excluder (and don't do it next to an open window).

2) Put 50 g of water in the copper can and <u>record its temperature</u>.

3) <u>Weigh the spirit burner</u> and lid.

4) Put the spirit burner underneath the can, and light the wick. Heat the water, <u>stirring constantly</u>, until the temperature reaches about <u>50 °C</u>.

5) <u>Put out the flame</u> using the burner lid, and measure the <u>final temperature</u> of the water.

6) <u>Weigh</u> the spirit burner and lid <u>again</u>.

7) You can then use the measurements you've taken to <u>calculate the enthalpy change</u> — see the next page.

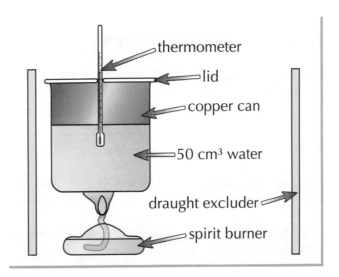

thermometer
lid
copper can
50 cm³ water
draught excluder
spirit burner

Measure the temperature change to find enthalpy changes

So you've seen two methods for measuring enthalpy changes. On the next page, you'll see how the results of the experiment on this page can be used in a calculation to work out the heat energy transferred.

Calculating Enthalpy Changes

If you've read the previous page, you'll know how to get <u>temperature measurements</u> from the start and end of reactions and to work out how much <u>fuel</u> was used for combustion. Now it's calculations time...

Calculate the Heat Energy Transferred

1) The <u>combustion</u> experiment on the previous page involves <u>heating water</u> by burning a <u>liquid fuel</u>.

2) If you measure (i) <u>how much fuel</u> you've burned and (ii) the <u>temperature change</u> of the water, you can work out how much energy is supplied by <u>each gram of fuel</u>. You need this equation:

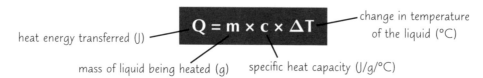

heat energy transferred (J)

$$Q = m \times c \times \Delta T$$

change in temperature of the liquid (°C)

mass of liquid being heated (g)   specific heat capacity (J/g/°C)

3) You also need to know water's <u>specific heat capacity</u> — this is the <u>amount of energy</u> needed to raise the temperature of <u>1 gram</u> of water by <u>1 °C</u>. The specific heat capacity of <u>water</u> is <u>4.2 J/g/°C</u> — so it takes 4.2 joules of energy to raise the temperature of 1 g of water by 1 °C.

<u>Example:</u> work out the heat energy change per gram of methylated spirit (meths)

Temperature of water in copper can before heating = 21.5 °C
Temperature of water in copper can after heating = 52.5 °C
⟹ Temperature rise of 50 g of water due to heating = <u>31.0 °C</u>

Using the equation, Q = m × c × ΔT,   You'll be given this value in the exam
the heat energy transferred in this experiment = 50 × 4.2 × 31 = 6510 joules.

Mass of spirit burner + lid before heating = 68.75 g
Mass of spirit burner + lid after heating = 67.85 g
⟹ Mass of meths burnt = 0.90 g

So 0.90 g of meths produces 6510 joules of energy...
...meaning 1 g of meths produces 6510/0.90 = <u>7230 J</u> or <u>7.23 kJ</u>

Energy's wasted heating the can, air, etc. So this figure will often be much lower than the <u>actual</u> energy content.

Calculate the Molar Enthalpy Change

Once you've calculated the <u>heat energy change</u> (Q) you can use it to work out the <u>molar enthalpy change, ΔH</u> (the enthalpy change given out by one mole of the reactant). See page 44 for more on moles. You need the <u>same info</u> as before and the <u>M_r</u> of the fuel (see page 43).

<u>Example:</u> work out the energy change per mole of methylated spirit (meths)

1) First calculate the <u>heat energy change</u> (Q). From the calculation above, we know the energy transferred in this experiment = 6510 J or 6.51 kJ.

2) Next, you need to find <u>how many moles of fuel</u> produced this energy change. The M_r of meths is 44.6.

To find the number of moles, use the equation: $\text{moles} = \dfrac{\text{mass (g)}}{M_r}$.

So, number of moles $= \dfrac{0.90}{44.6} = 0.020$ moles

The sign has changed to <u>negative</u> because combustion is an <u>exothermic</u> reaction.

3) So, the <u>heat transferred by 1 mole</u> of fuel (ΔH) $= \dfrac{-6.51}{0.020} = -325.5$ kJ/mol

---

Bond Energies

You can calculate the enthalpy change for a reaction by looking at the bonds that are made and broken.

Energy Must Always be Supplied to Break Bonds

There's more on energy transfer on page 97.

1) During a chemical reaction, old bonds are broken and new bonds are formed.
2) Energy must be supplied to break existing bonds — so bond breaking is an endothermic process.
3) Energy is released when new bonds are formed — so bond formation is an exothermic process.

BOND BREAKING — ENDOTHERMIC

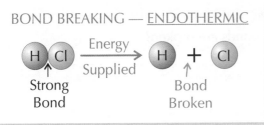

BOND FORMING — EXOTHERMIC

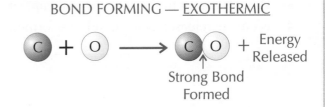

4) In endothermic reactions, the energy used to break bonds is greater than the energy released by forming them.
5) In exothermic reactions, the energy released by forming bonds is greater than the energy used to break them.

Bond Energy Calculations — Need to be Practised

1) Each type of chemical bond (e.g. C–C or C–H) has a particular bond energy associated with it.
2) This bond energy can vary slightly depending on what compound the bond is in — so you'll be given average bond energies in the exam.
3) You can use these to calculate the enthalpy change for a reaction. The basic idea is really simple — add up the energy of the bonds that are broken and subtract the energy of the bonds that are made.

$$\text{Enthalpy change } (\Delta H) = \text{Total energy absorbed to break bonds} - \text{Total energy released in making bonds}$$

4) A positive energy change means an endothermic reaction and a negative energy change means an exothermic reaction.
5) You need to practise a few of these, but the basic idea is really very simple...

Example: Using the bond energy values below, calculate the enthalpy change for the following reaction, where hydrogen and chlorine react to produce hydrogen chloride

$$H–H + Cl–Cl \rightarrow 2H–Cl$$

H–H: 436 kJ/mol   Cl–Cl: 242 kJ/mol   H–Cl: 431 kJ/mol

In this reaction, the energy released by forming bonds is greater than the energy used to break them so the reaction is exothermic.

1) Work out the energy required to break the original bonds in the reactants. $(1 \times H–H) + (1 \times Cl–Cl) = 436 + 242 = 678$ kJ/mol
2) Work out the energy released by forming the new bonds in the products. $(2 \times H–Cl) = 2 \times 431 = 862$ kJ/mol
3) Work out the enthalpy change. $\Delta H = 678 – 862 = –184$ kJ/mol

Take care when answering enthalpy change questions

When doing enthalpy change calculations, pay close attention to the number of bonds and the number of molecules involved in the reaction and be careful with positive and negative numbers.

Warm-Up & Exam Questions

Funny diagrams, a few different calculations and some practicals — there's a lot to get your head around in just a few pages here. Here are some questions so that you can check how you're getting on.

Warm-Up Questions

1) What is an endothermic reaction?
2) In a calorimetry experiment involving neutralisation, why should a beaker containing the reagents be insulated?
3) What is meant by the specific heat capacity of water?
4) Is energy released when bonds are formed or when bonds are broken?

Exam Questions

1 During the following reaction, the temperature of the reaction mixture decreases.

$$AB + C \rightarrow AC + B$$

(a) State, with a reason, whether the reaction is exothermic or endothermic.

[2 marks]

(b) (i) What is meant by the **enthalpy change** of a reaction?

[1 mark]

(ii) State whether the enthalpy change of the above reaction is positive or negative.

[1 mark]

(iii) Give the symbol that is used to represent enthalpy change.

[1 mark]

PAPER 2

2 The thermal decomposition of calcium carbonate is an endothermic reaction.

Sketch and label a reaction profile for this reaction on the axes below.
Label the enthalpy change.

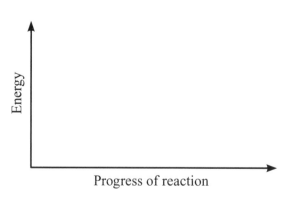

[3 marks]

Exam Questions

PAPER 2

3   Calculate the enthalpy change during the combustion of methane.
    The equation for the reaction, displayed formulae of the products
    and reactants, and bond energies are given below.

$$CH_4 + 2O_2 \rightarrow CO_2 + 2H_2O$$

C–H = +412 kJ/mol   O=O = +498 kJ/mol   C=O +743 kJ/mol   O–H = +463 kJ/mol

[4 marks]

PRACTICAL

4   A student measured the temperature change during a reaction between
    sodium hydroxide and hydrochloric acid using the apparatus shown below.

(a) Before mixing the reagents, the student measured
    the temperature of each of them. Explain why.

    [1 mark]

(b) State the purpose of:
    (i) the cotton wool

    [1 mark]

    (ii) the lid

    [1 mark]

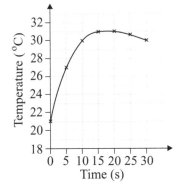

(c) The student measured the temperature over
    the first 30 seconds of the reaction. Her results
    are plotted on the graph shown on the right.
    What was the temperature increase during the reaction?

    [1 mark]

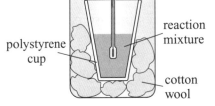

(d) What is the dependent variable in this experiment?

    [1 mark]

(e) How could the reliability of the results be improved?

    [1 mark]

(f) This is a neutralisation reaction. Give **one** other
    type of reaction this method could be used to study.

    [1 mark]

5   A student found that burning 1.15 g of ethanol (C_2H_5OH) raised the temperature of
    50.0 g of water by 34.5 °C. He calculated that this was a heat energy change of 7245 J.

(a) Calculate the number of moles of ethanol that the student burnt in his experiment.

    [2 marks]

(b) Calculate the molar enthalpy change (in kJ/mol) for the combustion of ethanol.

    [2 marks]

Rates of Reaction

In the chemical industry, the faster you make chemicals, the faster you make money. This all comes down to rates of reaction — and you need to know all about them.

Reactions Can Go at All Sorts of Different Rates

1) The rate of a chemical reaction is how fast the reactants are changed into products.
2) One of the slowest is the rusting of iron.
3) An example of a moderate speed reaction would be the metal magnesium reacting with an acid to produce a gentle stream of bubbles.
4) Burning is a fast reaction, but explosions are even faster and release a lot of gas. Explosive reactions are all over in a fraction of a second.

You Need to Understand Graphs for the Rate of Reaction

1) You can find the speed of a reaction by recording the amount of product formed, or the amount of reactant used up over time (see page 109).

2) The steeper the line on the graph, the faster the rate of reaction. Over time the line becomes less steep as the reactants are used up.

3) The quickest reactions have the steepest lines and become flat in the least time.

4) The plot below uses the amount of product formed over time to show how the speed of a particular reaction varies under different conditions.

For more on the conditions that affect the rate of reaction — see next page.

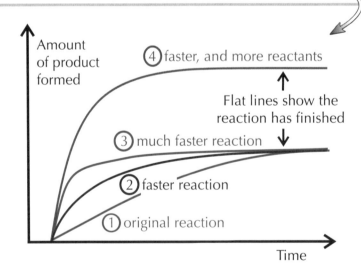

- Graph 1 represents the original reaction.
- Graphs 2 and 3 represent the reaction taking place quicker, but with the same initial amounts of reactants. The slopes of the graphs are steeper than for graph 1.
- Graphs 1, 2 and 3 all converge at the same level, showing that they all produce the same amount of product although they take different times to produce it.
- Graph 4 shows more product and a faster reaction. This can only happen if more reactant(s) are added at the start.

Factors Affecting Rates of Reaction

I'd ask you to <u>guess</u> what these two pages are about, but the <u>title</u> pretty much says it all really. Read on...

Particles Must **Collide** with **Enough Energy** in Order to **React**

1) Reaction rates are explained perfectly by <u>collision theory</u>. The <u>rate</u> of a chemical reaction depends on:

- The <u>collision frequency</u> of reacting particles (how <u>often</u> they collide). The <u>more</u> collisions there are the <u>faster</u> the reaction is. E.g. doubling the frequency of collisions doubles the rate.
- The energy <u>transferred</u> during a collision. Particles have to collide with <u>enough energy</u> for the collision to be successful.

A successful collision is a collision that ends in the particles reacting to form products.

2) The <u>minimum</u> amount of energy that particles need to react is called the <u>activation energy</u>. Particles need this much energy to <u>break the bonds</u> in the reactants and start the reaction. The <u>greater</u> the activation energy, the <u>more</u> energy needed to <u>start</u> the reaction — this has to be <u>supplied</u>, e.g. by <u>heating</u> the reaction mixture.

3) Factors that <u>increase</u> the <u>number</u> of collisions (so that a <u>greater proportion</u> of reacting particles collide) or the amount of <u>energy</u> particles collide with will <u>increase</u> the <u>rate</u> of the reaction.

The **Rate of Reaction** Depends on **Four Things**

1) <u>Temperature</u>.
2) The <u>concentration</u> of a solution or the <u>pressure</u> of gas.
3) <u>Surface area</u> — this changes depending on the size of the lumps of a solid.
4) The presence of a <u>catalyst</u> (see page 107).

The **More Collisions**, the **Higher** the Rate of Reaction

The <u>effects</u> of temperature, concentration (or pressure) and surface area on the <u>rate of reaction</u> can be explained in terms of <u>how often</u> the reacting particles <u>collide</u> and how much <u>energy</u> they collide with...

Increasing the **Temperature** Increases **Rate**

The effects of concentration (or pressure) and surface area are covered on the next page.

1) When the <u>temperature is increased</u> the particles <u>move faster</u>. If they move faster, they're going to have <u>more collisions</u>.

2) Higher temperatures also increase the <u>energy</u> of the collisions, since the particles are moving <u>faster</u>. Reactions <u>only happen</u> if the particles collide with <u>enough energy</u>.

3) This means that at <u>higher</u> temperatures there will be more <u>successful collisions</u> (more <u>particles</u> will <u>collide</u> with <u>enough energy</u> to react). So <u>increasing</u> the temperature <u>increases</u> the rate of reaction.

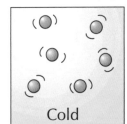

Cold

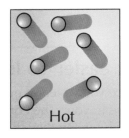

Hot

106

Factors Affecting Rates of Reaction

Increasing **Concentration** (or **Pressure**) Increases **Rate**

1) If a solution is made more concentrated its means there are more particles of reactant in the same volume. This makes collisions more likely, so the reaction rate increases.

2) In a gas, increasing the pressure means that the particles are more crowded. This means that the frequency of collisions between particles will increase — so the rate of reaction will also increase.

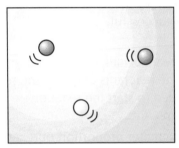 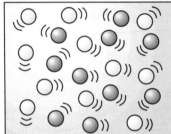

Low concentration (Low pressure) High concentration (High pressure)

Smaller Solid Particles (or **More Surface Area**) Means a Higher **Rate**

1) If one of the reactants is a solid, then breaking it up into smaller pieces will increase its surface area to volume ratio (i.e. more of the solid will be exposed, compared to its overall volume).

2) The particles around it will have more area to work on, so the frequency of collisions will increase.

3) This means that the rate of reaction is faster for solids with a larger surface area to volume ratio.

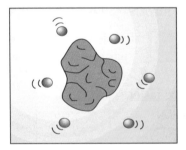 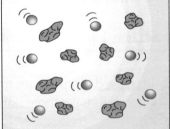

Small surface area to volume ratio Big surface area to volume ratio

It's easier to learn stuff when you know the reasons for it

Once you've learnt everything on these two pages, the rates of reaction stuff should start making a lot more sense to you. The concept's fairly simple — the more often particles bump into each other, and the harder they hit when they do, the faster the reaction happens. Right, onwards to some more rates of reaction fun...

Catalysts

Catalysts are very important for commercial reasons — they increase reaction rate and reduce energy costs in industrial reactions. They might come up in your exams too, so get reading this page.

A Catalyst Increases the Rate of a Reaction

1) A catalyst is a substance which increases the rate of a reaction, without being chemically changed or used up in the reaction.

2) Using a catalyst won't change the products of the reaction — so the equation will stay the same.

3) Because it isn't used up, you only need a tiny bit to catalyse large amounts of reactants.

4) Catalysts tend to be very fussy about which reactions they catalyse though — you can't just stick any old catalyst in a reaction and expect it to work.

5) Catalysts work by decreasing the activation energy (see page 105) needed for a reaction to occur.

6) They do this by providing an alternative reaction pathway that has a lower activation energy.

7) As a result, more of the particles have at least the minimum amount of energy needed for a reaction to occur when the particles collide.

You Can Show the Effect of a Catalyst using Reaction Profiles

1) The activation energy for a reaction can be shown on a reaction profile — it's the difference between the energy of the reactants and the highest point on the curve.

2) You can use reaction profiles to compare the activation energy of a reaction with and without a catalyst. There's more on reaction profiles on p.97.

3) The highest point on the curve for a reaction with a catalyst will be lower than without a catalyst.

4) Here are reaction profiles showing how a catalyst affects the activation energy for an exothermic and endothermic reaction (see page 97 for more on exo- and endothermic reactions).

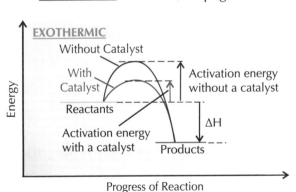

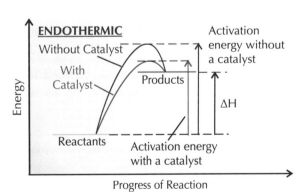

You can carry out experiments to investigate how catalysts affect the rate of a reaction — see page 113 for more.

Paper 2

Catalysts reduce the activation energy needed for reactions to occur

Some reactions take a very long time to happen by themselves, which isn't good for industrial reactions. Catalysts help to produce an acceptable amount of product in an acceptable length of time.

Warm-Up & Exam Questions

It's easy to think you've understood something when you've just read through it. These questions should test whether you really understand the previous chunk of pages, and get you set for the next bit.

Warm-Up Questions

1) Give an example of a reaction that happens very slowly, and one that is very fast.
2) True or False? A catalyst is unchanged chemically during a reaction.

Exam Questions

1   This question is about the rate of reaction between magnesium and hydrochloric acid. The chemical equation for the reaction is:

$$Mg_{(s)} + 2HCl_{(aq)} \rightarrow MgCl_{2(aq)} + H_{2(g)}$$

(a) The graph on the right shows how the volume of hydrogen produced changes over the course of the reaction when a small lump of magnesium is added to excess hydrochloric acid.

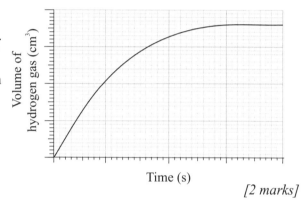

On the same axes, sketch a curve to show how the volume of hydrogen produced would change over time if an identical piece of magnesium was added to excess hydrochloric acid with a higher concentration.

[2 marks]

(b) State **two** properties of the collisions between particles that affect the rate of a reaction.

[2 marks]

(c) Use collision theory to explain why increasing the concentration of a reactant increases the rate of the reaction.

[2 marks]

(d) How would you expect the reaction rate to change if the magnesium was cut into smaller pieces?

[1 mark]

(e) Explain why cutting the magnesium into smaller pieces affects the rate of this reaction.

[2 marks]

(f) State **one** change that could be made to alter the rate of reaction, other than changing the concentration and the size of the magnesium pieces.

[1 mark]

2   A student carries out a reaction between hydrogen gas and iodine gas to form hydrogen iodide (HI).

(a) When cerium oxide is mixed with the hydrogen and iodine gases, the rate of reaction increases.
(i) What does this suggest about cerium oxide?

[1 mark]

(ii) Explain how cerium oxide increases the rate of the reaction.

[2 marks]

(b) State whether the reaction equation will change if cerium oxide is present in the reaction vessel. Explain your answer.

[2 marks]

Measuring Rates of Reaction

All this talk about rates of reaction is fine and dandy, but it's no good if you can't <u>measure</u> them.

The **Speed** of a Reaction Can be **Measured**

1) The <u>speed of a reaction</u> can be observed <u>either</u> by how quickly the reactants are used up or how quickly the products are formed. It's usually a lot easier to measure <u>products forming</u>.

2) The rate of reaction can be calculated using the following equation:

$$\text{Rate of Reaction} = \frac{\text{Amount of reactant used or amount of product formed}}{\text{Time}}$$

You Can Do **Experiments** to Follow **Reaction Rates**

There are different ways that the rate of a reaction can be <u>measured</u>.
Here's one example, and there are another two on the next page:

Precipitation

1) This method works for any reaction where mixing <u>two see-through solutions</u> produces a <u>precipitate</u>, which <u>clouds</u> the solution.

2) You <u>mix</u> the two reactant solutions and put the flask on a piece of paper that has a <u>mark</u> on it.

3) <u>Observe</u> the mark through the mixture and measure how long it takes for the mark to be <u>obscured</u>. The <u>faster</u> it disappears, the <u>faster</u> the reaction.

4) The result is <u>subjective</u> — <u>different people</u> might not agree on <u>exactly</u> when the mark 'disappears'.

You can use this method to investigate how temperature affects the rate of the reaction between sodium thiosulfate and hydrochloric acid. See page 112.

Make sure you use a method appropriate to your experiment

The method shown on this page only works if there's a <u>really obvious</u> change in the solution. If there's only a <u>small change</u> in colour, it <u>might not be possible</u> to observe and time the change.

Measuring Rates of Reaction

Change in Mass (Usually Gas Given Off)

1) You can measure the rate of a reaction that produces a gas using a mass balance.

2) As the gas is released, the lost mass is easily measured on the balance. The quicker the reading on the balance drops, the faster the reaction.

3) You know the reaction has finished when the reading on the balance stops changing.

4) You can use your results to plot a graph of change in mass against time.

5) This method does release the gas produced straight into the room — so if the gas is harmful, you must take safety precautions, e.g. do the experiment in a fume cupboard.

Putting cotton wool in the top of the flask lets the gas escape but stops the acid spitting out.

The Volume of Gas Given Off

1) This involves the use of a gas syringe to measure the volume of gas given off.

2) The more gas given off during a set time interval, the faster the reaction.

3) You can tell the reaction has finished when no more gas is produced.

4) You can use your results to plot a graph of gas volume against time elapsed.

5) You need to be careful that you're using the right size gas syringe for your experiment though — if the reaction is too vigorous, you can blow the plunger out of the end of the syringe.

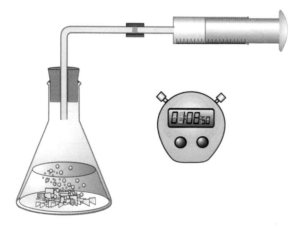

Each of these three methods has pros and cons

The mass balance method is only accurate as long as the flask isn't too hot, otherwise the loss in mass that you see might be partly due to the evaporation of liquid as well as being due to the loss of gas formed during the reaction. The first method (on the previous page) is subjective so it isn't very accurate, but if you're not producing a gas you can't use either of the other two.

Section 5 — Physical Chemistry

Rate of Reaction Experiments

You'll probably have to <u>measure</u> the <u>rate of a reaction</u> in class at some point. Time to learn how to do it...

You Can Measure how **Surface Area** Affects **Rate**

Here's how you can carry out an experiment to measure the effect of <u>surface area</u> on <u>rate</u>, using marble chips and hydrochloric acid:

1) Set the apparatus up as shown in the diagram on the right.
2) Measure the <u>volume</u> of gas produced using a <u>gas syringe</u>. Take readings at <u>regular time intervals</u> and record the results in a table.
3) You can plot a <u>graph</u> of your results — <u>time</u> goes on the <u>x-axis</u> and <u>volume</u> goes on the <u>y-axis</u>.
4) <u>Repeat</u> the experiment with <u>exactly the same volume</u> and <u>concentration</u> of acid, and <u>exactly the same mass</u> of marble chips, but with the marble <u>more crunched up</u>.
5) Then <u>repeat</u> with the same mass of <u>powdered chalk</u>.

It's important your system is air tight so no gas escapes.

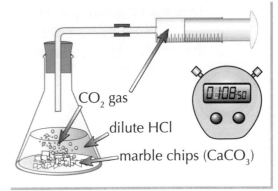

Marble and chalk are both made of calcium carbonate ($CaCO_3$).

Finer Particles of **Solid** Mean a **Higher Rate**

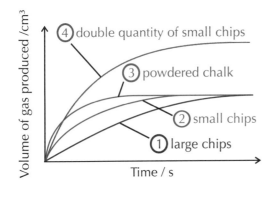

1) Using <u>finer particles</u> means that the marble has a <u>larger surface area</u>.
2) <u>Lines 1 to 3</u> on the graph on the left show that the <u>finer</u> the particles are (and the <u>greater</u> the surface area of the solid reactants), the <u>sooner</u> the reaction finishes and so the <u>faster</u> the reaction.
3) <u>Line 4</u> shows the reaction if a <u>greater mass</u> of small marble chips is added. The <u>extra surface area</u> gives a <u>faster reaction</u> and there is also <u>more gas evolved</u> overall.

Changing the **Concentration** of Acid Affects the **Rate** too

The reaction between marble chips and hydrochloric acid is also good for measuring how <u>changing the reactant concentration</u> affects reaction rate.

You could also measure the rate of these reactions by measuring the loss of mass as the gas is produced.

More Concentrated Solutions Mean a **Higher Rate**

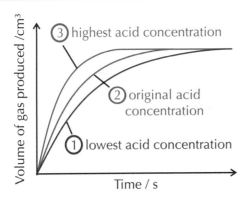

1) You can measure the effect of <u>concentration</u> on rate by following the <u>same method</u> described above. However, this time you repeat the experiment with exactly the same mass and surface area of marble chips and exactly the same volume of acid, but using <u>different concentrations</u> of acid.
2) <u>Lines 1 to 3</u> on the graph show that a <u>higher</u> concentration gives a <u>faster reaction</u>, with the reaction <u>finishing</u> sooner.

The graphs allow you to visually compare rates of reactions
However, to get exact numerical values for the rates you need to use a calculation (see page 109).

Rate of Reaction Experiments

Here's how to use the method you last saw on page 109. It's a bit <u>less accurate</u> than using a mass balance or a gas syringe, but it's handy because it lets you investigate a reaction that <u>doesn't produce a gas</u>.

Reaction Rate is Affected by Temperature

1) Sodium thiosulfate and hydrochloric acid are both <u>clear solutions</u>. They react together to form a <u>yellow precipitate</u> of <u>sulfur</u>.

2) You can measure the rate by watching the black mark <u>disappear</u> through the <u>cloudy sulfur</u> and <u>timing</u> how long it takes to go.

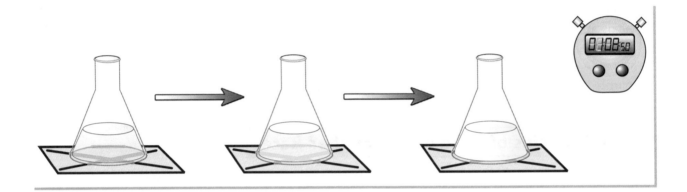

3) The reaction can be <u>repeated</u> for solutions at different <u>temperatures</u>. In practice, that's quite hard to do accurately and safely (it's not a good idea to heat an acid directly). The best way to do it is to use a <u>water bath</u> to heat both solutions to the right temperature <u>before you mix them</u>.

4) The <u>depth</u> of liquid must be kept the <u>same</u> each time, of course.

5) The results will of course show that the <u>higher</u> the temperature the <u>quicker</u> the reaction and therefore the <u>less time</u> it takes for the mark to <u>disappear</u>. These are typical results:

	Temperature (°C)	20	25	30	35	40
independent variable ⟶	Time taken for mark to disappear (s)	193	151	112	87	52

(row labels: "Temperature (°C)" is the independent variable; "Time taken for mark to disappear (s)" is the dependent variable)

6) This reaction can <u>also</u> be used to test the effects of <u>concentration</u>.

7) This reaction <u>doesn't</u> give you a set of graphs like those on the previous page. All you get is a set of <u>readings</u> of how long it took till the mark disappeared for each temperature.

Although you could draw a graph of temperature against 1/time, which will give you an approximate rate of reaction.

Make sure you can clearly see the cross at the start

With all of these experiments, you need to make sure you're only changing <u>one thing</u> for each repeat. So for this one, you need to make sure only <u>temperature</u> is changed, and not, e.g. the <u>concentration</u> of HCl. That way you'll know that it's definitely the temperature affecting the rate.

Rate of Reaction Experiments

Good news — this is the last rate experiment. This one looks at how a catalyst affects rate of reaction.

You Can Measure How Using Catalysts Affects Rate

This is a good reaction for showing the effect of different catalysts.
The decomposition of hydrogen peroxide (H_2O_2) is:

$$2H_{2}O_{2\,(aq)} \quad \rightarrow \quad 2H_{2}O_{(l)} \quad + \quad O_{2\,(g)}$$

1) This is normally quite slow but a bit of manganese(IV) oxide (MnO_2) catalyst speeds it up no end. Other catalysts which work are copper(II) oxide (CuO) and zinc oxide (ZnO).

2) Oxygen gas is given off, which provides an ideal way to measure the rate of reaction using the gas syringe method:

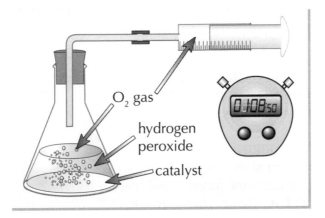

O_2 gas

hydrogen peroxide

catalyst

- Set up the apparatus as shown in the diagram above. Add some MnO_2 powder to the H_2O_2.
- Measure the volume of gas produced at regular time intervals. Record the results in a table.
- Repeat the experiment with the same volume and concentration of hydrogen peroxide, using a different catalyst, e.g. copper oxide. The amount of catalyst used must be kept the same though.

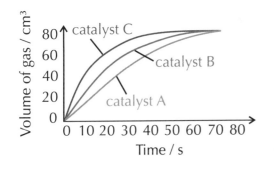

3) You can then draw a graph showing your results — time goes on the x-axis and volume goes on the y-axis.

4) Better catalysts give a quicker reaction, which is shown by a steeper graph which levels off quickly.

5) This reaction can also be used to measure the effects of temperature, or of concentration of the H_2O_2 solution. The graphs will look just the same.

The rate of reaction depends on what catalyst you use

You don't need to know all the details of these reactions — it's the experimental methods you need to learn.

Reversible Reactions

In a <u>reversible reaction</u>, both the forward and the backward reactions are happening <u>at the same time</u>.

Reversible Reactions Can Go Forwards and Backwards

A <u>reversible reaction</u> is one where the <u>products</u> of the reaction can react with each other and <u>convert back</u> to the original reactants. In other words, <u>it can go both ways</u>.

$$A + B \rightleftharpoons C + D$$

This is the symbol for a reversible reaction.

1) The <u>thermal decomposition of ammonium chloride</u> is a reversible reaction:

$$NH_4Cl_{(s)} \rightleftharpoons NH_{3(g)} + HCl_{(g)}$$

2) Ammonium chloride is a <u>white solid</u>. When it's heated it breaks down into the gases <u>ammonia</u> and <u>hydrogen chloride</u> — this is the <u>forward reaction</u>.

3) If you let it cool, the <u>ammonia</u> and <u>hydrogen chloride</u> react to <u>re-form</u> the solid — this is the <u>backward reaction</u>.

The dehydration of copper(II) sulfate is another example of a reversible reaction (see page 94).

Reversible Reactions Will Reach Dynamic Equilibrium

1) If a reversible reaction takes place in a <u>closed system</u> then a state of <u>equilibrium</u> will always be reached.

2) <u>Equilibrium</u> means that the <u>concentrations</u> of reactants and products will reach a certain <u>balance</u> and stay there. (A 'closed system' just means that none of the reactants or products can <u>escape</u>.)

3) It is in fact a <u>DYNAMIC EQUILIBRIUM</u>, which means that the reactions are still taking place in <u>both directions</u>, but the <u>overall effect is nil</u> because the forward and reverse reactions <u>cancel</u> each other out. The reactions are taking place at <u>exactly the same rate</u> in both directions.

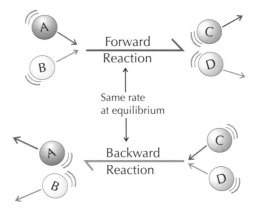

Changing Temperature and Pressure Can Get You More Product

1) In a reversible reaction the '<u>position of equilibrium</u>' (the relative amounts of reactants and products) depends <u>very strongly</u> on the <u>temperature</u> and <u>pressure</u> of the reacting mixture.

2) If you <u>deliberately alter</u> the temperature and pressure you can <u>move</u> the position of equilibrium to give <u>more product</u> and <u>less</u> reactants — so the position shifts to the <u>right</u>.

Temperature

- All reactions are <u>exothermic</u> in one direction and <u>endothermic</u> in the other (see page 97).
- If you <u>raise</u> the <u>temperature</u>, the <u>endothermic</u> reaction will increase to <u>use up</u> the extra heat.
- If you <u>reduce</u> the <u>temperature</u>, the <u>exothermic</u> reaction will increase to <u>give out</u> more heat.

Pressure

- Most gaseous reactions have <u>more moles</u> of gas on one side than on the other.
- If you <u>raise</u> the <u>pressure</u> it will encourage the reaction which produces <u>fewer moles</u> of gas.
- If you <u>lower</u> the <u>pressure</u> it will encourage the reaction which produces <u>more moles</u> of gas.

3) Adding a catalyst has <u>no effect</u> on the position of equilibrium. This is because it <u>speeds up</u> the forward reaction and the backward reaction by the <u>same amount</u>.

Paper 2

Warm-Up & Exam Questions

Try your hand at these questions — it's the best way to see what you've learnt so far.

Warm-Up Questions

1) What unit would you usually use to measure the amount of a gaseous product?
2) Give one disadvantage of using the 'precipitation' method to follow rate of reaction.
3) Explain what is meant by the term 'reversible reaction'.
4) What is dynamic equilibrium?

Exam Questions

PRACTICAL

1   Oxygen and water can be produced by the decomposition of hydrogen peroxide (H_2O_2).   **Grade 4-6**

Samples of three catalysts with the same surface area were added to hydrogen peroxide solution. The same volume and concentration of hydrogen peroxide was used each time. The volume of oxygen produced over time was measured and recorded, and is shown in the graph.

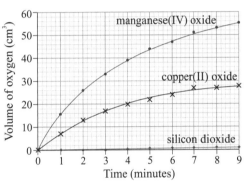

(a)   How much oxygen was produced after 3 minutes with copper(II) oxide?

[1 mark]

(b)   State, with a reason, the most effective catalyst.

[2 marks]

2   The rate of a reaction can be measured using different methods.   **Grade 6-7**

(a)   If one of the products is a gas, the rate of reaction can be measured by recording the change in mass of the reaction vessel using a mass balance.

   (i)   Suggest **one** disadvantage of this method.

[1 mark]

   (ii) Describe a method, other than measuring a change in mass, that could be used to measure the rate of a reaction when one of the products is a gas.

[1 mark]

(b)   (i)   Briefly describe how you could measure the rate of a reaction that produces a precipitate.

[2 marks]

   (ii) A student is investigating how the concentration of a reactant affects the rate of a reaction that produces a precipitate. She carries out the reaction with different concentrations of reactant and measures the rate of reaction for each concentration. What is the dependent variable in this method?

[1 mark]

Exam Questions

3 A student wanted to calculate the rate of reaction between nitric acid and zinc. He carried out two experiments under the same conditions, but in one he used zinc ribbons and in the other he used zinc powder.

The graph below shows the rate of reaction for both experiments, labelled Q and R.

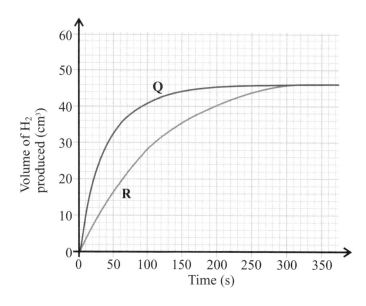

(a) (i) Calculate the rate of reaction Q at 50 seconds.

[3 marks]

(ii) Calculate the rate of reaction R at 120 seconds.

[3 marks]

(b) State which reaction, Q or R, used powdered zinc. Explain your answer.

[3 marks]

(c) State one variable that the student would have controlled in order to make the experiment scientifically valid. Explain why this variable needed to be controlled.

[2 marks]

PAPER 2

4 When ammonium chloride is heated, it breaks down into ammonia and hydrogen chloride. The reaction is reversible.

$$NH_4Cl_{(s)} \rightleftharpoons NH_{3(g)} + HCl_{(g)}$$

Two students are trying to deduce the optimum conditions to favour the forward reaction.

The first student suggests a temperature of 375 °C and a pressure of 1 atmosphere.
The second student suggests a temperature of 250 °C and a pressure of 5 atmospheres.

Using your knowledge of equilibrium reactions, deduce which conditions are more favourable for the forward reaction. Explain your answer.

[5 marks]

Revision Summary for Section 5

Well you've almost made it — you're just one more page away from a lovely cup of tea and a biscuit...
* Try these questions and <u>tick off each one</u> when you <u>get it right</u>.
* When you've done <u>all the questions</u> under a heading and are <u>completely happy</u> with it, tick it off.

Energy Transfer in Reactions (p.97-99) ☑

1) In an exothermic reaction is heat transferred to or from the surroundings? ☑
2) Draw a reaction profile for an exothermic reaction. ☑
3) Describe how you could measure the temperature change in a neutralisation reaction. ☑
4) Why are draught excluders used in calorimetry experiments when investigating combustion? ☑

Calculating Enthalpy Changes (p.100-101) ☑

5) What is the equation for calculating the heat energy transferred in a reaction? ☑
6) For the following sentences, use either 'endothermic' or 'exothermic' to fill in the blanks:
   a) Bond breaking is an _____ process.
   b) Bond forming is an _____ process. ☑
7) Describe how you could calculate the enthalpy change of a reaction using bond energies. ☑

Rates of Reaction (p.104-113) ☑

8) Sketch a graph to show how the amount of product formed in a reaction changes over time. ☑
9) Name four things that the rate of a reaction depends on. ☑
10) Explain how each of the four factors that affect reaction rate
    increases the number of successful collisions between particles. ☑
11) What is a catalyst? ☑
12) Show the effect of a catalyst on the reaction profile of an exothermic reaction. ☑
13) Describe how you could investigate the effect of increasing HCl concentration
    on the rate of reaction between HCl and marble chips. ☑
14) Describe how you could measure the rate of reaction for the decomposition of hydrogen peroxide. ☑

Reversible Reactions (p.114) ☑

15) What is the symbol for a reversible reaction? ☑
16) Which one of the following statements is true?
    a) In a reaction at equilibrium, there is the same amount of products as reactants.
    b) If the forward reaction in a reversible reaction is exothermic,
       then the reverse reaction is endothermic.
    c) If the equilibrium of a system lies towards the products, then the concentration
       of products is less than the concentration of reactants. ☑
17) Name two things that affect the position of the equilibrium in a reversible reaction. ☑

Organic Compounds

This section's all about <u>organic chemistry</u> — in other words, molecules that contain <u>carbon</u>.

There are **Loads of Ways** of Representing **Organic Compounds**

Type of formula	What it shows you	Formula for Ethene
General formula	An algebraic formula that can describe <u>any member</u> of a family of compounds.	C_nH_{2n} (for all alkenes)
Empirical formula	The <u>simplest whole number ratio</u> of atoms of each element in a compound (cancel the numbers down if possible).	CH_2
Molecular formula	The <u>actual</u> number of atoms of each element in a molecule.	C_2H_4
Displayed formula	Shows how all the atoms are <u>arranged</u>, and all the bonds between them.	$\underset{H}{\overset{H}{\diagdown}}C=C\underset{H}{\overset{H}{\diagup}}$
Structural formula	Shows the arrangement of atoms <u>carbon by carbon</u>, with the attached hydrogens and functional groups (see below).	CH_2CH_2

Organic Compounds can Belong to a Certain **Homologous Series**

1) A homologous series is a <u>group of compounds</u> that can all be represented by the <u>same general formula</u>.

2) You can use a general formula to work out the <u>molecular formula</u> of <u>any member</u> of a homologous series.

> E.g. <u>Alkanes</u> are a <u>homologous series</u> that <u>only</u> contain <u>carbon</u> and <u>hydrogen</u> atoms — there's more about them on page 126-127.
> The <u>general formula</u> for alkanes is C_nH_{2n+2}. So the first alkane in the series is $C_1H_{(2\times1)+2} = CH_4$, the second is $C_2H_{(2\times2)+2} = C_2H_6$, etc.

3) Molecules in a homologous series contain the same <u>functional group</u>.

4) A <u>functional group</u> is a group of atoms that determine how a compound typically reacts.

5) This means that compounds in a homologous series often <u>react in similar ways</u> — they share similar chemical properties.

6) These are the functional groups you need to know:

Alkenes

Functional Group: $\underset{H}{\overset{R}{\diagdown}}C=C\underset{R}{\overset{H}{\diagup}}$

R is used in place of a carbon chain that is attached to the functional group.

There's more on alkenes on p.128-129

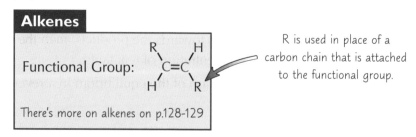

Alcohols

Functional Group: $R-O-H$

There's more on alcohols on p.132-133

Carboxylic Acids

Functional Group: $R-\overset{\overset{O}{\parallel}}{C}-OH$

There's more on carboxylic acids on p.135-136

Esters

Functional Group: $R-\overset{\overset{O}{\parallel}}{C}-O-R$

There's more on esters on p.137

Naming Organic Compounds

Organic compounds used to be given whatever names people fancied, but these names led to confusion between different countries. Luckily, chemists got together and came up with a system...

Nomenclature is the Naming of Organic Compounds

The IUPAC system for naming organic compounds was invented as an international language for chemistry. It can be used to give any organic compound a name using these rules of nomenclature...

1) Count the carbon atoms in the carbon chain — this gives you the stem.

No. of Carbons	1	2	3	4	5	6
Stem	meth-	eth-	prop-	but-	pent-	hex-

2) The main functional group of the molecule usually tells you what homologous series the molecule is in (see previous page), and so gives you the prefix or suffix — see the table below.

Homologous Series	Prefix or Suffix	Example
alkanes	–ane	propane — $CH_3CH_2CH_3$
alkenes	–ene	but-2-ene — $CH_3CHCHCH_3$
alcohols	–ol	ethanol — CH_3CH_2OH
carboxylic acids	–oic acid	ethanoic acid — CH_3COOH
esters	Prefix: alkyl– (–yl) Suffix: –anoate	ethyl ethanoate — $CH_3C(=O)OCH_2CH_3$

Paper 2

Paper 2

3) Number the carbon chain so that the functional group has the lowest possible number.

4) If there's more than one identical functional group, use di- (2), tri- (3) or tetra- (4) before the suffix.

There are some examples of how to name compounds on the following page.

The rules of nomenclature help you name compounds correctly

It's not the most exciting task, but setting to and learning all those stems and suffixes (and prefixes for esters) will really help you out in the rest of this section. You can work out an awful lot about organic molecules just from understanding what their names are telling you. Go back and re-read this page 'til you've got it.

Naming Organic Compounds

Here are a couple of <u>examples</u> of how the <u>rules</u> of <u>nomenclature</u> work.

You Can Work Out the **Name** of an **Alkene** Like This...

Here's how you'd go about <u>naming</u> the <u>alkene</u> $CH_2CHCH_2CH_3$:

H H H H
| 1 | 2 | 3 | 4
C = C — C — C — H
| | |
H H H

$CH_2CHCH_2CH_3$

1) The carbon chain is <u>4</u> carbons long. So the stem is '<u>but–</u>'.

2) The main functional group is a carbon-carbon double bond. So it is an alkene and the name will end in '<u>–ene</u>'.

3) Numbering the carbon chain so that one of the carbons in the C=C group has the lowest possible number puts the C=C group on <u>carbon 1</u>.

4) This means that the systematic name for the molecule is: <u>but-1-ene</u>.

...And an **Alcohol** Like This...

You can follow the same sort of procedure to name <u>any type</u> of <u>organic compound</u>. For example the <u>alcohol</u> $CH_3CH_2CH_2OH$:

H H H
| 3 | 2 | 1
H — C — C — C — OH
| | |
H H H

$CH_3CH_2CH_2OH$

If this molecule had 2 -OH groups it would be called propane<u>diol</u> — see page 142.

1) The carbon chain is <u>3</u> carbons long. So the stem is '<u>prop-</u>'.
2) The main functional group is <u>-OH</u>, so the suffix is <u>-ol</u>.
3) Numbering the carbon chain puts the OH on <u>carbon 1</u>.
4) This means that the systematic name for the molecule is: <u>propan-1-ol</u>.

This molecule can sometimes be called just propanol.

Start by counting the carbon atoms

You might be given the <u>name</u> of a compound and asked to draw its <u>displayed formula</u>. But don't panic — it's not actually too tricky. The <u>stem</u> tells you how many <u>carbon atoms</u> to draw and the <u>number</u> tells you which carbon to attach the <u>functional group</u> to. Then just look at the <u>suffix</u> to check which <u>group</u> you're drawing.

Isomers

The molecular formula alone can't tell you the <u>structure</u> of a molecule, thanks to the existence of <u>isomers</u>.

Isomers Have the Same **Molecular Formula**

1) Two molecules are isomers of one another if they have the <u>same molecular formula</u> but the atoms are <u>arranged differently</u>.

2) This means their <u>structural formulae</u> are different.

3) Isomers can be hard to spot — here are some things you need to look out for:

Differently Shaped Carbon **Chains**

1) The <u>carbons</u> could be arranged differently — for example, as a <u>straight chain</u>, or <u>branched</u> (one of the carbons being bonded to more than two other carbons) in different ways.

2) These isomers have <u>similar chemical properties</u> (they will react in similar ways) — but their <u>physical properties</u>, like boiling point, will be <u>different</u> because of the change in shape of the molecule.

E.g. <u>both</u> of these molecules have the formula C_4H_{10}:

Butane

Methylpropane

Functional Groups in **Different Places**

1) The <u>arrangement</u> of carbon atoms could be the same, and the isomers could have the same <u>functional group</u>, but the functional group could be attached to a <u>different carbon atom</u>.

2) These isomers also have <u>different physical properties</u>.

E.g. <u>both</u> of these molecules have the formula C_4H_8:

But-1-ene

But-2-ene

Different Functional Groups

1) The same atoms could be arranged into <u>different functional groups</u>.

2) These isomers have very <u>different physical</u> and <u>chemical</u> properties.

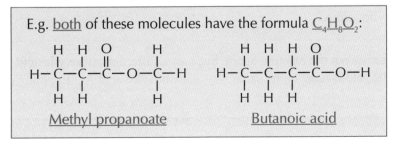

E.g. <u>both</u> of these molecules have the formula $C_4H_8O_2$:

Methyl propanoate

Butanoic acid

Warm-Up & Exam Questions

Well, you've made a start on organic chemistry — better check all that new information's going in okay...

Warm-Up Questions

1) What is the empirical formula of the alkene with molecular formula C_3H_6?
2) What is a functional group?
3) How many carbon atoms are there in a molecule of butanoic acid?
4) Give the name of the alcohol which has one carbon atom in its carbon chain.
5) What are isomers?

Exam Questions

1   Which of the following is a structural formula?

☐ **A** C_nH_{2n} ☐ **B** $CH_3CH_2CH_3$ ☐ **C**   CH   ☐ **D** C_2H_4

[1 mark]

2   Draw the displayed formula of a molecule of hexane.

[1 mark]

3   The displayed formula of a molecule is shown below.

```
        H  H  H
        |  |  |
   Br − C− C− C−H
        |  |  |
        H  H  H
```

(a)   Draw the displayed formula of an isomer of the molecule shown above.

[1 mark]

(b)   The molecular formula of a straight chain molecule is C_4H_9Cl.
Draw the displayed formula of **both** isomers of this molecule.

[2 marks]

PAPER 2

4   A student carries out the reaction between ethanol and a carboxylic acid, **A**.
The displayed formula of carboxylic acid **A** is shown below.

```
        H  H  H  H      O
        |  |  |  |     ⁄⁄
   H − C− C− C− C− C
        |  |  |  |     ⁄
        H  H  H  H    O−H
```

(a)   Name carboxylic acid **A**.

[1 mark]

(b)   The student carries out the reaction again, but uses a different carboxylic acid, **B**.
Will carboxylic acid **B** react in the same way as carboxylic acid **A**? Explain your answer.

[1 mark]

Crude Oil

Over millions of years, high temperatures and pressures cause the buried remains of plants and animals to turn into <u>crude oil</u>. Then we come along and drill it up.

Crude Oil is **Separated** into Different Hydrocarbon **Fractions**

Crude oil is a <u>mixture</u> of substances, most of which are <u>hydrocarbons</u> — molecules which are made of only <u>carbon and hydrogen</u>. The different compounds in crude oil are <u>separated</u> by <u>fractional distillation</u>:

1) The oil is <u>heated</u> until most of it has turned into <u>gas</u>. The gases enter a <u>fractionating column</u> (and the liquid bit, <u>bitumen</u>, is <u>drained off</u> at the bottom).

2) In the column there's a <u>temperature gradient</u> (i.e. it's <u>hot</u> at the <u>bottom</u> and gets gradually <u>cooler</u> as you go up). When the substances that make up crude oil reach a part of the column where the temperature is <u>lower</u> than their <u>boiling point</u> they <u>condense</u> (turn back into a liquid).

3) The <u>longer hydrocarbons</u> have <u>high boiling points</u>. They <u>condense</u> and <u>drain out</u> of the column <u>early on</u>, when they're near the <u>bottom</u>.

4) The <u>shorter</u> hydrocarbons have <u>lower boiling points</u>. They turn to liquid and drain out much <u>later on</u>, near to the <u>top</u> of the column where it's cooler.

5) <u>Bubble caps</u> in the fractionating column stop the separated liquids from running back down the column and <u>remixing</u>. You end up with the crude oil mixture separated out into <u>different fractions</u>.

Each fraction contains a mixture of hydrocarbons with <u>similar boiling points</u>.
Each fraction may contain <u>saturated</u> or <u>unsaturated</u> hydrocarbons.
<u>Saturated hydrocarbons</u> only contain single bonds between carbon atoms whereas <u>unsaturated hydrocarbons</u> have double or triple bonds between carbon atoms.

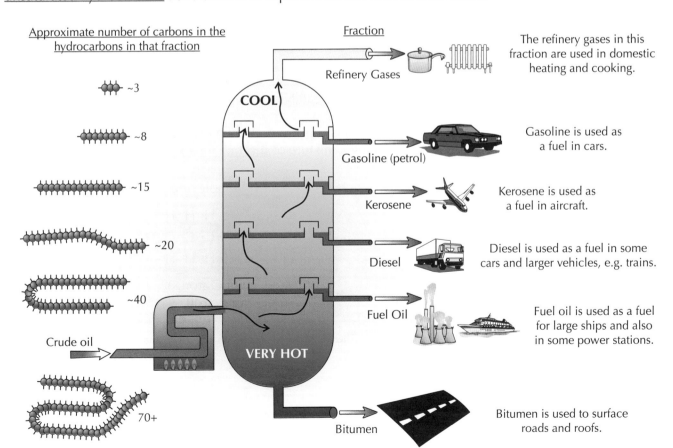

Cracking

Really <u>long hydrocarbons</u> aren't that useful — but it's OK because they can be <u>made smaller</u> by <u>cracking</u>.

Cracking — **Splitting Up** Long-Chain Hydrocarbons

1) <u>Long</u> hydrocarbons have <u>high</u> boiling points and are <u>viscous</u> (thick and gloopy).
2) <u>Shorter</u> hydrocarbons have <u>lower</u> boiling points and are much <u>thinner</u> and <u>paler</u> in colour.
3) Demand for <u>short-chain</u> hydrocarbons like octane, which is used in petrol (gasoline), is much <u>higher</u> than for longer-chain hydrocarbons.
4) So, to <u>meet</u> this demand, long-chain hydrocarbons are <u>split</u> into <u>more useful</u> short-chain molecules using <u>cracking</u>.

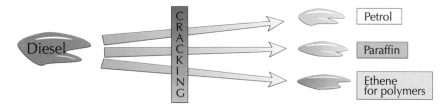

5) <u>Cracking</u> is a form of <u>thermal decomposition</u>, which just means <u>breaking</u> molecules down into <u>simpler</u> molecules by <u>heating</u> them.
6) Cracking also produces <u>alkenes</u>, which are used to make <u>polymers</u> (see page 140).

Conditions for Cracking: **Heat**, Plus a **Catalyst**

In industry, <u>vaporised hydrocarbons</u> are passed over a <u>powdered catalyst</u> at about <u>600 °C – 700 °C</u>. <u>Silica</u> (SiO_2) or <u>alumina</u> (Al_2O_3) are used as the <u>catalyst</u>. You can carry out the reaction in the lab using simple equipment. Like this...

Cracking using a catalyst is called catalytic cracking.

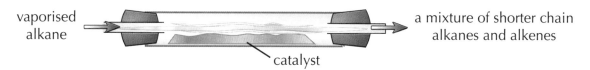

vaporised alkane

a mixture of shorter chain alkanes and alkenes

catalyst

During this reaction, the alkane is heated until it is <u>vaporised</u>. It then breaks down when it comes into contact with the catalyst, producing a mixture of <u>short-chain alkanes</u> and <u>alkenes</u>.

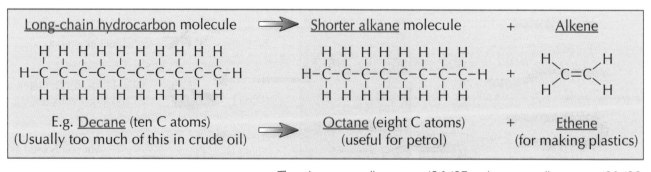

<u>Long-chain hydrocarbon</u> molecule ⟹ <u>Shorter alkane</u> molecule + <u>Alkene</u>

E.g. <u>Decane</u> (ten C atoms) ⟹ <u>Octane</u> (eight C atoms) + <u>Ethene</u>
(Usually too much of this in crude oil)   (useful for petrol)   (for making plastics)

There is more on alkanes on p.126-127 and more on alkenes on p.128-129.

Cracking breaks down long hydrocarbons into shorter ones

<u>Hydrocarbons</u> are used in all areas of industry. Unfortunately it's really only the <u>smaller molecules</u> which are really <u>useful</u>. Luckily, we have cracking to get as many useful products from crude oil as possible.

Burning Hydrocarbons

The great thing about <u>oil</u> is the amount of energy that gets released when it's burnt. However, this does come with some downsides. For example, some of the by-products of <u>combustion</u> contribute to <u>pollution</u>.

Fuels Release Energy in Combustion Reactions

1) When you <u>burn</u> a <u>fuel</u>, it releases <u>energy</u> in the form of <u>heat</u>.

2) Burning is also known as a <u>combustion reaction</u> (see page 48) — the substance being burned reacts with <u>oxygen</u>.

3) <u>Hydrocarbons</u> make great fuels because the <u>combustion reactions</u> that happen when you burn them in <u>oxygen</u> give out <u>lots of energy</u> — the reactions are very <u>exothermic</u> (see page 97).

4) When you burn hydrocarbons in plenty of oxygen, the only products are <u>carbon dioxide</u> and <u>water</u> — this is called <u>complete combustion</u>.

> hydrocarbon + oxygen → carbon dioxide + water

Incomplete Combustion Produces Carbon Monoxide and Soot

1) If there's <u>not enough oxygen</u> around for complete combustion, you get <u>incomplete combustion</u>. This can happen in some appliances, e.g. boilers, that use carbon compounds as fuels.

2) The products of incomplete combustion contain <u>less oxygen</u> than carbon dioxide.

3) As well as carbon dioxide and water, incomplete combustion produces <u>carbon monoxide</u> (CO), a <u>toxic gas</u>, and <u>carbon</u> in the form of soot.

In reality, incomplete combustion reactions will usually produce a mixture of H_2O, CO_2, CO and C.

- <u>Carbon monoxide</u> can combine with red blood cells and stop your blood from doing its proper job of <u>carrying oxygen</u> around the body.
- A lack of oxygen in the blood supply to the brain can lead to <u>fainting</u>, a <u>coma</u> or even <u>death</u>.

Acid Rain is Caused by Sulfur Dioxide and Nitrogen Oxides

1) A lot of the fractions obtained from <u>crude oil</u> are burnt as <u>fuels</u>.

2) When they're burnt, <u>sulfur dioxide</u> and <u>nitrogen oxides</u> may be produced.

3) The <u>sulfur dioxide</u> comes from <u>sulfur impurities</u> in the hydrocarbon fuels.

4) <u>Nitrogen oxides</u> are created when the temperature is <u>high</u> enough for the nitrogen and oxygen <u>in the air</u> to react. This often happens in car engines. Nitrogen oxides include <u>nitrogen monoxide</u> (NO) and <u>nitrogen dioxide</u> (NO_2).

5) When <u>sulfur dioxide and nitrogen oxides</u> mix with <u>water vapour</u> in clouds they form <u>dilute sulfuric acid</u> and <u>nitric acid</u>.

6) The rain that falls from these clouds is called <u>acid rain</u>.

7) <u>Acid rain</u> causes <u>lakes</u> to become <u>acidic</u> and many plants and animals <u>die</u> as a result.

Alkanes

We're now going to look at the different types of hydrocarbons you can get. First up is the <u>alkanes</u>...

Alkanes are **Saturated Hydrocarbons**

1) Alkanes are hydrocarbons — they're <u>chains of carbon atoms</u> surrounded by <u>hydrogen atoms</u>.

2) Different alkanes have chains of different <u>lengths</u>.

3) Alkanes have the <u>general formula</u> C_nH_{2n+2}.

> **Alkanes = C_nH_{2n+2}**

4) You need to know the <u>names</u> and the <u>structures</u> of the first five alkanes.

1) Methane

Molecular formula: CH_4
Structural formula: CH_4

$$H-\overset{\displaystyle H}{\underset{\displaystyle H}{C}}-H$$

2) Ethane

Molecular formula: C_2H_6
Structural formula: CH_3CH_3

$$H-\overset{\displaystyle H}{\underset{\displaystyle H}{C}}-\overset{\displaystyle H}{\underset{\displaystyle H}{C}}-H$$

3) Propane

$$H-\overset{\displaystyle H}{\underset{\displaystyle H}{C}}-\overset{\displaystyle H}{\underset{\displaystyle H}{C}}-\overset{\displaystyle H}{\underset{\displaystyle H}{C}}-H$$

Molecular formula: C_3H_8
Structural formula: $CH_3CH_2CH_3$

4) Butane

$$H-\overset{\displaystyle H}{\underset{\displaystyle H}{C}}-\overset{\displaystyle H}{\underset{\displaystyle H}{C}}-\overset{\displaystyle H}{\underset{\displaystyle H}{C}}-\overset{\displaystyle H}{\underset{\displaystyle H}{C}}-H$$

Molecular formula: C_4H_{10}
Structural formula: $CH_3CH_2CH_2CH_3$

5) Pentane

$$H-\overset{\displaystyle H}{\underset{\displaystyle H}{C}}-\overset{\displaystyle H}{\underset{\displaystyle H}{C}}-\overset{\displaystyle H}{\underset{\displaystyle H}{C}}-\overset{\displaystyle H}{\underset{\displaystyle H}{C}}-\overset{\displaystyle H}{\underset{\displaystyle H}{C}}-H$$

Molecular formula: C_5H_{12}
Structural formula: $CH_3CH_2CH_2CH_2CH_3$

To help remember the names of the first four alkanes just remember: Mice Eat Peanut Butter. Pentane is five, just like a pentagon, so you'll have to remember that one on its own.

5) The diagrams above show that all the atoms have formed bonds with as many other atoms as they can. There are only <u>single bonds</u> between the <u>carbon</u> atoms — this means the molecules are <u>saturated</u>.

Hydrocarbons only contain hydrogen and carbon

If you're asked to draw the <u>displayed formula</u> of an alkane in the exam, don't worry if you can't remember it. You can use the <u>stem</u> of the name of the alkane (see p.119) to <u>draw</u> a chain with the right number of <u>C atoms</u>, then just add in <u>H atoms</u> so that each C atom has <u>4 single bonds</u> in total.

Alkanes

You saw on page 118 that compounds in a <u>homologous series</u> react in <u>similar</u> ways. <u>Alkanes</u> are no exception — here are two <u>reactions</u> of alkanes that you need to <u>know</u> about.

Alkanes Burn in **Combustion Reactions**

<u>Alkanes</u> make up the majority of hydrocarbons in crude oil and tend to combust completely in a <u>good supply of oxygen</u>. For example:

$$\textbf{propane + oxygen} \rightarrow \textbf{carbon dioxide + water}$$
$$\textbf{C}_3\textbf{H}_8 \; + \; 5\textbf{O}_2 \; \rightarrow \; 3\textbf{CO}_2 \; + \; 4\textbf{H}_2\textbf{O}$$

Halogens React with **Alkanes** to make **Haloalkanes**

1) <u>Chlorine</u> and <u>bromine</u> react with alkanes in the presence of <u>ultraviolet light</u>.

Ultraviolet light can also be called ultraviolet radiation.

2) In these reactions a <u>hydrogen</u> atom from the alkane is <u>substituted</u> with (replaced by) <u>chlorine</u> or <u>bromine</u>. So this is called a <u>substitution reaction</u>.

3) This is how bromine and methane react together to form <u>bromomethane</u>.

methane + bromine → bromomethane + hydrogen bromide

$$\text{H-C-H} + \text{Br}_2 \xrightarrow{\text{UV}} \text{H-C-H} + \text{HBr}$$

The UV here shows that the reaction needs ultraviolet light.

Alkanes are useful fuels as they release energy when burnt

REVISION TIP They can also take part in <u>substitution</u> reactions with the <u>halogens</u> chlorine and bromine, but <u>only</u> in the presence of <u>ultraviolet light</u>. Try writing word and symbol <u>equations</u> for the complete combustion of methane, and for the substitution reactions of methane with chlorine and bromine. Then do it all over again for ethane, propane, butane and pentane. Then treat yourself to a biscuit.

Alkenes

Alkenes are another type of hydrocarbon. They are different to alkanes because they contain a double bond.

Alkenes Have a C=C Double Bond

1) Alkenes are hydrocarbons which have a double bond between two of the carbon atoms in their chain.

2) They are unsaturated molecules because they can make more bonds — the double bond can open up, allowing the two carbon atoms to bond with other atoms (see next page).

3) The first three alkenes are ethene (with two carbon atoms), propene (three Cs) and butene (four Cs).

4) All alkenes have the general formula: C_nH_{2n} — they have twice as many hydrogens as carbons.

Alkenes = C_nH_{2n}

1) Ethene

Molecular Formula: C_2H_4
Structural Formula: CH_2CH_2

Hydrogen atoms only make one bond.

This is a double bond — so each carbon atom is still making four bonds.

2) Propene

Molecular Formula: C_3H_6
Structural Formula: CH_3CHCH_2

3) Butene

There are two different structures for butene — these are isomers (see page 121).

But-1-ene

or

But-2-ene

Molecular Formula: C_4H_8
Structural Formula: $CH_2CHCH_2CH_3$

Molecular Formula: C_4H_8
Structural Formula: $CH_3CHCHCH_3$

Alkanes and alkenes are both types of hydrocarbon

Watch out — it's easy to get confused between alkanes and alkenes. They may look (and sound) similar, but that double bond makes a lot of difference, especially to their reactivities (see next page for more).

Alkenes

Now that you've met some alkenes, it's time to learn a bit about how they <u>react</u> with <u>halogens</u>. It's all down to the double bond splitting...

Halogens React with Alkenes, Forming Haloalkanes

1) <u>Halogens</u> can react with alkenes to make <u>haloalkanes</u>.

2) For example bromine and ethene react together to form <u>dibromoethane</u>.

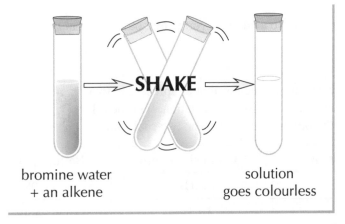

ethene + bromine → dibromoethane

$$\underset{H}{\overset{H}{>}}C=C\underset{H}{\overset{H}{<}} + Br_2 \longrightarrow \overset{Br\ Br}{\underset{\underset{H\ H}{|\ |}}{H-C-C-H}}$$

There are two bromine atoms so it's called <u>dibromoethane</u>.

3) These are called <u>addition reactions</u> because the C=C double bond is split and a halogen atom is <u>added</u> to each of the carbons.

Alkenes Turn Bromine Water Colourless

1) The reaction between bromine and alkenes is often used as a <u>test</u> for carbon-carbon double bonds.

2) When you shake an alkene with <u>orange bromine water</u>, the solution becomes <u>colourless</u> — this is because the <u>bromine</u> molecules, which are <u>orange</u>, are reacting with the <u>alkene</u> to make a <u>dibromoalkane</u>, which is <u>colourless</u>.

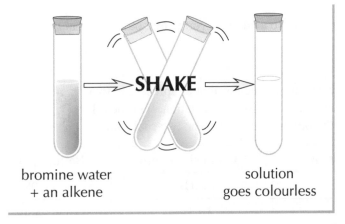

SHAKE

bromine water + an alkene

solution goes colourless

3) <u>Alkanes</u> don't react with bromine water as they <u>don't have a double bond</u>. So if you add an alkane to <u>bromine water</u>, the solution will stay <u>orange</u>.

PRACTICAL TIP

Alkenes don't need UV light to react with halogens

It's important to give the test tube a good <u>shake</u> when using <u>bromine water</u> to test for an alkene. This way, you can be sure that any alkene present will have actually <u>reacted</u> with the bromine.

Warm-Up & Exam Questions

It's that time again... See what you've learnt with this set of questions.

1) When does complete combustion happen?
2) Name the first five alkanes.
3) Why are alkenes described as unsaturated hydrocarbons?
4) What is the general formula of the alkenes?

Exam Questions

1 Fumes from faulty central heating boilers can contain carbon monoxide. Grade 4-6

    (a) What can cause carbon monoxide to be produced when fuel is burnt in a boiler?

[1 mark]

    (b) Describe the effect that carbon monoxide has on the human body.

[1 mark]

2 Nitrogen oxides can be produced when fossil fuels are burnt. Grade 4-6

    (a) (i) Describe the conditions needed for nitrogen oxides to form.

[1 mark]

       (ii) Give an example of where this reaction might take place.

[1 mark]

    (b) Nitrogen oxides react with moisture in the atmosphere.
        Name the product that is formed when this occurs.

[1 mark]

    (c) Nitrogen oxides contribute to acid rain. Name **one** other gas that contributes to acid rain.

[1 mark]

3 Heptane and triacontane are two molecules that are present in two
of the fractions produced by the fractional distillation of crude oil. Grade 6-7
The table below shows the boiling points of these two molecules.

Hydrocarbon	Chemical formula	Boiling point (°C)
Heptane	C_7H_{16}	98
Triacontane	$C_{30}H_{62}$	450

    (a) Triacontane is present in the fuel oil fraction. Give **two** uses of fuel oil.

[2 marks]

    (b) Which of these two hydrocarbons would you expect to
        be collected **further down** the fractionating column?
        Explain your answer, with reference to the boiling points of the hydrocarbons.

[3 marks]

Exam Questions

4 Cracking alters the molecules obtained in fractional distillation.

(a) The apparatus shown on the right can be used to crack kerosene in the lab.

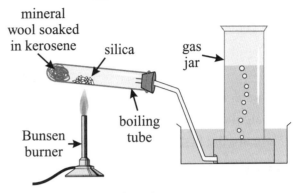

(i) Suggest the role of the silica.

[1 mark]

(ii) The alkanes produced by cracking collect in the boiling tube. Suggest what collects in the gas jar.

[1 mark]

(b) Why is cracking necessary? Discuss both types of hydrocarbon produced.

[4 marks]

5 Alkanes are a group of saturated hydrocarbon compounds.

(a) State the general formula of the alkane homologous series.

[1 mark]

(b) (i) Name the alkane that contains **two** carbon atoms.

[1 mark]

(ii) State the number of hydrogen atoms that this alkane contains.

[1 mark]

(c) Draw the displayed formula of butane.

[1 mark]

(d) Methane will react with bromine in the presence of UV light.
(i) Copy and complete the word equation for this reaction.

methane + bromine $\xrightarrow{\text{UV}}$ .... + ...

[2 marks]

(ii) Name the type of reaction shown in part (i).

[1 mark]

6 A student investigated the reactivity of some hydrocarbons.

(a) The student added a sample of a hydrocarbon, **A**, to bromine water. A reaction took place.
(i) The molecular formula of the product formed was $C_3H_6Br_2$.
Write the structural formula of hydrocarbon **A**.

[1 mark]

(ii) What would the student expect to observe when hydrocarbon **A** was added to bromine water?

[1 mark]

(iii) Name the type of reaction that took place between the hydrocarbon and the bromine water.

[1 mark]

(b) The student took some bromine water and added it to a hydrocarbon with the chemical formula C_2H_6. What would you expect the student to have observed? Explain your answer.

[3 marks]

Alcohols

This page is about different types of <u>alcohol</u> — and that's not just beer, wine and other pub favourites...

Alcohols Have an '-OH' Functional Group

1) The <u>general formula</u> of an alcohol is:

$$C_nH_{2n+1}OH$$

So an alcohol with 2 carbons has the formula C_2H_5OH.

2) All alcohols contain an <u>-OH functional group</u>.

3) Here are the <u>first four</u> alcohols in the homologous series:

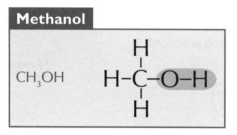

Methanol

CH_3OH

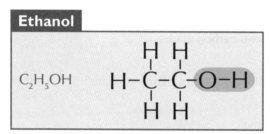

Ethanol

C_2H_5OH

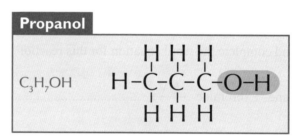

Propanol

C_3H_7OH

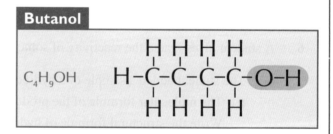

Butanol

C_4H_9OH

4) Don't write CH_4O instead of CH_3OH — it doesn't show the <u>-OH functional group</u>.

5) It is possible to get alcohols where the -OH group is attached to <u>different carbon atoms</u> in the carbon chain, or alcohols with <u>more than one</u> -OH group (like the ones that form condensation polymers on page 142).

EXAM TIP

The general formula of alcohols is $C_nH_{2n+1}OH$

For the exam, make sure you learn the structures of the <u>first four alcohols</u>. You also need to be able to recognise alcohols from their <u>names</u> or <u>formulae</u>, but as long as you know the basic <u>naming system</u> (see p.119), it shouldn't be too hard to figure out a given alcohol in the exam.

Alcohols

Read on for not one, not two, but three different ways in which <u>alcohols</u> can be <u>oxidised</u>.

Alcohols Can Be Oxidised to Form Carboxylic Acids

Oxidation can also describe the loss of electrons (see page 65).

1) When something's <u>oxidised</u>, it gains oxygen.

2) Alcohols can be oxidised to form <u>carboxylic acids</u> (see page 135-136). You need an oxidising agent for this, such as <u>potassium dichromate(VI) in dilute sulfuric acid</u>.

3) You need to know what happens when ethanol is <u>heated</u> with acidified potassium dichromate(VI):

Ethanol + potassium dichromate(VI) in sulfuric acid.

4) You'll see a colour change during this reaction — potassium dichromate(VI) turns from orange to green as it oxidises the alcohol.

5) Alcohols can <u>only</u> form carboxylic acids in this way if the <u>-OH group</u> is attached to a carbon that's only attached to <u>one</u> carbon itself.

Microbial Oxidation Also Forms Carboxylic Acids from Alcohols

1) Some microorganisms are able to use <u>alcohols</u> as an <u>energy source</u>. To do this, they use <u>oxygen in the air</u> to oxidise alcohols.

2) <u>Carboxylic acids</u> are made as a by-product.

3) For example, the oxidation of <u>ethanol</u> produces <u>ethanoic acid</u>.

Alcohols are Oxidised when they are Burnt

1) When alcohols are burnt in enough <u>oxygen</u> (or air), they undergo <u>complete combustion</u> (see page 125).

2) The products of this reaction are <u>water</u> and <u>carbon dioxide</u>.

3) The alcohol is <u>oxidised</u> in this reaction. For example:

$$\text{ethanol} + \text{oxygen} \rightarrow \text{carbon dioxide} + \text{water}$$
$$C_2H_5OH + 3O_2 \rightarrow CO_2 + H_2O$$

When an alcohol is oxidised, it gains oxygen...

... and this can result in <u>different products</u>, depending on how the oxidation is carried out. Oxidation by <u>microorganisms</u> or an <u>oxidising agent</u> (such as potassium dichromate(VI) in dilute sulfuric acid) produces a <u>carboxylic acid</u>, whereas oxidation by <u>complete combustion</u> gives the usual <u>carbon dioxide</u> and <u>water</u>.

Production of Ethanol

The best way to make <u>ethanol</u> often depends on which <u>resource</u> is most easily available — <u>oil</u> or <u>sugar</u>.

Ethanol Can Be Produced from Ethene and Steam

1) <u>Ethene</u> is produced from <u>crude oil</u> (by cracking — see page 124).
2) Ethene (C_2H_4) will react with <u>steam</u> (H_2O) to make <u>ethanol</u>.
3) This is an <u>addition reaction</u> because water is added to the molecule.
4) The reaction needs a <u>temperature</u> of 300°C and a <u>pressure</u> of 60-70 atmospheres.
5) <u>Phosphoric acid</u> is used as a <u>catalyst</u>.

$$C_2H_4 + H_2O \rightarrow C_2H_5OH$$

6) At the moment this is a <u>cheap</u> process, because ethene's fairly <u>cheap</u> and <u>not much</u> of it is <u>wasted</u>.
7) The trouble is that <u>crude oil</u> is a <u>non-renewable</u> resource, which will start running out fairly soon. This means that using ethene to make ethanol will become very <u>expensive</u>.

Ethanol Can Also Be Produced by Fermentation

The alcohol in beer and wine, etc. isn't made from ethene — it's made by <u>fermentation</u>.

1) The raw material for fermentation is <u>sugar</u>, e.g. glucose. This is converted into <u>ethanol</u> using <u>yeast</u>.

This is the formula for glucose — a common sugar.

$$C_6H_{12}O_6 \xrightarrow{yeast} 2C_2H_5OH + 2CO_2$$

The products are ethanol and carbon dioxide.

2) Yeast cells contain an <u>enzyme</u>. Enzymes are naturally occurring <u>catalysts</u> (see page 107) — they speed up reactions.
3) The fermentation mixture needs to be about <u>30 °C</u> — fermentation happens fastest at this temperature. At <u>lower temperatures</u>, the reaction slows down. If it's <u>too hot</u> the enzyme in the yeast <u>denatures</u> (is destroyed) and the <u>reaction would stop</u>.
4) It's important to keep the mixture in <u>anaerobic conditions</u> (no oxygen). Oxygen converts the <u>ethanol</u> to <u>ethanoic acid</u> (which is what you get in <u>vinegar</u> — it doesn't exactly enhance the drinking experience).
5) An advantage of this process compared to the reaction of <u>ethene</u> with steam is that the raw materials are all <u>renewable resources</u>. Sugar (sugar cane) is <u>grown</u> as a major crop in several parts of the world, including many poorer countries. <u>Yeast</u> is also easy to grow.
6) There are some <u>disadvantages</u> to fermentation though. The ethanol you get from this process <u>isn't very concentrated</u>, so it needs to be <u>distilled</u> to increase its strength (as in whisky distilleries). It also needs to be <u>purified</u>.

Yeast enzymes work best at a specific temperature

Remember — it's very important to keep the <u>temperature</u> as close as possible to <u>30 °C</u> during <u>fermentation</u>.

Carboxylic Acids

So you will have seen <u>carboxylic acids</u> mentioned on page 133. Well, they're a <u>homologous series</u> too and deserve a couple of pages all to themselves. Here's some more about the <u>first four</u> in the series.

Carboxylic Acids Have the Functional Group -COOH

1) <u>Carboxylic acids</u> are a homologous series of compounds that all have '-COOH' as a <u>functional group</u>.
2) Make sure you know the <u>names</u> and the <u>structures</u> of the first four carboxylic acids.

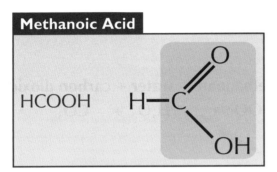

Methanoic Acid

HCOOH

Ethanoic Acid

CH₃COOH

Make sure you know the names and the structures of these four carboxylic acids. You could be asked about them in the exam.

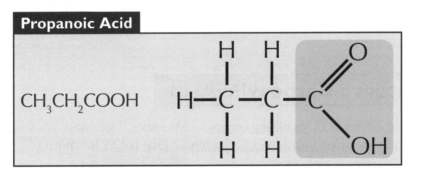

Propanoic Acid

CH₃CH₂COOH

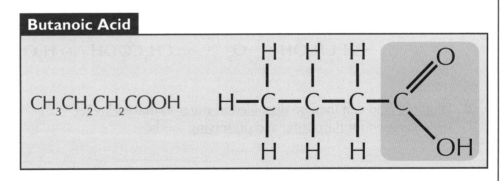

Butanoic Acid

CH₃CH₂CH₂COOH

Carboxylic acids end in '-anoic' acid

EXAM TIP Take care when drawing the <u>displayed formulas</u> of carboxylic acids in the exam — make sure you've got the <u>right number</u> of <u>atoms</u> and the <u>right type</u> of <u>bonds</u>. Don't forget, carbon atoms only form <u>four</u> bonds and the carbon of the -COOH group is <u>included</u> in the <u>stem</u> when naming.

Paper 2

Carboxylic Acids

You might not realise it, but you're probably already familiar with ethanoic acid. There's more on this at the bottom of the page, but first it's time to take a look at how carboxylic acids react.

Carboxylic Acids React Like Other Acids

1) Carboxylic acids can react to form salts (like any other acid). The salts formed end in -anoate — e.g. methanoic acid will form a methanoate, ethanoic acid an ethanoate, etc.

2) Carboxylic acids in aqueous solution react with metal carbonates to form a salt, water and carbon dioxide. For example:

ethanoic acid + sodium carbonate → sodium ethanoate + water + carbon dioxide
$$2CH_3COOH_{(aq)} + Na_2CO_{3(aq)} \rightarrow 2CH_3COONa_{(aq)} + H_2O_{(l)} + CO_{2(g)}$$

Aqueous means that a substance is dissolved in water.

3) Aqueous carboxylic acids react with metals to produce a salt and hydrogen. For example:

ethanoic acid + magnesium → magnesium ethanoate + hydrogen
$$2CH_3COOH_{(aq)} + 2Mg_{(s)} \rightarrow 2CH_3COOMg_{(aq)} + H_{2(g)}$$

4) Carboxylic acids are also used in the preparation of esters. Carboxylic acids react with alcohols in the presence of an acid catalyst to form esters — there's more on this on the next page.

Vinegar Contains a Carboxylic Acid

1) Ethanoic acid can be made by oxidising ethanol. Microbes, like yeast, cause the ethanol to ferment. Ethanol can also be oxidised using oxidising agents. (See p.133 for more.)

ethanol + oxygen → ethanoic acid + water
$$CH_3CH_2OH + O_2 \rightarrow CH_3COOH + H_2O$$

If you leave wine open, the ethanol in it is oxidised — this is why it goes off.

2) Ethanoic acid can then be dissolved in water to make vinegar, which is used for flavouring and preserving foods.

A metal plus a carboxylic acid makes a salt plus hydrogen

If you know the products of the reaction of a metal or metal carbonate with a normal acid (see p.83), you can predict the products of its reaction with a carboxylic acid. Make sure you can name the salts formed — to work out the second part of the name, replace the '-anoic acid' ending of the carboxylic acid with '-anoate'.

Esters

Mix an alcohol from p.132 and a carboxylic acid from p.135, and what have you got... an <u>ester</u>, that's what.

Esters Have the Functional Group -COO-

1) <u>Esters</u> are formed from an <u>alcohol</u> and a <u>carboxylic acid</u>.

> alcohol + carboxylic acid → ester + water

2) An <u>acid catalyst</u> is usually used (e.g. concentrated <u>sulfuric acid</u>).

CH_3COOH
Ethanoic acid

CH_3CH_2OH
Ethanol

$CH_3COOCH_2CH_3$
Ethyl ethanoate

H_2O
Water

3) Their names end in '<u>-oate</u>'. The <u>alcohol</u> forms the <u>first</u> part of the ester's name, and the <u>acid</u> forms the <u>second</u> part.

> ethanol + ethanoic acid → ethyl ethanoate + water
> methanol + propanoic acid → methyl propanoate + water

You Can Make Esters in the Lab | PRACTICAL

The reaction between <u>alcohols</u> and <u>carboxylic acids</u> can be carried out in the <u>lab</u>. Here's how you would make <u>ethyl ethanoate</u>:

1) First, add a few drops of <u>concentrated sulfuric acid</u> to a boiling tube using a <u>dropping pipette</u>.
2) Add about 10 drops of <u>ethanoic acid</u>.
3) Then add an equal volume of <u>ethanol</u>.
4) Place the boiling tube in a beaker of water and place on a tripod.
5) Heat using a <u>Bunsen burner</u> until the water starts to boil, and then turn off the Bunsen.
6) After <u>1 minute</u>, remove the <u>tube</u> and allow it to <u>cool</u>.
7) Once it's cool, pour the mixture into a test tube of <u>sodium carbonate</u> solution and mix. A <u>layer of the ester</u> should form on top of the solution.

Mixture containing sulfuric acid, ethanoic acid and ethanol.

The ester should smell sweet, like pear drops.

Esters Smell Nice

1) Many esters have <u>pleasant smells</u> — often quite <u>sweet and fruity</u>. They're also <u>volatile</u>, which means they <u>evaporate</u> (turn into gases) easily. Because of these properties, esters are used in <u>perfumes</u> (the evaporated molecules can be detected by smell receptors in your nose).

2) Esters are also used to make <u>food flavourings</u> — e.g. there are esters that smell or taste of rum, apple, orange, banana, grape, pineapple, etc.

Warm-Up & Exam Questions

Time to test how much you know about alcohols, carboxylic acids and esters...

Warm-Up Questions

1) What is the general formula of an alcohol?
2) What gas is produced when methanoic acid reacts with potassium?
3) What type of catalyst is usually used when reacting an alcohol and a carboxylic acid to produce an ester?
4) Name the ester which has the structural formula $CH_3COOCH_2CH_3$.

Exam Questions

PAPER 2

1 Yeast can be used to convert sugars into ethanol. What is the name given to this process?

Grade 3-4

    ☐ **A** extraction   ☐ **C** denaturing

    ☐ **B** fermentation   ☐ **D** distillation

[1 mark]

PAPER 2

2 Alcohols are a series of organic compounds with a wide range of industrial applications.

Grade 4-6

(a) An alcohol containing 3 carbons is commonly used as a solvent. What is the name given to this alcohol?

[1 mark]

(b) Butanol is also commonly used as a solvent. Give the structural formula for butanol.

[1 mark]

(c) Methanol can be used as an additive to fuels to improve combustion. Draw the displayed formula for methanol.

[1 mark]

PAPER 2

3 Esters are volatile compounds that are often used in perfumes.

Grade 4-6

(a) Explain what is meant by the term **volatile**.

[1 mark]

(b) Apart from volatility, give **one** other property of esters that makes them suitable for use in perfumes.

[1 mark]

(c) Other than perfumes, give **one** use of esters in the chemical industry.

[1 mark]

Exam Questions

PAPER 2

4 Two different methods can be used to manufacture ethanol.
The incomplete table below shows some information about the two methods.

(a) Copy and complete the table.

Method	Reaction	Temperature needed
A	$C_2H_4 +$ .... $\rightarrow C_2H_5OH$	....
B	$C_6H_{12}O_6 \rightarrow 2CO_2 +$ ....C_2H_5OH	....

[4 marks]

(b) Method A requires a high temperature.
State the pressure and type of catalyst that are typically used in the reaction.

[2 marks]

(c) Method B should be carried out in an environment without oxygen.

(i) Predict the pH of the solution that would form if method B was
carried out in a flask that was open to the air. Explain your answer.

[2 marks]

(ii) A scientist attempted to use method B to produce ethanol at 250 °C.
After 24 hours, no product had been formed. Explain why.

[2 marks]

PAPER 2

5 A student reacts a small sample of a carboxylic acid, A, with potassium carbonate.

(a) The structural formula of carboxylic acid A is $CH_3CH_2CH_2COOH$.
(i) Name carboxylic acid A.

[1 mark]

(ii) Draw the displayed formula of carboxylic acid A.

[1 mark]

(b) A salt is produced in the reaction of carboxylic acid A with potassium carbonate.
Name the other **two** products of this reaction.

[2 marks]

(c) The student has an aqueous solution of a second carboxylic acid, B. She opens the bottle
and notices a strong smell of vinegar. Suggest the identity of carboxylic acid B.

[1 mark]

PAPER 2

6 Draw the displayed formulae of the carboxylic acid and the alcohol
that can be reacted together to produce propyl methanoate.

[2 marks]

Addition Polymers

Polymers are made by joining lots of little molecules together in long chains.

Addition Polymers are Made From Unsaturated Monomers

1) Polymers are substances of high average relative molecular mass made by joining up lots of small repeating units called monomers.

2) The monomers that make up addition polymers have a double covalent bond.

3) Lots of unsaturated monomer molecules (alkenes — see p.128) can open up their carbon-carbon double bonds and join together to form polymer chains. This is called addition polymerisation.

Ethene (C_2H_4) becoming poly(ethene) — $(C_2H_4)_n$:

The 'n' represents 'any number' — it just means you start with lots of ethene molecules.

many single ethenes → pressure and catalyst → poly(ethene)

Propene (C_3H_6) becoming poly(propene) — $(C_3H_6)_n$:

many single propenes → pressure and catalyst → poly(propene)

This is a shorthand way of showing polymer chains. See the next page for how to draw them.

4) The name of the polymer comes from the type of monomer it's made from — you just put brackets around it and stick the word "poly" in front of it. So propene becomes poly(propene), etc.

5) To get the formula of the polymer, you just put the formula of the monomer in brackets and put a little 'n' after it. So C_3H_6 becomes $(C_3H_6)_n$. Simple.

Addition polymerisation usually needs high pressure and a catalyst
The name of a polymer is determined by the monomers that were used to make it. So you can work out what monomers a polymer is made of from its name — e.g. poly(butene) is made up of butene monomers.

Addition Polymers

Polymers aren't usually drawn in diagrams as long chains — they're represented using repeat units.

You Can Draw the Repeat Unit of a Polymer

1) Drawing the displayed formula of an addition polymer from the displayed formula of its monomer is easy.

- Join the carbons together in a row with no double bonds between them.
- Stick a pair of brackets around the repeating bit, and put an 'n' after it (to show that there are lots of monomers).
- You should also draw a bond from each of the two carbons in the chain that pass through the brackets — this shows the chain continues.

Chloroethene → Poly(chloroethene)

2) To get from the displayed formula of the polymer to the displayed formula of the monomer, just do the reverse.

Draw out the repeating bit of the polymer, get rid of the two bonds going out through the brackets and put a double bond between the carbons.

Poly(tetrafluoroethene) → Tetrafluoroethene

Most Polymers are Hard to Get Rid Of

1) Most addition polymers are inert — they don't react easily. This is because the carbon-carbon bonds in the polymer chain are very strong and aren't easily broken.

2) This means that it takes a really long time for addition polymers to biodegrade (be broken down by bacteria or other organisms) — if you bury them in a landfill site, they'll still be there years later.

3) Burning plastics can release toxic gases, so that's not a great idea either.

4) So it's difficult to dispose of polymers. The best thing is to reuse them as many times as possible and then recycle them if you can.

Addition polymer carbon chains have no C=C bonds

Make sure you can recognise and draw polymers and their monomers. Cover up the method at the top of the page and try writing it out — then check how much you managed to remember.

Polyesters

Polyesters are polymers that contain ester links that join together repeating units.
Oh yeah, it's about time to get into the exciting world of condensation polymerisation.

Polymers Can be Made by **Condensation Polymerisation**

1) Condensation polymerisation usually involves two different types of monomer.
2) The monomers react together and bonds form between them, making polymer chains.
3) Each monomer has to contain at least two functional groups, one on each end of the molecule.
4) Each functional group can react with the functional group of another monomer, creating long chains of alternating monomers. For each new bond that forms, a small molecule (e.g. water) is lost.

Polyesters are **Condensation Polymers**

There's more on alcohols on page 132-133 and carboxylic acids on page 135-136.

1) Polyesters form when dicarboxylic acid monomers and diol monomers react together.

Dicarboxylic acid monomer   Diol monomer   The blocks represent the rest of each molecule.   Polyester   Water

Example:

Ethanedioic acid   Ethanediol   Poly(ethyl ethanoate)   Water

2) The dicarboxylic acid monomers contain two carboxylic acid (-COOH) groups and the diol monomers contain two alcohol (-OH) groups.
3) When the carboxylic acid group reacts with the alcohol group, it forms an ester link.
4) Polyesters are condensation polymers — each time an ester link is formed, a molecule of water is lost.

You may see polymers shown using their structural formula, e.g.

Some **Polyesters** are **Biodegradable**

1) Biodegradable polyesters, known as biopolyesters, can be broken down by bacteria and other living organisms in the environment over time.
2) This means they decompose and don't stay in landfill forever, reducing the polymers' pollutant effect.

Water can be released when condensation polymers are made
This happens when an ester link is formed between a carboxylic acid and an alcohol to produce a polyester.

Warm-Up & Exam Questions

I'm sure you have everything on these pages learnt and understood. But just to check, try these questions.

Warm-Up Questions

1) What is a polymer?
2) Butene has the formula C_4H_8. Give the formula for poly(butene).
3) True or false? Condensation polymerisation reactions always produce two products.
4) What is a biopolyester?

Exam Questions

1 The polymer poly(propene) can be made by addition polymerisation. The diagram on the right shows the displayed formula for part of a poly(propene) molecule. **Grade 6-7**

(a) (i) Draw the structure of the repeat unit of poly(propene).

[1 mark]

(ii) Draw the structure of the monomer that is used to make poly(propene).

[1 mark]

(iii) Give the name of the monomer used to make poly(propene).

[1 mark]

(b) The repeat unit of a different polymer is shown on the right. Name the polymer formed from this repeat unit.

[1 mark]

(c) Most addition polymers are difficult to dispose of, so it's good for the environment to reuse them as many times as possible. Explain why addition polymers are difficult to dispose of.

[2 marks]

PAPER 2

2 A condensation polymerisation reaction between butanedioic acid and ethanediol produces a polyester, **D**, and another product, **E**. **Grade 7-9**

(a) (i) Draw the displayed formula of the repeat unit of polyester **D**.

[2 marks]

(ii) What is the formula of the product, **E**?

[1 mark]

(b) In a different polymerisation reaction, pentanedioic acid, $HOOC(CH_2)_3COOH$, reacts with propanediol, $HO(CH_2)_3OH$. A polyester, **F**, is formed. Draw the repeat unit of **F**.

[2 marks]

Revision Summary for Section 6

Woohoo — you did it. But before you run off, time to have a go at a few questions.
*   Try these questions and <u>tick off each one</u> when you <u>get it right</u>.
*   When you've done <u>all the questions</u> under a heading and are <u>completely happy</u> with it, tick it off.

Formulae, Names and Isomers (p.118-121) ☐

1) Give the name of the type of formula shown
    a) C_2H_4 b) CH_2CH_2 ☐
2) What is a homologous series? ☑
3) Give the stem of the name of a hydrocarbon that contains 5 carbon atoms. ☑

Hydrocarbons (p.123-129) ☐

4) What is crude oil? ☑
5) How do the boiling points of hydrocarbons change as the chain length gets longer? ☑
6) What is cracking? ☑
7) Write out the word equation for the complete combustion of a hydrocarbon. ☑
8) Describe how acid rain is formed. ☑
9) a) Write out the symbol equation for the reaction between
        methane and bromine in the presence of UV light.
    b) Give the names of the products of this reaction. ☐
10) True or false? Alkenes contain C=C bonds. ☑
11) Which hydrocarbon has the general formula C_nH_{2n}? ☑
12) Write out the equation for the reaction between ethene and bromine water. ☐

Alcohols, Carboxylic Acids and Esters (p.132-137) ☐

13) State the names of the first four alcohols. ☑
14) Give three ways that alcohols can be oxidised. ☑
15) What type of reaction occurs between ethene and steam? ☑
16) What are the ideal conditions for the fermentation of sugar by yeast to take place at? ☑
17) Give the structural formula of the functional group in carboxylic acids. ☑
18) What ester is produced when ethanol and ethanoic acid
    react together in the presence of an acid catalyst? ☐

Polymers (p.140-142) ☐

19) a) What kind of polymers are made from monomers with a carbon-carbon double bond?
    b) Why is it not a good idea to dispose of these polymers by burning them? ☑
20) What type of polymerisation produces polyesters? ☑

Experimental Know-How

Scientists need to know how to plan and carry out scientific experiments. Unfortunately, the examiners think you should be able to do the same. But don't worry — that's what this section is all about.

You Might Get Asked Questions on Reliability and Validity

1) RELIABLE results come from experiments that give the same data:

- each time the experiment is repeated (by you),
- each time the experiment is reproduced by other scientists.

2) VALID results are both reliable AND come from experiments that were designed to be a fair test.

In the exam, you could be asked to suggest ways to improve the reliability or validity of some experimental results. If so, there are a couple of things to think about:

Controlling Variables Improves Validity

1) A variable is something that has the potential to change, e.g. temperature.
In a lab experiment you usually change one variable and measure how it affects another variable.

> Example: you might change only the temperature of a chemical reaction and measure how this affects the rate of reaction.

2) To make it a fair test, everything else that could affect the results should stay the same — otherwise you can't tell if the thing you're changing is causing the results or not.

> Example continued: you need to keep the concentration of the reactants the same, otherwise you won't know if any change in the rate of reaction is caused by the change in temperature, or a difference in reactant concentration.

3) The variable you CHANGE is called the INDEPENDENT variable.
4) The variable you MEASURE is called the DEPENDENT variable.
5) The variables that you KEEP THE SAME are called CONTROL variables.

> Example continued:
> Independent variable = temperature
> Dependent variable = rate of reaction
> Control variables = concentration of reactants, volume/mass of reactants, etc.

6) Because you can't always control all the variables, you often need to use a CONTROL EXPERIMENT — an experiment that's kept under the same conditions as the rest of the investigation, but doesn't have anything done to it. This is so that you can see what happens when you don't change anything at all.

Carrying Out Repeats Improves Reliability

1) To improve reliability you need to repeat any measurements you make and calculate the mean (average).
2) You need to repeat each measurement at least three times.

Getting valid, reliable results is very important

You might be asked to suggest what variables need to be controlled in an experiment. You might also be asked how you'd control the variables, e.g. temperature can be controlled using a water bath.

More Experimental Know-How

You Might Have to Suggest Ways to Make an Experiment Safer

1) It's important that experiments are safe. If you're asked to suggest ways to make an experiment safer, you'll first need to identify what the <u>potential hazards</u> might be. Hazards include things like:

> - <u>Chemicals</u>, e.g. sulfuric acid can burn your skin and alcohols catch fire easily.
> - <u>Fire</u>, e.g. an unattended Bunsen burner is a fire hazard.
> - <u>Electricity</u>, e.g. faulty electrical equipment could give you a shock.

You can find out about potential hazards by looking in textbooks, doing some internet research, or asking your teacher.

2) Then you'll need to suggest ways of <u>reducing</u> the <u>risks</u> involved with the hazard, e.g.

> - If you're working with <u>sulfuric acid</u>, always wear gloves and safety goggles. This will reduce the risk of the acid coming into contact with your skin and eyes.
> - If you're using a <u>Bunsen burner</u>, stand it on a heat proof mat. This will reduce the risk of starting a fire.
> - If you're working with <u>chemicals</u> that give off <u>harmful gases</u>, you need to use a fume cupboard. This will reduce the risk of you breathing in the gases.

You Could be Asked About Accuracy...

1) <u>Accuracy</u> is important. Accurate results are those that are <u>really close</u> to the <u>true answer</u>.
2) The accuracy of your results usually depends on your <u>method</u>.

> E.g. say you wanted to measure the <u>rate</u> of a <u>chemical reaction</u> that releases a <u>gas</u> as a product. The rate of the reaction would be the <u>amount of gas produced per unit time</u>. You could <u>estimate</u> how much gas is produced by <u>counting</u> the number of <u>bubbles</u> that are released. But the bubbles could be <u>different sizes</u>, and if they're produced really quickly you might <u>miss some</u> when counting. It would be more accurate to <u>collect the gas</u> (e.g. using a gas syringe) and <u>measure</u> its <u>volume</u>.

3) To make your results as <u>accurate</u> as possible, you need to make sure you measure the <u>right thing</u> and that you <u>don't miss</u> anything or <u>include</u> anything that shouldn't be included in the measurements.

> E.g. if you're measuring the volume of gas produced using a gas syringe, you need to make sure the syringe is <u>empty</u> at the start of the experiment. If there's any air in it the reading will be <u>wrong</u>.

...And Precision

Results also need to be <u>precise</u>. Precise results are ones where the data is <u>all really close</u> to the <u>mean</u> (average) of your repeated results (i.e. not spread out).

Sometimes, results are described as precise if they've been taken using sensitive instruments that can measure in small increments, e.g. using a ruler with a millimetre scale gives more precise data than a ruler with a scale in centimetres.

Repeat	Data set 1	Data set 2
1	12	11
2	14	17
3	13	14
Mean	13	14

Data set 1 is more precise than data set 2.

If you're asked how to carry out an experiment in the exam...

...then all this stuff about safety, accuracy and precision will apply then too. Flick back through this book to find an example of a practical experiment, then list all the <u>potential hazards</u> it might have. For each hazard, come up with a way of reducing the <u>risk</u> involved with it.

Processing Data

Processing your data means doing some <u>calculations</u> with it to make it more useful.

You Should Be Able to Identify **Anomalous Results**

1) Most results vary a bit, but any that are <u>totally different</u> are called <u>anomalous results</u>.

2) They're <u>caused</u> by <u>human errors</u>, e.g. by a mistake made when measuring or by not setting up a piece of equipment properly.

3) You could be asked to <u>identify</u> an anomalous result in the exam and suggest what <u>caused</u> it. To do this, just look for a result that <u>doesn't fit in</u> with the rest (e.g. it's <u>too high</u> or <u>too low</u>) then try to figure out what could have <u>gone wrong</u> with the experiment to have caused it.

4) If you're calculating an <u>average</u>, you can <u>ignore</u> any anomalous results.

You Might Have to **Process Your Data**

1) When you've done repeats of an experiment you should always calculate the <u>mean</u> (average). To do this, <u>add together</u> all the data values and <u>divide</u> by the total number of values in the sample.

Ignore anomalous results when calculating these.

2) You might also need to calculate the <u>range</u> (how spread out the data is). To do this, find the <u>largest</u> number and <u>subtract</u> the <u>smallest</u> number from it.

<u>Example</u>: The results of an experiment to find the mass of gas lost from two reactions are shown below. Calculate the mean and the range for the mass of gas lost in each reaction.

Test tube	Repeat 1 (g)	Repeat 2 (g)	Repeat 3 (g)	Mean (g)	Range (g)
A	28	37	32	$(28 + 37 + 32) \div 3 = \underline{32}$	$37 - 28 = \underline{9}$
B	47	51	60	$(47 + 51 + 60) \div 3 = \underline{53}$	$60 - 47 = \underline{13}$

Don't forget your calculator...

In an exam you could be given some data and asked to <u>process</u> it in some way. Make sure you're comfortable with things like calculating a mean or a percentage (using the right number of significant figures). Check you know what an anomalous result is and how to <u>identify</u> them, too.

Drawing Graphs

Once you've processed your data, you can present your results in a <u>chart</u> or <u>graph</u>.

Bar Charts can be Used to Show Different Types of Data

<u>Bar charts</u> can be used to display:

1) <u>Categoric data</u> — data that comes in <u>distinct categories</u>, e.g. alkane chain length, metals.
2) <u>Discrete data</u> — data that can be counted in <u>chunks</u>, where there's no in-between value, e.g. number of protons is discrete because you can't have half a proton.
3) <u>Continuous data</u> — <u>numerical</u> data that can have any <u>value</u> in a <u>range</u>, e.g. length, volume, temperature.

There are some <u>golden rules</u> you need to follow for <u>drawing</u> bar charts:

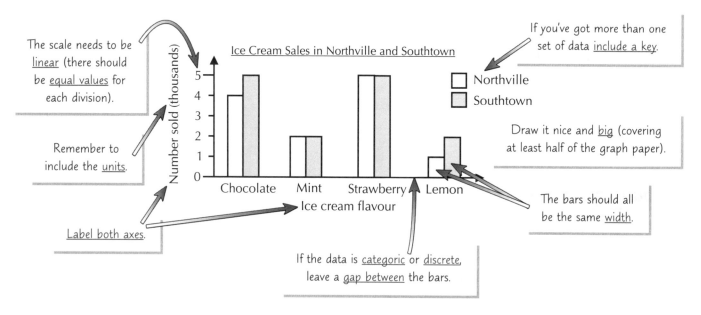

The scale needs to be <u>linear</u> (there should be <u>equal values</u> for each division).

Remember to include the <u>units</u>.

Label both axes.

If you've got more than one set of data <u>include a key</u>.

Draw it nice and <u>big</u> (covering at least half of the graph paper).

The bars should all be the same <u>width</u>.

If the data is <u>categoric</u> or <u>discrete</u>, leave a <u>gap between</u> the bars.

Graphs can be Used to Plot Continuous Data

1) If both variables are <u>continuous</u> you should use a <u>graph</u> to display the data.
2) Here are the <u>rules</u> for plotting points on a graph:

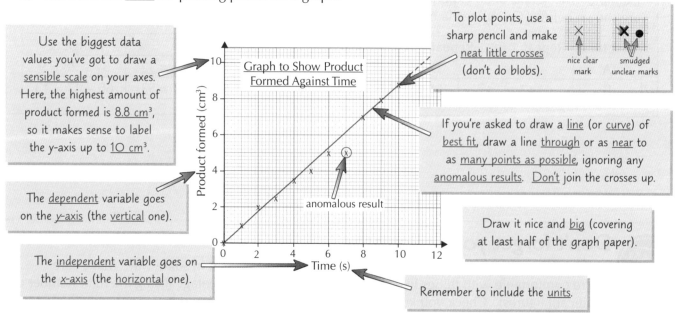

Use the biggest data values you've got to draw a <u>sensible scale</u> on your axes. Here, the highest amount of product formed is <u>8.8 cm³</u>, so it makes sense to label the y-axis up to <u>10 cm³</u>.

The <u>dependent</u> variable goes on the <u>y-axis</u> (the <u>vertical</u> one).

The <u>independent</u> variable goes on the <u>x-axis</u> (the <u>horizontal</u> one).

To plot points, use a sharp pencil and make <u>neat little crosses</u> (don't do blobs).

nice clear mark / smudged unclear marks

If you're asked to draw a <u>line</u> (or <u>curve</u>) of <u>best fit</u>, draw a line <u>through</u> or as <u>near</u> to as <u>many points as possible</u>, ignoring any <u>anomalous results</u>. <u>Don't</u> join the crosses up.

Draw it nice and <u>big</u> (covering at least half of the graph paper).

Remember to include the <u>units</u>.

Interpreting Graphs

You Need to be Able to **Interpret** Graphs

1) A graph is used to show the <u>relationship</u> between two variables —
   you need to be able to look at a graph and <u>describe</u> this relationship.

> E.g. the graph on the previous page shows that as
> <u>time goes on</u>, <u>more product is formed</u> and that the
> amount of product formed is <u>directly proportional</u> to time.

A relationship is directly proportional if one variable increases at the same rate as the other variable (so if one variable doubles, the other also doubles, etc.). A graph shows direct proportion when the line is straight and goes through the origin (O,O).

2) You also need to be able to <u>read information</u> off a graph.

> In the example on the previous page, if you wanted to know
> how much product had been formed by <u>11 s</u>, you'd draw a <u>vertical line up</u>
> to the graph line from the *x*-axis at 11 s and a <u>horizontal line across</u> to the *y*-axis.
> This would tell you that the amount of product formed by <u>11 s</u> was around <u>9.8 cm³</u>.

Graphs Show the **Correlation** Between Two Variables

1) You can get <u>three</u> types of <u>correlation</u> (relationship) between variables:

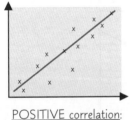

<u>POSITIVE correlation</u>:
as one variable <u>increases</u>
the other <u>increases</u>.

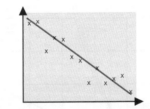

<u>INVERSE (negative) correlation</u>:
as one variable <u>increases</u>
the other <u>decreases</u>.

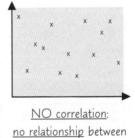

<u>NO correlation</u>:
<u>no relationship</u> between
the two variables.

2) Just because there's correlation, it doesn't mean the change in one variable is
   <u>causing</u> the change in the other — there might be <u>other factors</u> involved.

3) There are three possible reasons for a correlation:

- <u>CHANCE</u>: It might seem strange, but two things can show a correlation purely due to <u>chance</u>.

- <u>LINKED BY A 3RD VARIABLE</u>: A lot of the time it may <u>look</u> as if a change in one variable is causing a change in the other, but it <u>isn't</u> — a <u>third variable links</u> the two things.

- <u>CAUSE</u>: Sometimes a change in one variable does <u>cause</u> a change in the other. You can only conclude that a correlation is due to cause when you've <u>controlled all the variables</u> that could be affecting the result.

Correlation is just a relationship

It's very important to not get carried away if you notice a <u>correlation</u> between two variables. It doesn't mean that a change in one is causing a change in the other — there could be <u>another explanation</u> for the results. However, if you've controlled <u>all</u> other variables properly, it's a sign there <u>might</u> be a pattern there.

150

Calculating Rates from Graphs

You saw how to carry out some rate of reaction <u>experiments</u> back on pages 111-113. If you plot the results of experiments like those on a graph, you can <u>calculate</u> the rate of reaction. Here's how...

Faster Rates of Reaction are Shown by Steeper Gradients

1) If you have a graph of <u>amount of product formed</u> (or <u>reactant used up</u>) against <u>time</u>, then the <u>gradient</u> (slope) of the graph will be equal to the rate of the reaction — the <u>steeper</u> the slope, the <u>faster</u> the rate.

2) The gradient of a <u>straight line</u> is given by the equation:

> **gradient = change in y ÷ change in x**

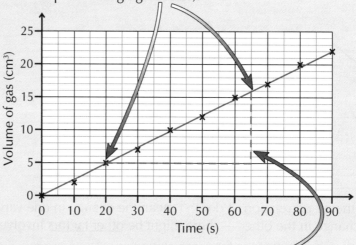

Example: Calculate the rate of the reaction shown on the graph below.

1) Find two <u>points on the line</u> that are <u>easy to read</u> the x and y values of (ones that pass through grid lines).

2) Draw a line straight <u>down</u> from the higher point and straight <u>across</u> from the lower one to make a <u>triangle</u>.

3) The <u>height</u> of your triangle = <u>change in y</u>   The <u>base</u> of your triangle = <u>change in x</u>
   Change in y = 16 − 5 = 11   Change in x = 65 − 20 = 45

4) Use the formula to work out the <u>gradient</u>, and therefore the rate.
   Gradient = change in y ÷ change in x = 11 ÷ 45 = 0.24 cm³/s   The units of the rate are just "units of y-axis ÷ units of x-axis".

Use a gradient to work out reaction rate

When calculating rates, always be sure to give your answer to an appropriate number of <u>significant figures</u>. And don't forget to write the <u>units</u>, too. You can work out the correct units for the rate by taking the units on the y-axis and dividing them by the units on the x-axis.

Describing Experiments

Calculating Rates from Graphs

Unfortunately, graphs aren't always nice straight lines. If they're <u>curved</u>, things start to get a bit trickier.

Draw a **Tangent** to Find the Gradient of a **Curve**

1) If your graph (or part of it) is a <u>curve</u>, the gradient, and therefore <u>rate</u>, is different at different points along the curve.

2) To find the <u>gradient</u> of the graph at a certain point, you'll have to draw a <u>tangent</u> at that point.

3) A tangent is just a line that <u>touches the curve</u> and has the <u>same gradient</u> as the line at that point.

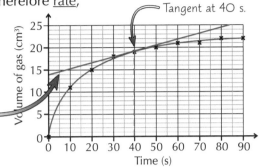

4) To draw a tangent:

- Place a <u>ruler</u> on the line of best fit at the point you're interested in, so you can see the <u>whole curve</u>.
- Adjust the ruler so the space between the ruler and the curve is the same on both sides of the point.
- Draw a line <u>along the ruler</u> to make the <u>tangent</u>.

5) The rate at that point is then just the <u>gradient</u> of the <u>tangent</u>.

<u>Example</u>: The graph below shows the concentration of product formed, measured at regular intervals during a chemical reaction. What is the rate of reaction at 3 minutes?

1) Position a <u>ruler</u> on the graph at the point where you want to know the rate — here it's <u>3 minutes</u>.

2) Adjust the ruler until the <u>space</u> between the ruler and the curve is <u>equal</u> on <u>both sides</u> of the point.

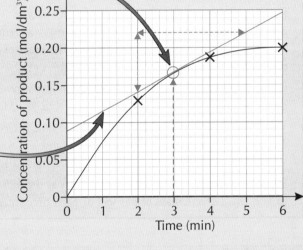

3) Draw a line along the ruler to make the <u>tangent</u>. Extend the line <u>right across</u> the graph.

4) Pick <u>two points</u> on the line that are easy to read. Use them to calculate the <u>gradient</u> of the tangent in order to find the <u>rate</u>:

gradient = change in y ÷ change in x
$\quad\quad$ = (0.22 − 0.14) ÷ (5.0 − 2.0)
$\quad\quad$ = 0.08 ÷ 3.0
$\quad\quad$ = 0.027

So, the rate of reaction at 3 minutes was 0.027 mol/dm³/min.

Units = units of y-axis ÷ units of x-axis.
$\quad\quad$ = mol/dm³ ÷ min
$\quad\quad$ = mol/dm³/min

Tangents should only touch one point on the curve

Don't <u>rush</u> if you need to draw a tangent in an exam. <u>How</u> you draw your line will affect what <u>answer</u> you get out at the end, so it's always worth checking you've positioned the ruler correctly.

Describing Experiments

Planning Experiments

You could be asked to <u>plan</u> or <u>describe</u> how you'd <u>carry out</u> an experiment. The experiment might be one you've already come across or you might be asked to come up with an <u>experiment of your own</u>.

You Need to Be Able to Plan a **Good Experiment**

Here are some <u>general tips</u> on what to include when planning an experiment:

1) Say <u>what</u> you're <u>measuring</u> (i.e. what the <u>dependent variable</u> is going to be).

2) Say <u>what</u> you're <u>changing</u> (i.e. what the <u>independent variable</u> is going to be) and describe <u>how</u> you're going to change it.

3) Describe the <u>method</u> and the <u>apparatus</u> you'd use.

4) Describe what <u>variables</u> you're keeping <u>constant</u> — and <u>how</u> you're going to do it.

5) Say that you need to <u>repeat</u> the experiment at least three times, to make the results <u>more reliable</u>.

6) Say whether you're using a <u>control</u> or not.

Even if you can't remember all the details of an experimental method you've learned about, you could still get marks for describing things like the independent and dependent variables.

Here's an <u>idea</u> of the sort of thing you might be asked in the exam and what your answer might be...

Exam-style Question

1) Describe an experiment to investigate the effect of concentration on the reaction of dilute hydrochloric acid and magnesium metal. **(6 marks)**

Example Answer

In this experiment you should change the concentration of the dilute hydrochloric acid. You can see what effect this has by measuring the mass of the reaction mixture.

Set up a flask containing a measured mass of magnesium metal. Place the flask on a mass balance.

Pour a measured volume of dilute hydrochloric acid into the flask and start the timer. Take readings of the mass at regular time intervals until the mass doesn't change anymore. The mass of gas lost from the reaction mixture can be calculated using this data.

Carry out the experiment again with different concentrations of dilute hydrochloric acid (e.g. 0.1 mol/dm³, 0.2 mol/dm³, 0.3 mol/dm³ and 0.4 mol/dm³).

The mass should be measured at the same time intervals for each acid concentration. The volume of acid should always be the same and the same mass of magnesium metal should be used each time. The temperature must also remain constant.

Repeat the experiment three times at each acid concentration and use the results to find the average mass of gas lost at each time interval for each concentration.

You could also collect the hydrogen in a gas syringe and measure its volume.

Experiments Test **Hypotheses**

1) A <u>hypothesis</u> is a possible <u>explanation</u> for something that you've observed.

2) You can use experiments to <u>test</u> whether a hypothesis might be <u>right or not</u>. This involves making a <u>prediction</u> based on the hypothesis and testing it by <u>gathering evidence</u> (i.e. <u>data</u>) from <u>investigations</u>. If <u>evidence</u> from <u>experiments</u> backs up a prediction, you're a step closer to figuring out if the hypothesis is true.

All investigations need be planned before you begin

The number of marks available for a question like the one above will vary, but it'll usually be around five or six. Think about what you're going to say <u>beforehand</u> and in what <u>order</u> — that way you're less likely to forget something important. Like what you're <u>actually measuring</u>, say.

Drawing Conclusions

Congratulations — you're nearly at the end of a gruelling investigation, time to draw some <u>conclusions</u>.

You Can **Only Conclude** What the Data Shows and **No More**

1) Drawing conclusions might seem pretty straightforward — you just <u>look at your data</u> and <u>say what pattern or relationship you see</u> between the dependent and independent variables.

> The table below shows the rate of a reaction in the presence of two <u>different catalysts</u>.
>
> | Catalyst | Rate of reaction (cm³/s) |
> |:---:|:---:|
> | A | 13.5 |
> | B | 19.5 |
> | No catalyst | 5.5 |
>
> <u>CONCLUSION</u>:
> Catalyst <u>B</u> makes <u>this reaction</u> go faster than catalyst A.

2) But you've got to be really careful that your conclusion <u>matches the data</u> you've got and <u>doesn't go any further</u>.

> You <u>can't</u> conclude that catalyst B increases the rate of <u>any other reaction</u> more than catalyst A — the results might be completely different.

3) You also need to be able to <u>use your results</u> to <u>justify your conclusion</u> (i.e. back up your conclusion with some specific data).

> The rate of this reaction was <u>6 cm³/s faster</u> using catalyst B compared with catalyst A.

4) When writing a conclusion you need to <u>refer back</u> to the original hypothesis and say whether the data <u>supports it</u> or not.

> - The <u>hypothesis</u> for this experiment might have been that adding a catalyst would <u>increase the rate of reaction</u> because it would <u>decrease</u> the <u>activation energy</u>.
> - The <u>prediction</u> may have been that <u>catalyst B</u> would decrease the activation energy by a greater amount so would <u>increase the rate of reaction more</u> than catalyst A.
> - If so, the data <u>supports</u> the hypothesis.

5) You could also make more <u>predictions</u> based on your conclusion, then <u>further experiments</u> could be carried out to test them.

Conclusions sum up what you've learnt from your data

There's no point doing an investigation unless you're going to draw some kind of <u>conclusion</u> from it — even if that conclusion is that you were <u>completely wrong</u> about your original hypothesis. <u>Don't worry</u> if you're wrong, there will still be something that you can <u>learn</u> from your data. That's how science works, after all.

Evaluations

So you've planned and carried out an investigation, processed and interpreted your data and drawn some conclusions. There's only <u>one thing</u> left to do — an <u>evaluation</u>.

Evaluations — Describe **How** it Could be **Improved**

An evaluation is a <u>critical analysis</u> of the whole investigation.

1) You should comment on the <u>method</u> — was it <u>valid</u>? Did you control all the other variables to make it a <u>fair test</u>?

2) Comment on the <u>quality</u> of the <u>results</u> — was there <u>enough evidence</u> to reach a valid <u>conclusion</u>? Were the results <u>reliable</u>, <u>valid</u>, <u>accurate</u> and <u>precise</u>?

3) Were there any <u>anomalous</u> results? If there were <u>none</u> then <u>say so</u>. If there were any, try to <u>explain</u> them — were they caused by <u>errors</u> in measurement? Were there any other <u>variables</u> that could have <u>affected</u> the results?

4) All this analysis will allow you to say how <u>confident</u> you are that your conclusion is <u>right</u>.

5) Then you can suggest any <u>changes</u> to the <u>method</u> that would <u>improve</u> the quality of the results, so that you could have <u>more confidence</u> in your conclusion. For example, you might suggest <u>changing</u> the way you controlled a variable, or <u>increasing</u> the number of <u>measurements</u> you took. Taking more measurements at <u>narrower intervals</u> could give you a <u>more accurate result</u>.

For example, <u>enzymes</u> have an <u>optimum temperature</u> (a temperature at which they <u>work best</u>). Say you do an experiment to find an enzyme's optimum temperature and take measurements at 10 °C, 20 °C, 30 °C, 40 °C and 50 °C. The results of this experiment tell you the optimum is <u>40 °C</u>. You could then <u>repeat</u> the experiment, taking <u>more measurements around 40 °C</u> to get a <u>more accurate</u> value for the optimum.

6) You could also make more <u>predictions</u> based on your conclusion, then <u>further experiments</u> could be carried out to test them.

When suggesting improvements to the investigation, always make sure that you say why you think this would make the results better.

Evaluations help us to improve scientific methods

That's it for this section. Around <u>20%</u> of your marks will come from being able to <u>describe experiments</u> and <u>analyse</u> and <u>evaluate</u> data and methods in an appropriate way. So it's crucial that you make sure you're completely happy with everything in this section before you go into the exam. Best of luck.

Candidate Surname		Candidate Forename(s)	

Centre Number	Candidate Number

Edexcel
International GCSE

Chemistry
Paper 1C

Practice Paper
Time allowed: 2 hours

You must have:
- A ruler.
- A calculator.

Total marks:

Instructions to candidates
- Use **black** ink to write your answers.
- Write your name and other details in the spaces provided above.
- Answer **all** questions in the spaces provided.
- In calculations, show clearly how you worked out your answers.
- You will need to answer some questions by placing a cross in a box, like this: ☒
  To change your answer, draw a line through the box like this: ☒
  Then mark your new answer as normal.

Information for candidates
- The marks available are given in brackets at the end of each question.
- There are 110 marks available for this paper.

Advice for candidates
- Read all the questions carefully.
- Write your answers as clearly and neatly as possible.
- Keep in mind how much time you have left.

Answer **all** questions

1   Atoms contain protons, neutrons and electrons.

(a)   The diagram below shows the structure of an atom.
Label a proton.

[1]

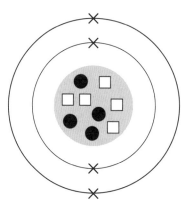

(b)   The table below shows the numbers of protons, neutrons and electrons in six different atoms.

Atom	Number of protons	Number of neutrons	Number of electrons
A	5	6	5
B	7	7	7
C	6	8	6
D	6	6	6
E	10	10	10
F	4	5	4

Which **two** atoms are isotopes of the same element? Explain your answer.

Atoms .... and ....

Explanation ....

....

....

[2]

Zinc appears in the periodic table as shown below.

| 65 |
| Zn |
| 30 Zinc |

(c)   How many protons, neutrons and electrons are there in an atom of zinc?

Protons .... Neutrons .... Electrons ....

[3]

(d)   Zinc sulfate is a compound with the formula $ZnSO_4$.

(i)   Describe what is meant by the term **compound**.

....

....

[2]

(ii)   Calculate the relative formula mass of zinc sulfate.

Relative formula mass = ...

[2]

[Total 10 marks]

Turn over ▶

158

2   Nitrogen dioxide is an atmospheric pollutant.

(a)   Suggest why nitrogen dioxide levels can be particularly high in cities.

....

....

....

....

[2]

(b)   Nitrogen dioxide can react with water in the atmosphere to form nitric acid, which falls as acid rain. Acid rain can damage buildings made from limestone, which is mainly calcium carbonate.

    (i)   Complete the word equation for the reaction between nitric acid and calcium carbonate.

    nitric acid + calcium carbonate $\rightarrow$

    .... + ... + ...

[2]

    (ii) Name **one** other gas that can cause acid rain.

....

[1]

(c)   Nitrogen dioxide is a covalent compound with a boiling point of 21 °C. Explain, in terms of its structure and bonding, why nitrogen dioxide has such a low boiling point.

....

....

....

....

....

[3]

[Total 8 marks]

3   The halogens make up Group 7 of the periodic table.
The table below shows some of the physical properties of the first four halogens.

Halogen	Atomic number	Melting Point (°C)	Boiling Point (°C)	Colour at room temperature
Fluorine	9	−220	−188	very pale yellow
Chlorine	17		−34	green
Bromine	35	−7	59	
Iodine	53	114	185	dark grey

(a) (i) Predict the melting point of chlorine, using the data in the table.

☐ **A** −231 °C

☐ **B** −216 °C

☐ **C** −101 °C

☐ **D**   107 °C

[1]

(ii) Explain your answer to part (i).

....

....
[1]

(b)   Describe the appearance of bromine at room temperature.

....
[2]

(c)   Write down the balanced symbol equation for the reaction between
bromine and potassium iodide.

....
[2]

Turn over ▶

160

(d) (i) Complete the diagram below to show the electronic structure of a chlorine atom.
Mark each electron using an 'X'.

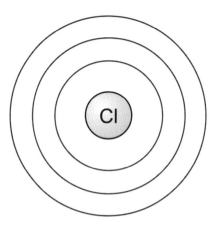

[1]

(ii) Explain how the group number of chlorine in the periodic table
is related to its electronic structure.

....

....

....

[2]

(e) Chlorine is bubbled through sodium iodide solution. What will happen?
Explain your answer in terms of the relative positions of chlorine and iodine in
the periodic table.

....

....

....

....

....

[3]

(f) Chlorine can combine with hydrogen to form hydrogen chloride.
Explain why hydrogen chloride forms an acidic solution in water.

....

....

....

[2]

[Total 14 marks]

4 A student wanted to find out which of five dyes could be present in a particular black ink.

(a) The student was asked to suggest a method. This is the method the student suggested:

- Take a piece of filter paper. Draw a pencil line near the bottom.

- Add spots of the dyes to the line at regular intervals.

- Put the paper into a beaker of water with the line just touching the water.

- Repeat these steps with a spot of the black ink on a second piece of filter paper, and put this paper into a beaker of ethanol.

- Place a lid on each beaker, and wait for the solvents to travel to the top of the paper.

- Compare the positions of the spots created by the black ink with those created by the dyes.

Identify **two** problems with this method. For each problem, suggest how you would alter the method to carry out the experiment correctly.

You can assume the student takes sensible safety precautions.

Problem 1 ....

....

....

Correction ....

....

....

....

Problem 2 ....

....

Correction ....

....

....

....

[4]

(b) The student repeated the experiment using the correct method.
The results are shown below.

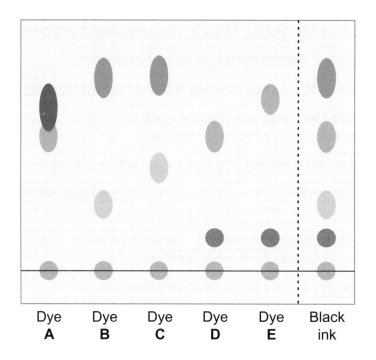

Diagram not to scale.

Dye **A** Dye **B** Dye **C** Dye **D** Dye **E** Black ink

Which dyes (**A-E**) could have been present in the black ink? Explain your answer.

Dyes ....

Explanation ....

....

....

....

[2]

(c) The student measured the distances moved by the solvent and one
of the spots in the black ink. He found that the solvent had moved
6.4 cm from the baseline, and that the spot had moved 4.8 cm.
Calculate the R_f value of the spot in the black ink.

R_f value = ...

[1]

[Total 7 marks]

5   Carbon dioxide is a simple molecule whose displayed formula is shown below.

$$O=C=O$$

(a)   Carbon dioxide can be formed from the thermal decomposition of magnesium carbonate.
        Name the other product of this reaction.

....

[1]

(b)   Draw a dot and cross diagram to show the bonding in carbon dioxide.
        Only show the outer electrons.

[2]

(c)   The molecular formula of magnesium carbonate is $MgCO_3$.
        Calculate the percentage mass of carbon in magnesium carbonate.

mass of carbon = ... %

[2]

(d)   Carbon dioxide is a greenhouse gas.

    (i)   Explain what is meant by the term **greenhouse gas**.

....

....

....

[2]

    (ii) State the percentage of the air that is made up of carbon dioxide.

....

[1]

    (iii) Give **one** possible effect of increasing the amount of carbon dioxide in the atmosphere.

....

....

[1]

[Total 9 marks]

6   Analytical tests can be used to identify different substances.

(a) (i) A test is carried out to distinguish between a solution of iron(II) chloride
          and a solution of iron(III) chloride.

          Describe the test and the result expected for each solution.

          ....

          ....

          ....

          ....

          ....

                                                                                                    [2]

(ii)   Another test is carried out to distinguish between a solution of sodium chloride
          and a solution of sodium iodide.

          Describe the test and the result expected for each solution.

          ....

          ....

          ....

          ....

          ....

                                                                                                    [2]

(b)   When an unknown compound is placed in a blue Bunsen flame, it gives a yellow colour.
          If dilute acid is added to the compound, a gas is produced.
          When this gas is bubbled through limewater, the limewater goes cloudy.

          Identify the compound by its chemical name.

          ....

                                                                                                    [2]
                                                                                        [Total 6 marks]

Turn over ▶

7   A student reacts four different metals with dilute sulfuric acid.
She controls all of the relevant variables to make sure that the test is fair.
She collects the gas given off by each reaction in a gas syringe.
The diagrams below show all four reactions after 30 seconds.

Reaction A   **Reaction B**   **Reaction C**   **Reaction D**

unknown metal   iron   copper   magnesium

gas syringe

dilute $H_2SO_{4(aq)}$

(a)   State the dependent variable in this experiment.

....

[1]

(b)   Name the gas that is being collected in the gas syringes.

....

[1]

(c)   Which reaction, **A**, **B**, **C**, or **D**, contains the **most reactive** metal?
Explain how you can tell.

....

....

[3]

(d)   Use your knowledge of the reactivity series to suggest a
possible identity for the unknown metal used in reaction **A**.

....

[1]

(e)   In another experiment, the student placed pieces of different metals in metal salt solutions. She left them for 10 minutes. The student then recorded whether any reaction had occurred. The results of this experiment are shown in the table below.

	Did any reaction occur with:		
	iron sulfate	magnesium sulfate	copper sulfate
iron	No	No	....
magnesium	....	No	Yes
copper	No	No	No

Complete the table by filling in the gaps.

[2]

(f)   The equation for the reaction between magnesium and copper sulfate solution is:

$$Mg_{(s)} + CuSO_{4(aq)} \rightarrow MgSO_{4(aq)} + Cu_{(s)}$$

Which substance was oxidised in this reaction?

....

[1]

[Total 9 marks]

8 The displayed formulae of two gases are shown below.

Gas **A** $H-C-C-C-H$ (with H atoms above and below each carbon)

Gas **B** $H-C-C=C$ (with H atoms shown)

(a) Name gas **B**.

....

[1]

(b) State the name given to unsaturated hydrocarbons like gas **B**.

....

[1]

(c) Pentane is a saturated compound. Draw the displayed formula of pentane.

[1]

(d) Describe a test that you could use to distinguish between gas **A** and gas **B**.
State what you would observe in each case.

Test: ....

Observations:

Gas **A**: ....

Gas **B**: ....

[2]

(e) In terms of bond breaking and bond formation, explain the observation for gas **B**.

....

....

....

[2]

(f)   Gas **A** is burnt in a plentiful supply of oxygen.
        Write a balanced chemical equation for this reaction.

        ....
                                                                                                                    [2]

(g)   Demand for short chain hydrocarbons, such as gas **A** and gas **B**,
        is much higher than for longer chain hydrocarbons.

   (i) Name the process by which long chain hydrocarbons are split into short chain hydrocarbons.

        ....
                                                                                                                    [1]

   (ii) Decane, $C_{10}H_{22}$, can be split using the process in (i) into gas **B** and heptane, C_7H_{16}.
        Write these three hydrocarbons in order of increasing viscosity.

        ....
                                                                                                                    [1]
                                                                                                    [Total 11 marks]

Turn over ▶

9   Self-heating cans use exothermic chemical reactions to heat up their contents.
When a seal is broken two chemicals mix and react, heating up the can.
Calcium oxide and water can be used to heat up drinks in this way.

(a)   Explain what is meant by an **exothermic reaction**.

....

....

[1]

(b)   A student wanted to test the reaction of different substances with water
to see if they could be used to cool drinks down.

Outline an experiment the student could carry out to test different substances.

....

....

....

....

....

[3]

(c)   Calcium oxide (CaO) is produced when iron(III) oxide (Fe_2O_3) reacts with calcium.
Iron is also produced. Write a balanced chemical equation for this reaction.

....

[2]

[Total 6 marks]

10 The graph shows the volume of gas produced over time
when lumps of zinc are reacted with dilute sulfuric acid.

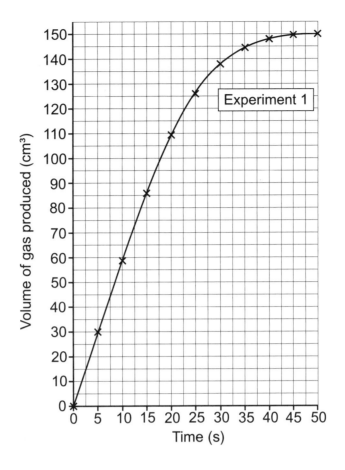

(a) Use the graph to calculate the rate of reaction at 25 s.

rate of reaction = ... cm³/s

[3]

In a second experiment, some copper sulfate catalyst was added to the acid.
The same amount of zinc was used as before, and the lumps were of a similar size.
The same volume of dilute sulfuric acid was also used.

The results are shown in the table below.

Time (s)	Volume of gas formed (cm³) Experiment 2
0	0
5	50
10	100
15	130
20	143
25	148
30	150
35	150
40	150
45	150
50	150

(b)   Plot the results of the second experiment on the graph on the previous page.
Draw a curve of best fit through the points. Label the line 'Experiment 2'.

[2]

(c)   How long does it take to form half of the total amount of gas collected
in the second experiment?

time taken = ... s

[1]

(d)   Describe what the curves show about how the rate of reaction changes as
the reaction proceeds.

....

[1]

(e)   State how the catalyst affects the reaction rate and explain
how you can tell this from the graph.

....

....

....

[1]

(f)   Explain, in terms of activation energy, how catalysts affect reaction rates.

....

....

....

[1]

[Total 9 marks]

Turn over ▶

Practice Paper 1C

11 Iron pipes need protection from rusting.

(a) State the conditions that cause iron to rust.

....

....

[2]

(b) Rusting is a type of corrosion. What causes corrosion?

☐ **A** distillation

☐ **B** electrolysis

☐ **C** oxidation

☐ **D** reduction

[1]

(c) Paint can be used to stop underground iron pipes rusting, but they will eventually need repainting or replacing. An alternative to this is to connect a large piece of magnesium to the pipe, as shown in the diagram below.

(i) State the name given to this kind of corrosion protection.

....

[1]

(ii) Explain why the magnesium protects the iron from rusting, and how this happens.

....

....

....

[2]

(d) A coat of zinc could be applied to the iron pipes to prevent them rusting. State the name given to this method of corrosion protection.

....

[1]

[Total 7 marks]

12 The balanced equation below shows what happens when a strip of magnesium metal is dissolved in a solution of hydrochloric acid.

$$Mg_{(s)} + 2HCl_{(aq)} \rightarrow MgCl_{2(aq)} + H_{2(g)}$$

(a) A student dissolved a piece of magnesium in an excess of hydrochloric acid.
7.60 g of $MgCl_2$ was produced. What mass of magnesium did the student start with?

Mass of magnesium = ... g
[3]

(b) Describe how the student could test for the gas produced in this reaction, and state what he would observe.

Test ....

....

Observation ....

....
[2]

(c) The student repeated the reaction, but added a few drops of methyl orange indicator to the acid before adding a magnesium strip.
Suggest a reason why no colour change occurred during the course of the reaction.

....
[1]
[Total 6 marks]

Turn over ▶

176

13   A student burns a piece of copper in air.

(a)   The copper reacts with oxygen in the air to form copper oxide.
Use the data in the table below to find the empirical formula of the copper oxide.

Mass of empty container	28.00 g
Mass of container + mass of copper oxide	34.36 g
Mass of container + copper	33.08 g

Empirical formula = ...
[5]

(b)   In another experiment, the student burns 1.08 g of magnesium in air.
She expected to produce 1.80 g of magnesium oxide.
The actual mass of magnesium oxide produced was 1.20 g.

(i)   Calculate the percentage yield of magnesium oxide.

Percentage yield = ... %
[2]

(ii)   Suggest a reason why the mass of magnesium oxide produced was less than expected.

....

....
[1]
[Total 8 marks]
[Total for paper 110 marks]

Candidate Surname		Candidate Forename(s)

Centre Number	Candidate Number

Edexcel
International GCSE

Chemistry
Paper 2C

Practice Paper
Time allowed: 1 hour 15 minutes

You must have:
- A ruler.
- A calculator.

Total marks:

Instructions to candidates
- Use **black** ink to write your answers.
- Write your name and other details in the spaces provided above.
- Answer **all** questions in the spaces provided.
- In calculations, show clearly how you worked out your answers.
- You will need to answer some questions by placing a cross in a box, like this: $\boxed{\text{x}}$
  To change your answer, draw a line through the box like this: $\boxed{\text{x}}$
  Then mark your new answer as normal.

Information for candidates
- The marks available are given in brackets at the end of each question.
- There are 70 marks available for this paper.

Advice for candidates
- Read all the questions carefully.
- Write your answers as clearly and neatly as possible.
- Keep in mind how much time you have left.

Answer **all** questions

1   The diagram shows the electronic structures of a sodium atom and a chlorine atom.

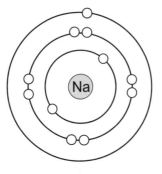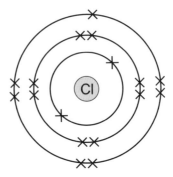

(a)   Chlorine has two major isotopes, ^{35}Cl and ^{37}Cl.
These isotopes are used to calculate the relative atomic mass of chlorine.

    (i)   State what is meant by the term **isotope**.

....

....

                                                                                                                 [1]

    (ii) ^{35}Cl has a relative abundance of 75%.

         The relative atomic mass of chlorine is 35.5. Show how this value is calculated.

....

....

                                                                                                               [2]

(b)   Sodium and chlorine react to form the ionic compound sodium chloride.

       Draw a dot and cross diagram of sodium chloride. Show only the outer electrons.

[3]

[Total 6 marks]

2   The Haber process is used to make ammonia from nitrogen and hydrogen.
The chemical equation for the reaction is:

$$N_{2(g)} + 3H_{2(g)} \rightleftharpoons 2NH_{3(g)}$$

(a)   The Haber process reaction reaches a dynamic equilibrium.
State **one** characteristic of a dynamic equilibrium.

....

....
[1]

(b)   The reaction between nitrogen and hydrogen is exothermic.

Explain what will happen to the yield of ammonia if the temperature is increased.

....

....

....
[2]

(c)   Explain what will happen to the yield of ammonia if the pressure is decreased.

....

....

....
[2]

(d)   At a particular pressure and temperature, the Haber process
was used to produce 85 g of ammonia.

(i)   Calculate the number of moles of ammonia produced.

Number of moles = ...
[2]

(ii) Calculate the volume of this amount of ammonia at room temperature and pressure.

Volume = ... dm³
[1]
[Total 8 marks]

Turn over ▶

3 The structural formula of an alcohol is shown below.

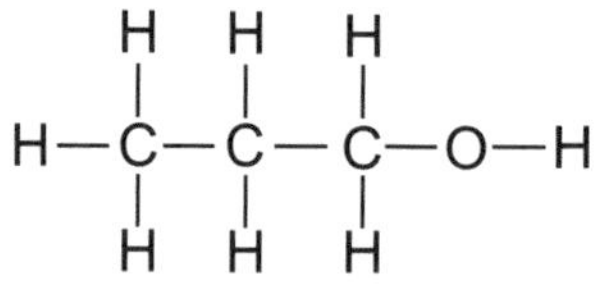

$$H-\underset{\underset{H}{|}}{\overset{\overset{H}{|}}{C}}-\underset{\underset{H}{|}}{\overset{\overset{H}{|}}{C}}-\underset{\underset{H}{|}}{\overset{\overset{H}{|}}{C}}-O-H$$

(a) Name the alcohol shown above.

....

[1]

(b) This alcohol can be used to make propyl propanoate.
The symbol equation for the formation of propyl propanoate is shown below.

$$C_3H_7OH + C_2H_5COOH \rightarrow C_2H_5COOC_3H_7 + H_2O$$

(i) Name the compound C_2H_5COOH.

....

[1]

(ii) State the homologous series propyl propanoate belongs to.

....

[1]

(iii) Propyl propanoate has a strong, fruity smell.
Suggest **one** other property of propyl propanoate.

....

[1]

(c) Ethanol is another alcohol. Ethanol can be oxidised by burning in air.

(i) Write down a balanced symbol equation for the complete combustion of ethanol.

....

[2]

(ii) Suggest another method that can be used to oxidise ethanol.

....

....

[1]

[Total 7 marks]

4   A student investigates the reactions of the Group 1 elements lithium, sodium and potassium with water. The student's observations are recorded in the table below.

Metal	Observations
lithium	Fizzes, moves across the surface
sodium	Fizzes strongly, melts into a round ball, moves across the surface
potassium	Fizzes violently, melts into a round ball, moves across the surface, a flame is seen

The student decides that the order of reactivity of the three elements is:

- potassium (most reactive)

- sodium

- lithium (least reactive)

(a)   Give **two** pieces of evidence from the table that support the student's conclusion.

1 ....

....

2 ....

....

[2]

(b)   Explain the pattern of reactivity that the student has noticed.

....

....

....

....

[2]

(c)   Write a balanced chemical equation for the reaction between lithium and water.

....

[2]

Turn over ▶

(d)   The student accidentally mixes up some unlabelled samples of lithium chloride and potassium chloride. The student decides to do a test to find out which is which, using a moistened wire loop. Briefly describe the test that the student could carry out, and what the results would be.

....

....

....

[2]

[Total 8 marks]

5   Hydrogen can be burned in oxygen and used as a fuel.

$$2H_2 + O_2 \rightarrow 2H_2O$$

(a)   Calculate the enthalpy change for the reaction. The bond energy values are given below.

Bond energy values (kJ/mol):

O=O   +498

H–H   +436

O–H   +464

Enthalpy change = ... kJ/mol

[4]

(b)   Is bond breaking an exothermic or endothermic process?

....

[1]

(c)   In another reaction, the energy change is exothermic.
Which of the following energy profiles show the enthalpy change of the reaction?

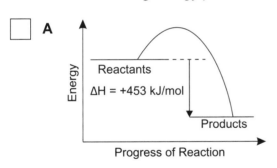

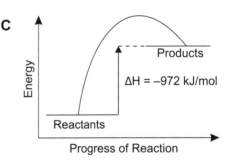

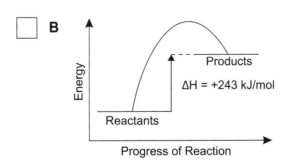

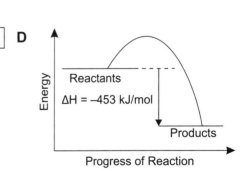

[1]

[Total 6 marks]

Turn over ▶

6   A student is investigating how the rate of the reaction between magnesium
strips and hydrochloric acid is affected by the concentration of the acid.
The student compares different concentrations of acid by measuring how
long it takes for the reaction to produce 20 cm³ of hydrogen gas.

The results of the experiment are shown below.

Concentration of acid (mol/dm³)	Time (s)
0.2	58
0.4	29
0.6	18
0.8	15
1.0	12

(a)   Plot the results on the axes below and draw a curve of best fit.

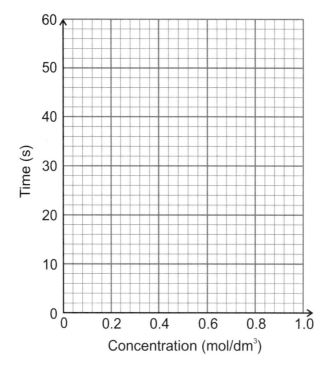

[2]

(b)   Use your graph to predict the time that it would take for 20 cm³ of hydrogen gas to form with
0.5 mol/dm³ hydrochloric acid.

.... s

[1]

(c) How could the student make his results more reliable?

....

[1]

(d) Describe what the graph shows about the effect of concentration on the rate of reaction.

....

....

[1]

(e) Explain, in terms of collision theory, why concentration affects the rate of a reaction.

....

....

....

....

[2]

(f) The student carries out the experiment again using 0.6 mol/dm^3 hydrochloric acid.
This time, magnesium powder is used rather than strips of metal.

The student says "it will take longer than 18 seconds for 20 cm^3 of hydrogen gas to form".

Is the student's prediction correct? Explain your answer.

....

....

....

....

....

[3]
[Total 10 marks]

Turn over ▶

7 Titration with 0.050 mol/dm³ sulfuric acid was used to determine the concentration of calcium hydroxide solution. In the titration, 8.80 cm³ of sulfuric acid were needed to neutralise 10.0 cm³ of the calcium hydroxide solution.

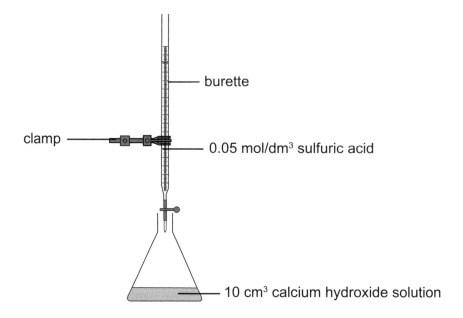

(a) Name a suitable indicator for the titration.

....

[1]

(b) Complete and balance the equation for this reaction below.

$$H_2SO_{4(aq)} + Ca(OH)_{2(aq)} \rightarrow \text{................}_{(aq)} + \text{................}H_2O_{(l)}$$

[2]

(c) (i) How many moles of sulfuric acid reacted with the calcium hydroxide in the titration?

Number of moles = ...

[1]

(ii) How many moles of calcium hydroxide reacted with the acid?

....

[1]

(iii) Calculate the concentration of the calcium hydroxide solution in mol/dm³.
Show clearly how you work out your answer.

Concentration = ... mol/dm³

[1]

[Total 6 marks]

8 A student is doing an experiment to investigate the electrolysis of sodium chloride solution.

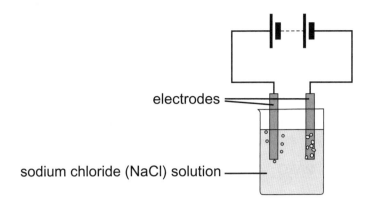

electrodes

sodium chloride (NaCl) solution

(a) Explain why the sodium chloride has to be in solution for electrolysis to occur.

....

....

[2]

(b) Write the half-equation for the reaction occurring at the positive electrode.

....

[1]

(c) Why is sodium not formed at the negative electrode?

....

....

[1]

(d) State the product that remains in solution.

....

[1]

(e) Electrolysis can be used to extract aluminium from aluminium oxide.

Some metals can also be extracted from their oxides in a reduction reaction with carbon. Give a reason why aluminium cannot be extracted using this method.

....

....

[1]

Turn over ▶

188

(f)   Aluminium is used as a material in the bodies of aircraft.
        Give **one** property of aluminium which would make it suitable for this application.

        ....

        ....
                                                                                                                              [1]

(g)   The equation for the electrolysis of aluminium oxide is shown below:

$$2Al_2O_3 \rightarrow 4Al + 3O_2$$

        A scientist carries out an experiment where aluminium oxide is electrolysed.
        The scientist starts off with 40.8 g of pure aluminium oxide.
        Predict the mass of aluminium she can extract from this mass of electrolyte.

                                                        mass = ... g
                                                                                                          [4]
                                                                                        [Total 11 marks]

9   Soluble salts can be made by reacting an acid with an insoluble base or an alkali.

(a)   An excess of zinc oxide is added to a beaker of dilute hydrochloric acid.
The mixture is stirred and the acid is neutralised.

dilute hydrochloric acid

excess of zinc oxide

(i)   How could you tell when all the acid has been neutralised?

....

[1]

(ii) Give the products of this reaction.

....

[2]

(b)   Describe how you could obtain a pure, dry sample of calcium chloride
from the alkali calcium hydroxide and dilute hydrochloric acid.

....

....

....

....

....

....

[3]

Turn over ▶

(c)   Which **two** substances from the list below could be mixed to obtain barium sulfate by precipitation? Write the letters of the substances.

   A $CaSO_4$

   B $BaCl_2$

   C $BaCO_3$

   D $PbSO_4$

   E Na_2SO_4

   F $Ba(OH)_2$

Substances .... and ....

[2]

[Total 8 marks]

[Total for paper 70 marks]

Answers

Section 1 — Particles and Mixtures

Pages 8-9
Warm-Up Questions
1) false
Energy is transferred to a solid through heating to convert it into a liquid, so the particles in a liquid must have more energy than in a solid.
2) freezing
3) A solute is the substance being dissolved.
A solvent is the liquid that the solute is dissolving into.
4) temperature

Exam Questions
1 a) solid *[1 mark]*
b) liquid *[1 mark]*
c) The particles in a gas move constantly with random motion in straight lines *[1 mark]*.
2 a) D *[1 mark]*
b) evaporation *[1 mark]*
c) The particles gain energy *[1 mark]* and vibrate more *[1 mark]*. This weakens the forces that hold the solid together and makes the solid expand *[1 mark]*. At the point of melting, many of the particles have enough energy to break free from their positions *[1 mark]*.
3 a) A mixture of a solute and a solvent *[1 mark]* that does not separate out *[1 mark]*.
b) The solution had become saturated, so no more sodium chloride can dissolve *[1 mark]*.
4 Both jars will be the same paler brown colour *[1 mark]* because the random motion of the bromine and air particles means that they will eventually be equally mixed throughout both jars *[1 mark]*.
5 a) B *[1 mark]*
b) E.g. if the solution was heated using a Bunsen burner, this could cause a fire hazard *[1 mark]*. The risk could be reduced by standing the Bunsen burner on a heat proof mat *[1 mark]*.
c) solubility (g per 100 g of solvent)
= mass of solid (g) ÷ mass of water removed (g) × 100
= (12.2 g ÷ 32.8 g) × 100
= 37.1951... = 37.2 g per 100 g of solvent
[2 marks for correct answer, otherwise 1 mark for correct working.]
d) E.g. repeating the experiment would improve the reliability *[1 mark]*.
e) The solubility of the substance *[1 mark]*.

Page 14
Warm-Up Questions
1) protons and neutrons
2) Electrons have a relative mass of 0.0005 and a relative charge of −1.
These masses and charges are measured <u>relative</u> to that of a proton.
3) false
Different isotopes of the same element have the same number of <u>protons</u> but a different number of <u>neutrons</u>.
4) A substance that consists of only one type of atom.

Exam Questions
1 Sample A *[1 mark]*. The purer the substance, the smaller the range of the melting point / pure substances have sharp melting points, whereas impure substances melt over a range of temperatures *[1 mark]*.
2 a) mass number = 55 *[1 mark]*
atomic number = 25 *[1 mark]*
b) protons = 25 *[1 mark]*
neutrons = mass number – atomic number
= 55 – 25 = **30** *[1 mark]*
electrons = 25 *[1 mark]*
3 a) The relative atomic mass of an element is the average mass of all isotopes of the element *[1 mark]*, compared to the mass of one atom of carbon-12 *[1 mark]*.
b) E.g. relative atomic mass is an average value/ result of a calculation *[1 mark]*.
4 % isotopic abundance of Ga-71 = 100 – 60.1 = 39.9
relative atomic mass = (69 × 60.1) + (71 × 39.9) ÷ 100
= (4146.9 + 2832.9) ÷ 100 = 69.8
[3 marks for correct answer, otherwise 1 mark for working out % abundance of Ga-71, 1 mark for correctly substituting in values for abundances and atomic masses.]

Pages 21-22
Warm-Up Questions
1) crystallisation
2) fractional distillation

Exam Questions
1 brown seaweed *[1 mark]*
2 a) A: fractionating column *[1 mark]*
B: condenser *[1 mark]*
b) The different liquids in the mixture will all have different boiling points *[1 mark]*. When the mixture is heated, the liquid with the lowest boiling point will evaporate first and it will reach the top of the fractionating column when the temperature there matches its boiling point *[1 mark]*. It can then be condensed and collected *[1 mark]*. When the first liquid has been collected, the temperature can be raised until the next liquid evaporates and reaches the top of the column, and so on *[1 mark]*.
3 a) E.g. mix the lawn sand with water to dissolve the ammonium sulfate *[1 mark]*. Filter the mixture using filter paper to remove the sharp sand *[1 mark]*. Pour the remaining solution into an evaporating dish and slowly heat it to evaporate the water *[1 mark]*. Dry the products in a drying oven/desiccator *[1 mark]*.
b) E.g. the products were not completely dry *[1 mark]*.
4 a) Distance from baseline to spot B = 2.4 cm / 24 mm *[1 mark]*
Distance from baseline to furthest point of solvent = 4.0 cm / 40 mm *[1 mark]*
R_f = distance travelled by solute ÷ distance travelled by solvent
= 2.4 ÷ 4.0 = **0.6**
[1 mark for correctly dividing measured distance to spot B by measured distance to solvent front.]
b) i) E.g. draw a pencil line near the bottom of a sheet of filter paper and add spots of the different inks, including the ink from the document, to the line at intervals *[1 mark]*. Put the paper in a beaker of solvent, e.g. water *[1 mark]*, so that the pencil line and the spots of ink are above the solvent *[1 mark]*.
ii) The ink from the printer that produced the document will have the same R_f values as the ink from the document *[1 mark]*.
5 The difference in the boiling points of ethanol and cyclopentane is quite large, so you could separate them using simple distillation *[1 mark]*. But the boiling points of ethanol and ethyl ethanoate are similar, so you would need to use fractional distillation to separate them *[1 mark]*.

Section 2 — The Periodic Table and Bonding

Page 28
Warm-Up Questions
1)   sodium

Potassium and sodium are both in Group 1 of the periodic table. Calcium is in Group 2. Elements in the same group have similar properties, so the properties of potassium should be more like sodium than calcium.

2) a)   2
  b)   8
3)   2.3
4)   Group 0 elements are inert/unreactive.

Exam Questions
1 a)   B *[1 mark]*
  b)   To the right of the line *[1 mark]*. Since it does not conduct electricity, it must be a non-metal *[1 mark]*.
2 a)   2.8.6 *[1 mark]*
  b)

[1 mark]

3 a)   The group number tells you how many electrons are in the outer shell, so magnesium has 2 outer shell electrons *[1 mark]*. The period number tells you how many electron shells the atom has in total, so magnesium has three shells *[1 mark]*. All the shells apart from the outer shell will be filled (the first holds 2 electrons and the second holds 8) *[1 mark]*.
  b)   2.8.2 *[1 mark]*

Page 33
Warm-Up Questions
1)   2+
2)   2−
3) Na_2SO_4

Sodium is a group 1 element, so it must form 1+ ions. The charge on a sulfate ion is 2−. So you need two sodium ions to balance the charge on the sulfate ion.

Exam Questions
1 a)   The oppositely charged ions are strongly attracted to each other *[1 mark]* by electrostatic attractions/forces *[1 mark]*.
  b) (i) K^+ *[1 mark]*
    (ii) Cl^- *[1 mark]*

Group 1 elements form positive ions by losing 1 electron. Group 7 elements form negative ions by gaining 1 electron.

2   positive: Al^{3+} *[1 mark]*
      negative: F^- *[1 mark]*

From the dots and the crosses, you can see how many electrons each ion has gained or lost. You can use the periodic table to work out what atom it was to start with.

3   magnesium hydroxide: $Mg(OH)_2$ *[1 mark]*
     potassium nitrate: KNO_3 *[1 mark]*

4 a)   Sodium chloride contains positive sodium ions (Na^+) *[1 mark]* and negative chloride ions (Cl^-) *[1 mark]* that are arranged in a giant ionic lattice *[1 mark]*. The oppositely charged ions are held together by a strong electrostatic attraction *[1 mark]*.
  b)   To melt sodium chloride, you have to overcome the very strong electrostatic forces/ionic bonds between the ions *[1 mark]*, which requires lots of energy *[1 mark]*.

Page 40
Warm-Up Questions
1)   two
2)   Because the intermolecular forces between the chlorine molecules are very weak.

Exam Questions
1   D *[1 mark]* — giant covalent substances have high melting points and don't normally conduct electricity, even when molten *[1 mark]*.
2 a)

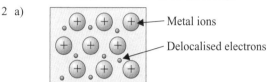

    — Metal ions
    — Delocalised electrons

[1 mark for regular arrangement of metal ions, 1 mark for delocalised electrons, 1 mark for correct labels.]

  b)   E.g. metals are good conductors of electricity because the delocalised electrons in the structure carry electrical charge *[1 mark]*. Most metals are malleable because the layers of atoms in metals can slide over each other allowing them to be hammered or rolled into sheets *[1 mark]*.
3 a)

[1 mark]

[1 mark]

[1 mark]

  b)   A pair of electrons (one from the hydrogen atom and one from the chlorine atom) is shared between the two atoms *[1 mark]*. The atoms are held together by the strong attraction between this shared pair and the nuclei of the atoms *[1 mark]*.
4 a)   A — graphite *[1 mark]*
     B — C_{60} fullerene *[1 mark]*
     C — diamond *[1 mark]*
  b)   Graphite/structure A can conduct electricity because it contains delocalised electrons that can move around *[1 mark]*. Diamond/structure C doesn't conduct electricity because it doesn't contain any charged particles that can move around *[1 mark]*. Diamond/structure C is hard because the strong covalent bonds hold the atoms in a rigid lattice structure *[1 mark]*. Graphite/structure A is soft, as the layers of graphite are held together by weak intermolecular forces *[1 mark]*.
  c)   Structure B is a simple molecular substance *[1 mark]* so only weak intermolecular forces need to be broken to separate the molecules *[1 mark]*. In order for A to sublime, strong covalent bonds need to be broken, which would require more energy *[1 mark]*.

Section 3 — Equations, Calculations and Electrolysis

Pages 46
Warm-Up Questions

1) s
2) $Zn(OH)_2 + 2HCl \rightarrow ZnCl_2 + \mathbf{2H_2O}$
3) $M_r = 23 + 1 + 12 + (16 \times 3) = 84$
4) 23 g
5) moles = mass ÷ M_r
     $= 54 \div 18$
     $= 3$ moles
6) percentage yield = (actual yield ÷ theoretical yield) × 100

Exam Questions

1 a) methane + oxygen → carbon dioxide + water *[1 mark]*
  b) $CH_4 + 2O_2 \rightarrow CO_2 + 2H_2O$ *[1 mark for correct reactants and products, 1 mark for correctly balancing the equation]*

For any question that involves balancing an equation, you would also get the mark if you have matching multiples of the correct numbers.

2   $M_r(C_9H_8O_4) = (12 \times 9) + (1 \times 8) + (16 \times 4) = 180$
    mass = moles × M_r = 12.4 × 180 = **2232 g**
    [2 marks for the correct answer, otherwise 1 mark for calculating the M_r of $C_9H_8O_4$.]

3   $M_r(MgO) = (24 + 16) = 40$
    3.52 kg × 1000 = 3520 g
    moles = mass ÷ M_r = 3520 ÷ 40 = **88 moles**
    [3 marks for the correct answer, otherwise 1 mark for calculating the M_r of MgO, 1 mark for converting between kg and g.]

4 a) $M_r(Fe_2O_3) = (56 \times 2) + (16 \times 3) = 160$
     $A_r(Fe) = 56$
     moles of Fe_2O_3 = mass ÷ M_r = 20 ÷ 160 = 0.125
     There is a 1:2 ratio between the number of moles of Fe_2O_3 and Fe in the balanced equation, so 0.125 moles of Fe_2O_3 react to give 0.25 moles of Fe.
     mass of Fe = moles × A_r = 0.25 × 56 = **14 g**
     [3 marks for correct answer, otherwise 1 mark for calculating the M_r of Fe_2O_3, 1 mark for calculating the moles of Fe_2O_3 and Fe.]
  b) $M_r(Fe_2O_3) = 160$
     $A_r(Al) = 27$
     moles of Fe_2O_3 = mass ÷ M_r = (32 × 1000) ÷ 160 = 200
     There is a 1:2 ratio between the number of moles of Fe_2O_3 and Al in the balanced equation, so 200 moles of Fe_2O_3 react with 400 moles of Al.
     mass of Al = moles × A_r = 400 × 27 = 10800 g = **10.8 kg**
     [2 marks for correct answer, otherwise 1 mark for calculating the moles of Fe_2O_3 and Al.]

5   $M_r(CaCO_3) = 40 + 12 + (16 \times 3) = 100$
    $M_r(CaO) = 40 + 16 = 56$
    Mass of $CaCO_3$ in g = 68.00 × 1000 = 68 000 g
    Moles = mass ÷ M_r
    Moles ($CaCO_3$) = 68 000 ÷ 100 = 680
    1 mole of $CaCO_3$ produces 1 mole of CaO.
    So 680 moles of $CaCO_3$ should produce 680 moles of CaO.
    Theoretical yield = 680 × 56 = 38 080 g = 38.08 kg
    Percentage yield = (28.56 ÷ 38.08) × 100 = **75%**
    [5 marks for correct answer, otherwise 1 mark for calculating the M_rs, 1 mark for correct moles of $CaCO_3$ and CaO, 1 mark for finding the theoretical yield of CaO, 1 mark for dividing actual yield by theoretical yield and multiplying by 100.]

If you didn't convert the mass of $CaCO_3$ from kg to g you should still have got the correct answer as long as you kept all the masses as kg throughout your working. If your answer is wrong, you should still get marks for your working.

Pages 54-55
Warm-Up Questions

1) CH_2O
2) anhydrous
3) concentration = moles ÷ volume
     $= 6.25 \div 25.0$
     $= 0.250$ mol/dm^3
4) false
All gases have a molar volume of 24 dm^3 at RTP.

Exam Questions

1 a) C *[1 mark]*
  b) i) mass of manganese = (mass of test tube and bung + manganese) − (mass of test tube and bung)
       $= 84.88 - 36.48 = \mathbf{48.40}$ *[1 mark]*
    ii) number of moles: Mn = 48.40 ÷ 55 = 0.88
                           O = 14.08 ÷ 16 = 0.88
       simplest whole number ratio:
       (0.88 ÷ 0.88) : (0.88 ÷ 0.88) = 1 : 1
       empirical formula: MnO
       [3 marks for correct answer, otherwise 1 mark for calculating the moles of both manganese and oxygen, 1 mark for correct whole number ratio.]

2 a) 24 dm^3 / 24 000 cm^3 *[1 mark]*
  b) 1.5 × 24 = 36 dm^3 *[1 mark]*

3   Calculate the mass of the empirical formula:
    (12 × 3) + (1 × 7) + 16 = 59 *[1 mark]*
    Divide the relative molecular mass by this mass:
    118 ÷ 59 = 2 *[1 mark]*
    Work out the molecular formula:
    empirical formula × 2 = $C_6H_{14}O_2$ *[1 mark]*

4 a) 125 cm^3 ÷ 1000 = 0.125 dm^3
     moles = concentration × volume
         $= 2.5 \times 0.125 = 0.3125$
         $= \mathbf{0.313}$ **moles** *[1 mark]*

Remember to convert the volume from cm^3 to dm^3 by dividing by 1000.

  b) 750 cm^3 ÷ 1000 = 0.75 dm^3
     concentration = moles ÷ volume
         $= 3 \div 0.75$
         $= \mathbf{4}$ **mol/dm^3** *[1 mark]*
  c) $M_r(Na_2SO_4) = (23 \times 2) + 32 + (16 \times 4) = 142$
     mass = moles × M_r = 4 × 142 = 568 g
     concentration in g/dm^3 = **568 g/dm^3**
     [2 marks for correct answer, otherwise 1 mark for calculating the M_r of Na_2SO_4]

5 a) E.g. to remove all of the water from the salt *[1 mark]*.
  b) i) 61.224 − 53.500 = **7.724 g** *[1 mark]*
    ii) 56.364 − 53.500 = **2.864 g** *[1 mark]*
  c) $M_r(Na_2CO_3) = (23 \times 2) + 12 + (16 \times 3) = 106$
     Moles of water lost:
     mass of water lost = 7.724 − 2.864 = 4.86 g
     moles of water lost = 4.86 ÷ 18 = 0.27 moles
     Moles of salt produced:
     moles of Na_2CO_3 produced = 2.864 ÷ 106 = 0.027 moles
     ratio of salt to water = 0.027 : 0.27
     so, 1 mole of Na_2CO_3 : (0.27 ÷ 0.027) = 10 moles of water
     x = **10** *[4 marks for the correct answer, otherwise 1 mark for calculating the M_r of Na_2CO_3, 1 mark for calculating the moles of water, 1 mark for calculating the moles of Na_2CO_3.]*

Page 59
Warm-Up Questions
1) electrolysis
2) It must be molten or dissolved in water.
3) the cathode

Exam Questions
1 a) $Pb^{2+} + 2e^- \rightarrow Pb$
   [1 mark for correct equation, 1 mark for correct balancing]
  b) $2Br^- \rightarrow Br_2 + 2e^-$
   [1 mark for correct equation, 1 mark for correct balancing]
2 a) i) potassium *[1 mark]*
     ii) iodine *[1 mark]*
  b) It is oxidation, as the iodide ions lose electrons *[1 mark]*.
3 a) E.g.

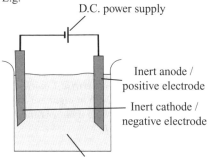

D.C. power supply

Inert anode /
positive electrode

Inert cathode /
negative electrode

Aqueous solution / electrolyte

   [1 mark for power supply, 1 mark for electrodes in solution, 1 mark for labels]
  b) i) Cu^{2+} *[1 mark]*, SO_4^{2-} *[1 mark]*, H^+ *[1 mark]*, OH^- *[1 mark]*
     ii) $Cu^{2+} + 2e^- \rightarrow Cu$ *[1 mark for correct reactants and products, 1 mark for correct balancing.]*
  c) Potassium is more reactive than hydrogen *[1 mark]* so hydrogen is produced *[1 mark]*. There are no halide ions *[1 mark]* so oxygen and water are produced *[1 mark]*.

Section 4 — Inorganic Chemistry

Page 66
Warm-Up Questions
1 lithium oxide
2 The boiling points increase as you go down the group.
3 iodine water / astatine
4 negative

Exam Questions
1 a) Metal B is the most reactive *[1 mark]* because it takes the least time to react completely with the water *[1 mark]*.
  b) A = sodium, B = potassium and C = lithium.
   [2 marks for all three answers correct, otherwise 1 mark for any one answer correct.]
  c) sodium hydroxide *[1 mark]*, hydrogen *[1 mark]*
  d) Rubidium is further down the group than potassium/metal B *[1 mark]*, so it is more reactive/ will take less time to react *[1 mark]*.
2 a) Before — colourless *[1 mark]*
   After — brown *[1 mark]*
  b) Yes *[1 mark]*, as chlorine is more reactive than astatine *[1 mark]*.
3 a) The halogens have seven electrons in their outer shell *[1 mark]*. As you go further down the group additional shells are added / the outer electrons are further away from the nucleus *[1 mark]*.

  b) Both astatine and fluorine have 7 outer shell electrons so should react in a similar way *[1 mark]*. So astatine should react with sodium to form sodium astatide *[1 mark]*. But astatine would react more slowly than fluorine, as it would be less reactive *[1 mark]*. This is because it would be more difficult for astatine to attract extra electrons/form ions, as the extra electron would be added to a shell further away from the nucleus *[1 mark]*.

Page 71
Warm-Up Questions
1 a) 78%
  b) 0.04%
2 $CuCO_3 \rightarrow CuO + CO_2$
3 E.g. deforestation / burning fossil fuels

Exam Questions
1 a) Heat detector B *[1 mark]*, e.g. because the nitrogen will absorb less heat than the carbon dioxide/the carbon dioxide will absorb more heat than the nitrogen *[1 mark]*.
  b) Carbon dioxide absorbs heat that would otherwise be radiated out into space *[1 mark]* and re-radiates some of it back towards the Earth *[1 mark]*.
2 a) pale blue *[1 mark]*
  b) A bright white flame *[1 mark]* and the formation of white powder *[1 mark]*.
  c) $2H_2 + O_2 \rightarrow 2H_2O$
   [1 mark for the correct reactants and products, 1 mark for correct balancing.]
3 Dry air is 21% oxygen
   $100\% - 21\% = 79\%$
   $50\ cm^3 \times 0.79 = \mathbf{39.5\ cm^3}$
   (accept 20-22% oxygen and a correctly calculated volume)
   [2 marks for correct answer, otherwise 1 mark for using any correct method]

Pages 80-81
Warm-Up Questions
1 magnesium chloride
2 Because the more reactive metal will bind more strongly to oxygen than the less reactive metal.
3 oxygen, water
4 You would extract tin from its ore by reducing it with carbon because tin is less reactive than carbon.
5 E.g. car bodies / bridges / cutlery

Exam Questions
1 a) magnesium, zinc, iron, copper
   [1 mark for putting magnesium as the most reactive and copper as the least reactive. 1 mark for putting zinc and iron in the correct order.]
  b) i) zinc oxide *[1 mark]*
     ii) Metal X was sodium, because it reacted vigorously with cold water *[1 mark]*.
2 a) electrolysis *[1 mark]*
  b) If the metal is more reactive than carbon, it can't be extracted using carbon *[1 mark]*.
3 a) Sacrificial protection involves attaching a metal that is more reactive than steel to the ship *[1 mark]*. The more reactive metal will lose electrons/be oxidised more easily than steel *[1 mark]*, so it will corrode instead of the steel *[1 mark]*.
  b) No, the zinc layer acts as sacrificial protection as well as a barrier / the zinc is more reactive than iron *[1 mark]* so it will lose electrons in preference to iron, even if it's scratched *[1 mark]*.

4   Aluminium *[1 mark]* because it has a low density/
     is light so the yacht would be able to move quickly
     in the water *[1 mark]* and aluminium doesn't corrode
     (unlike iron) so it would not be damaged over time
     by being in contact with water *[1 mark]*.
5 a) $Mg_{(s)} + FeCl_{2(aq)} \rightarrow MgCl_{2(aq)} + Fe_{(s)}$
     [1 mark for the correct reactants and products,
     1 mark for all state symbols correct.]
  b) Magnesium is oxidised / loses electrons to form magnesium
     ions *[1 mark]* and simultaneously iron ions are reduced /
     gain electrons to form iron metal *[1 mark]*.
  c) The solution would turn from blue to colourless *[1 mark]*.
     A brown precipitate would form *[1 mark]*.

Pages 89-90
Warm-Up Questions
1   0-14
2   neutral
3   pH 11-14
4   sulfuric acid + magnesium oxide $\rightarrow$ magnesium sulfate + water
5   E.g. phenolphthalein / methyl orange

Exam Questions
1

Indicator	Colour
Litmus paper	blue
Phenolphthalein	pink
Universal indicator	purple
Methyl orange	yellow

     [3 marks for whole table correct, otherwise
     1 mark for each correct answer.]
2 a) H^+ ions/hydrogen ions *[1 mark]*
  b) neutralisation *[1 mark]*
  c) $H^+_{(aq)} + OH^-_{(aq)} \rightarrow H_2O_{(l)}$
     [1 mark for the correct reactants and products,
     1 mark for all state symbols correct.]
3 a) carbon dioxide *[1 mark]*
Don't just give the formula of carbon dioxide — the question asks you to
name the gas.
  b) $2HNO_3 + MgCO_3 \rightarrow Mg(NO_3)_2 + H_2O + CO_2$ *[1 mark*
     for the correct formulae, 1 mark for correct balancing]
  c) hydrochloric acid *[1 mark]*
4 a) E.g. lead nitrate/$Pb(NO_3)_2$ and magnesium sulfate/$MgSO_4$
     [1 mark for any soluble lead salt, 1 mark
     for any soluble sulfate salt.]
  b) The student has poured too much solution into the
     funnel / the level of the solution goes above the filter
     paper *[1 mark]*. This means that some of the solid
     could pass down the sides of the filter paper and
     into the conical flask below, reducing the amount of
     solid that's extracted from the solution *[1 mark]*.
  c) E.g. calcium chloride/$CaCl_2$ and sodium carbonate/Na_2CO_3
     [1 mark for any soluble calcium salt,
     1 mark for any soluble carbonate.]
5 a) Moles KOH = 0.10 × (30.0 ÷ 1000) = 0.0030
     Reaction equation shows that 2 moles of KOH react with
     1 mole of H_2SO_4 so 0.0030 moles of KOH react with
     0.0030 ÷ 2 = 0.0015 moles of H_2SO_4
     Concentration = 0.0015 ÷ (10.0 ÷ 1000)
     = **0.15 mol/dm³**
     [3 marks for correct answer, otherwise 1 mark for correct
     moles of KOH, 1 mark for correct moles of H_2SO_4.]
There are 0.0015 moles in 10 cm³ of H_2SO_4. So you need to calculate
how many moles there are in 1 dm³ (1000 cm³) to get the concentration.

  b) M_r of H_2SO_4 is (2 × 1) + (1 × 32) + (4 × 16) = 98
     Concentration = 0.15 × 98 = **14.7 g/dm³**
     [2 marks for correct answer, otherwise 1 mark for
     correct working.]
6 a) $H_2SO_{4(aq)} + CuO_{(s)} \rightarrow CuSO_{4(aq)} + H_2O_{(l)}$
     [1 mark for correct reactants and products,
     1 mark for correct state symbols.]
  b) E.g. warm the sulfuric acid in a water bath *[1 mark]*.
     Add excess copper oxide to the acid *[1 mark]*. When the
     reaction is complete, filter the reaction mixture to remove
     the excess copper oxide *[1 mark]*. Heat the remaining
     solution gently (using a Bunsen burner) to evaporate
     off some of the water *[1 mark]*. Leave the solution to
     cool and allow the salt to crystallise *[1 mark]*. Filter off
     the solid salt and leave the crystals to dry *[1 mark]*.

Page 95
Warm-Up Questions
1   lithium / Li^+
2 a) Use a damp piece of red litmus paper. If there's
     ammonia present, the litmus paper will turn blue.
  b) You can add some sodium hydroxide to the substance
     and then test for ammonia. If ammonia is given
     off, there are ammonium ions in the substance.
3   Chlorine bleaches damp blue litmus paper, turning it white.
4   blue

Exam Questions
1 a) Test the gas with a lighted splint *[1 mark]*.
     Hydrogen will burn with a squeaky pop *[1 mark]*.
  b) Test the gas with a glowing splint *[1 mark]*.
     Oxygen will relight it *[1 mark]*.
2 a) E.g. take a clean platinum wire loop, dip it into
     the substance to be tested and put the material
     into the hot part of a Bunsen burner flame.
     [1 mark for any suitable method stated to transfer
     the material into the flame, 1 mark for saying that
     the material needs to be placed in the flame]
  b) Potassium would give a lilac flame *[1 mark]* but
     sodium would give a yellow-orange flame *[1 mark]*.
  c) The medicines also contain sodium ions *[1 mark]*,
     so the colour produced by the sodium could
     interfere with the flame test result *[1 mark]*.
3 a) CO_3^{2-} *[1 mark]*
  b) i) dilute hydrochloric acid *[1 mark]*, barium
         chloride solution *[1 mark]*
     ii) a white precipitate *[1 mark]*
4   The presence of chloride ions could be tested by
     adding dilute nitric acid followed by silver nitrate
     solution *[1 mark]*. If chloride ions were present,
     a white precipitate would form *[1 mark]*.
     The presence of carbonate ions could be tested by
     adding dilute hydrochloric acid *[1 mark]*.
     If carbonate ions were present, bubbles of gas
     (carbon dioxide) will be released *[1 mark]*.

Section 5 — Physical Chemistry

Pages 102-103
Warm-Up Questions

1   An endothermic reaction is one which takes in energy from the surroundings.

2   To reduce the amount of energy lost to the surroundings.

3   The amount of energy needed to raise the temperature of 1 gram of water by 1 °C.

4   When bonds are formed.

Exam Questions

1 a)   Endothermic *[1 mark]*. The temperature decrease shows that the reaction is taking in energy from the surroundings *[1 mark]*.

   b) i)   The overall change in energy during a reaction *[1 mark]*.

     ii)   positive *[1 mark]*

     iii)   ΔH *[1 mark]*

2   E.g.

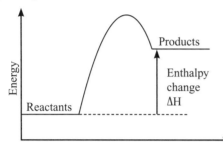

[1 mark for reactants and products correctly labelled and at appropriate energies, 1 mark for correct shape of curve, 1 mark for enthalpy change correctly labelled.]

3   (4 × 412) + (2 × 498) = 2644 kJ/mol *[1 mark]*
       (2 × 743) + (4 × 463) = 3338 kJ/mol *[1 mark]*
       Enthalpy change = 2644 − 3338 = −694 kJ/mol
       [1 mark for correct value, 1 mark for correct sign]

4 a)   To ensure that they are the same temperature before beginning the reaction / to know their initial temperature *[1 mark]*.

   b) i)   To insulate the cup *[1 mark]*.

     ii)   To reduce the energy lost by evaporation *[1 mark]*.

   c)   31 °C − 21 °C = 10 °C *[1 mark]*

   d)   The temperature of the reaction mixture *[1 mark]*.

   e)   The experiment could be repeated and an average temperature change calculated *[1 mark]*.

   f)   E.g. dissolving (or dissolution) / displacement *[1 mark]*.

5 a) M_r of ethanol = (2 × 12) + (6 × 1) + (1 × 16) = 46
       Number of moles = 1.15 ÷ 46 = 0.025 *[2 marks for correct answer, otherwise 1 mark for correct working.]*

   b)   7245 J = 7.245 kJ
       Molar enthalpy change = −7.245 ÷ 0.025
       = −289.8 kJ/mol *[2 marks for correct answer, otherwise 1 mark for correct working.]*

The molar enthalpy change (−289.8 kJ/mol) is negative because combustion is an exothermic reaction. You'd also get the marks if you rounded your answer to −290 kJ/mol.

Page 108
Warm-Up Questions

1   E.g. the corrosion of iron is a reaction that happens very slowly. Explosions are very fast reactions.

2   True

Exam Questions

1 a)   E.g.

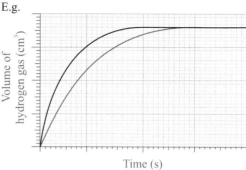

[1 mark for curve with steeper gradient at the start of the reaction, 1 mark for final volume being the same as for the other curve but reaching it in less time.]

   b)   The frequency of the collisions *[1 mark]* and the energy of the colliding particles *[1 mark]*.

   c)   There are more particles in a given volume/the particles are closer together *[1 mark]*, so the collisions between particles are more frequent *[1 mark]*.

   d)   The rate would increase *[1 mark]*.

   e)   Smaller pieces have a higher surface area to volume ratio *[1 mark]*. So for the same volume of solid, the particles around it will have more area to work on and collisions will be more frequent *[1 mark]*.

   f)   E.g. changing the temperature / adding a catalyst *[1 mark]*.

2 a) i)   It is a catalyst *[1 mark]*.

     ii)   It provides an alternative reaction pathway *[1 mark]* with a lower activation energy *[1 mark]*.

   b)   The reaction equation won't change *[1 mark]*. Cerium oxide isn't used up in the reaction, so doesn't appear in the reaction equation / the cerium oxide doesn't change the products of the reaction *[1 mark]*.

Pages 115-116
Warm-Up Questions

1   cm^3

2   E.g. it is subjective/inaccurate as different people might not agree on exactly when the cross disappears.

3   In a reversible reaction the products of the reaction can react with each other and convert back to the original reactants.

4   Dynamic equilibrium is the point at which both the forward and backward reactions of a reversible reaction are taking place at the same rate. Whilst both reactions continue, the overall effect is nil as they cancel each other out.

Exam Questions

1 a)   17 cm^3 *[1 mark]*

   b)   Manganese(IV) oxide was the most effective catalyst *[1 mark]* because it led to the greatest volume of oxygen being produced over the time period measured/increased the rate of reaction by the greatest amount *[1 mark]*.

2 a) i)   E.g. the gas is released directly into the room and may be toxic/hazardous *[1 mark]*.

     ii)   E.g. measure the volume of gas given off using a gas syringe *[1 mark]*.

   b) i)   E.g. observe a marker through the solution *[1 mark]*. Measure how long it takes for the marker to disappear (as the precipitate forms) *[1 mark]*.

     ii)   The time taken for the mark to be obscured. / The rate of reaction. *[1 mark]*

3 a) i) Draw a tangent to curve Q at 50 s, e.g.:

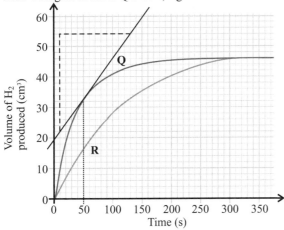

Then calculate the gradient of your tangent, e.g.:
Change in y = 54 – 22 = 32
Change in x = 130 – 10 = 120
Gradient = change in y ÷ change in x
= 32 ÷ 120 = 0.27 cm³/s
[Accept answers between 0.22 cm³/s and 0.32 cm³/s.
3 marks for correct answer, otherwise 1 mark for
drawing a correct tangent and 1 mark for using
the correct equation to calculate the gradient.]

It's OK if you've drawn your tangent slightly differently to this one, or if you've used a different bit of the tangent to calculate the gradient. As long as your tangent's sensible and your final answer is in the range given, you'll get the marks.
The same thing applies to the second tangent and calculation too.

ii) Draw a tangent to curve R at 120 s, e.g.:

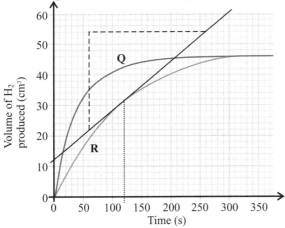

Then calculate the gradient of your tangent, e.g.:
Change in y = 54 – 22 = 32
Change in x = 260 – 60 = 200
Gradient = change in y ÷ change in x
= 32 ÷ 200 = 0.16 cm³/s
[Accept answers between 0.11 cm³/s and 0.21 cm³/s.
3 marks for correct answer, otherwise 1 mark for
drawing a correct tangent and 1 mark for using
the correct equation to calculate the gradient.]

b) Reaction Q must have used powdered zinc. Powdered zinc has a larger surface area to volume ratio than zinc ribbon *[1 mark]*, so the rate of reaction would be higher for powdered zinc than for zinc ribbon *[1 mark]*. The line for reaction Q has a steeper gradient / finishes sooner than the line for reaction R, so it must have a higher rate *[1 mark]*.

c) E.g. the student would have used the same volume / concentration of acid in each experiment *[1 mark]*. This variable needed to be controlled so that the student could tell that the variable he was changing was causing the results *[1 mark]*.

4 The first student's reaction conditions are better *[1 mark]*, because:
The forward reaction is endothermic *[1 mark]* so raising the temperature will increase this reaction *[1 mark]*.
There are more moles of gas on the right-hand side of the equation *[1 mark]*, and a lower pressure will encourage the reaction that produces more moles of gas *[1 mark]*.

Section 6 — Organic Chemistry

Page 122
Warm-Up Questions
1) CH_2
2) A group of atoms that determine how a compound typically reacts.
3) 4
4) methanol
5) Molecules which have the same molecular formula but differently arranged atoms.

Exam Questions
1 B *[1 mark]*
2

```
    H  H  H  H  H  H
    |  |  |  |  |  |
H—C—C—C—C—C—C—H
    |  |  |  |  |  |
    H  H  H  H  H  H
```
[1 mark]

3 a)
```
    H  Br H
    |  |  |
H—C—C—C—H
    |  |  |
    H  H  H
```
[1 mark]

b)
```
      H  H  H  H
      |  |  |  |
Cl—C—C—C—C—H
      |  |  |  |
      H  H  H  H
```
[1 mark]

```
    H  Cl H  H
    |  |  |  |
H—C—C—C—C—H
    |  |  |  |
    H  H  H  H
```
[1 mark]

Don't worry if your answer doesn't look identical to what's shown here — as long as you drew an isomer with the Cl attached to one of the end carbons, and an isomer where it's attached to one of the middle carbons, you'd get the marks.

4 a) pentanoic acid *[1 mark]*
   b) Yes it will, as compounds in the same homologous series react in similar ways *[1 mark]*.

Pages 130-131
Warm-Up Questions
1) When you burn something in plenty of oxygen.
2) methane, ethane, propane, butane, pentane
3) Because they can make more bonds.
4) C_nH_{2n}

198

Exam Questions

1 a) Carbon monoxide can form if the fuel is burnt without enough oxygen / if incomplete combustion occurs *[1 mark]*.

b) Carbon monoxide can interfere with the blood's role of carrying oxygen around the body, meaning it can carry less *[1 mark]*.

2 a) i) high temperatures *[1 mark]*
ii) E.g. in a car engine *[1 mark]*.

b) nitric acid *[1 mark]*

c) sulfur dioxide *[1 mark]*

3 a) E.g. fuel for large ships *[1 mark]* and in power stations *[1 mark]*.

b) Triacontane, e.g. because the fractionating column is hottest at the bottom *[1 mark]* so hydrocarbons with higher boiling points will be collected further down the column *[1 mark]*. Triacontane has a higher boiling point than heptane because triacontane is a bigger molecule *[1 mark]* (so triacontane will be collected lower down).

4 a) i) It acts as a catalyst / catalyses the reaction *[1 mark]*.
ii) alkenes *[1 mark]*

b) There is a greater demand for short-chain alkanes than for longer-chain alkanes *[1 mark]*. To meet this demand, long hydrocarbons are split into more useful short-chain molecules *[1 mark]*. Cracking also produces alkenes *[1 mark]* which are used to make polymers/plastic *[1 mark]*.

5 a) C_nH_{2n+2} *[1 mark]*

A general formula means you can replace the 'n's with a number to get the formula of a certain molecule in the series — so the 4th alkane is $C_4H_{(2\times4+2)} = C_4H_{10}$.

b) i) ethane *[1 mark]*
ii) 6 *[1 mark]*

c)

      H H H H
      | | | |
   H—C—C—C—C—H
      | | | |
      H H H H   *[1 mark]*

d) i) methane + bromine —UV→ bromomethane + hydrogen bromide
[1 mark for each correct product]

It doesn't matter which way round you write the two missing answers here.

ii) substitution reaction *[1 mark]*

6 a) i) CH_2CHCH_3/CH_3CHCH_2 *[1 mark]*
ii) The solution would turn from orange to colourless *[1 mark]*.
iii) An addition reaction *[1 mark]*.

b) Nothing would happen / the solution would stay orange *[1 mark]*. C_2H_6/ethane is a saturated hydrocarbon/an alkane/ doesn't contain a double bond *[1 mark]* so it can't react with bromine *[1 mark]*.

Pages 138-139
Warm-Up Questions

1) $C_nH_{2n+1}OH$
2) hydrogen
3) an acid catalyst / concentrated sulfuric acid
4) ethyl ethanoate

Exam Questions

1 B *[1 mark]*

2 a) propanol *[1 mark]*

b) $CH_3CH_2CH_2CH_2OH$ *[1 mark]*

c)

      H
      |
   H—C—O—H
      |
      H   *[1 mark]*

3 a) A volatile chemical evaporates easily *[1 mark]*.

b) They often smell nice/have distinctive smells *[1 mark]*.

c) e.g. as flavourings *[1 mark]*

---

4 a)

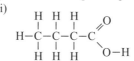

Method	Reaction	Temperature needed
A	$C_2H_4 + H_2O \rightarrow C_2H_5OH$	300 °C
B	$C_6H_{12}O_6 \rightarrow 2CO_2 + 2C_2H_5OH$	30 °C

[4 marks — 1 mark for each correct answer]

b) Pressure — 60-70 atmospheres *[1 mark]*
Catalyst — phosphoric acid *[1 mark]*

c) i) Any pH from 2-6 *[1 mark]*. The ethanol will react with oxygen in the air, converting it to ethanoic acid (which is acidic) *[1 mark]*.
ii) The enzyme in the yeast was denatured *[1 mark]* so it could not catalyse the reaction / the reaction could not happen *[1 mark]*.

5 a) i) butanoic acid *[1 mark]*
ii)

      H H H   O
      | | | ⫽
   H—C—C—C—C
      | | | \
      H H H   O—H
                    [1 mark]

b) water *[1 mark]*, carbon dioxide *[1 mark]*

c) ethanoic acid *[1 mark]*

6 carboxylic acid:

               O
              ⫽
        H—C
              \
               O—H   *[1 mark]*

alcohol:

      H H H
      | | |
   H—C—C—C—O—H
      | | |
      H H H
                  [1 mark]

Page 143
Warm-Up Questions

1) A substance of high average relative molecular mass made by joining lots of smaller molecules/monomers.
2) $(C_4H_8)_n$
3) True
4) A biodegradable polyester/a polyester that can be broken down by bacteria and other living organisms over time.

Exam Questions

1 a) i)

     ⎛ H   H ⎞
     ⎜ | | ⎥
    —⎜ C — C ⎟—
     ⎜ | | ⎥n
     ⎝ H   CH₃⎠ *[1 mark]*

ii)

    H   H
     \   ⁄
      C = C
     ⁄   \
    H   CH₃   *[1 mark]*

Don't worry if you put the CH₃ in another position — as long as it's attached to one of the carbon atoms, it's still correct.

iii) propene *[1 mark]*

b) poly(chloroethene) *[1 mark]*

c) E.g. most addition polymers are inert/don't react easily *[1 mark]*. This means that it takes a very long time for them to biodegrade and they can stay unchanged in landfill sites for a long time *[1 mark]*.

2 a) i)

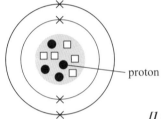

*[1 mark for correct ester link connecting monomers,
1 mark for rest of the structure being correct.]*
*You could also draw the repeat unit with the monomers the other
way round (so that the diol monomer is on the left-hand side and the
dicarboxylic acid is on the right-hand side).*

   ii) H_2O *[1 mark]*

b)

*[1 mark for correct ester link connecting monomers,
1 mark for rest of the structure being correct.]*

Practice Paper 1C

1 a) E.g.

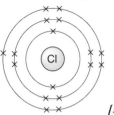

                              proton

                         [1 mark]

Remember that atoms have the same number of electrons and protons.

b) Atoms C and D *[1 mark]*
   Explanation — isotopes have the same number of protons but
   a different number of neutrons, and C and D are the only pair
   with the same number of protons *[1 mark]*.

c) Protons — 30 *[1 mark]*
   Neutrons — 35 *[1 mark]*
   Electrons — 30 *[1 mark]*

d) i) A compound is a substance made of two or more different
      elements *[1 mark]* that are chemically bonded together
      [1 mark].

   ii) $M_r = 65 + 32 + (4 \times 16) = $ **161**
       *[2 marks for the correct answer, otherwise 1 mark for
       correct working]*

2 a) Nitrogen dioxide is created when the temperature is high
     enough for the nitrogen and oxygen in the air to react
     [1 mark]. This often happens in car engines, which there are
     lots of in cities *[1 mark]*.

b) i) nitric acid + calcium carbonate → calcium nitrate +
      carbon dioxide + water
      *[1 mark for calcium nitrate, 1 mark for carbon dioxide and
      water.]*

*Think back to acid and metal carbonate reactions — you always get a salt,
carbon dioxide and water.*

   ii) e.g. sulfur dioxide *[1 mark]*

c) Nitrogen dioxide has a simple molecular structure *[1 mark]*
   and the molecules are held together by weak intermolecular
   forces *[1 mark]*. This means it has a very low boiling point,
   because not much energy is needed to break the molecules
   apart *[1 mark]*.

3 a) i) C *[1 mark]*

*Melting point increases down the group, so chlorine will have a melting
point about halfway between the melting points of fluorine and bromine.*

   ii) It is around halfway between the melting points of bromine
       and fluorine *[1 mark]*.

b) It is a red-brown *[1 mark]* liquid *[1 mark]*.

c) $Br_2 + 2KI \rightarrow I_2 + 2KBr$
   *[1 mark for correct reactants and products, 1 mark for
   correct balancing]*

d) i)

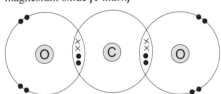

                         [1 mark]

   ii) The group number is equal to the number of electrons in the
       outer electron shell *[1 mark]*. Chlorine is in Group 7, so a
       chlorine atom has seven electrons in its outer shell *[1 mark]*.

e) Chlorine will displace the iodine in solution to form sodium
   chloride solution *[1 mark]*. This happens because chlorine
   is higher up Group 7 than iodine *[1 mark]*, which means that
   chlorine is more reactive *[1 mark]*.

f) When hydrogen chloride is dissolved in water, the hydrogen
   chloride molecules split up into H^+ ions and Cl^- ions
   [1 mark]. It is the H^+ ions that make the solution acidic
   [1 mark].

4 a) Any two from: Problem — the spots of dye/ink are touching
     the solvent *[1 mark]*. Correction — the student should put
     the filter paper in a beaker of solvent with the pencil line
     above the level of the solvent *[1 mark]*. / Problem — the ink
     and dyes are compared using different solvents *[1 mark]*.
     Correction — the student should use the same solvent for the
     black ink and the dyes so that it's a fair test *[1 mark]*. /
     Problem — the ink and dyes are compared on different
     pieces of filter paper which could make it difficult to directly
     compare them *[1 mark]*. Correction — the student should
     put the spots of the dyes and the ink on the same piece of
     filter paper *[1 mark]*.

b) Dyes B and D *[1 mark]*
   Explanation — the spots from these two dyes are in the same
   positions as the spots from the black ink *[1 mark]*.

c) $R_f = $ distance travelled by solute ÷ distance travelled by
   solvent = 4.8 ÷ 6.4 = **0.75** *[1 mark]*

5 a) magnesium oxide *[1 mark]*

b)

*[1 mark for all shared pairs correct, 1 mark for the
non-bonding electrons correct]*

c) $M_r(MgCO_3) = 24 + 12 + (16 \times 3) = 84$
   percentage mass of C = $(12 \div 84) \times 100 = $ **14%**
   *[2 marks for correct answer, otherwise 1 mark for
   correct working.]*

d) i) Greenhouse gases act like an insulating layer by absorbing
      heat that would normally be radiated from the Earth into
      space *[1 mark]* and re-radiating some of it back towards the
      Earth *[1 mark]*.

   ii) 0.04% *[1 mark]*

   iii) e.g. global warming / climate change / changing rainfall
        patterns / sea level rise *[1 mark]*

6 a) i) Add sodium hydroxide (NaOH) solution *[1 mark]*.
      Iron(II) chloride will form a green precipitate. Iron(III)
      chloride will form a reddish-brown precipitate *[1 mark]*.

   ii) Add dilute nitric acid (HNO_3) followed by silver nitrate
       ($AgNO_3$) solution *[1 mark]*. Sodium chloride will form
       a white precipitate. Sodium iodide will form a yellow
       precipitate *[1 mark]*.

b) sodium carbonate / sodium hydrogen carbonate *[1 mark for identifying the sodium ion and 1 mark for identifying the carbonate ion.]*

7 a) The volume of gas produced *[1 mark]*.

b) hydrogen/H_2 *[1 mark]*

c) Reaction D *[1 mark]*. The most reactive metal will react fastest with the acid *[1 mark]*. In reaction D the largest volume of gas has been collected in the syringe / the most bubbles are being given off *[1 mark]*.

d) e.g. zinc *[1 mark]*

You would get this mark if you named any metal between magnesium and iron in the reactivity series (for example, aluminium would be fine here too).

e) Reaction of copper sulfate with iron: yes *[1 mark]*
Reaction of iron sulfate with magnesium: yes *[1 mark]*

f) Mg / magnesium *[1 mark]*

Remember, when you're talking about oxidation and reduction in terms of electrons, oxidation is the loss of electrons. In this reaction, the magnesium went from being neutral atoms to positively charged ions — so they must have lost electrons.

8 a) propene *[1 mark]*

b) alkenes *[1 mark]*

c)
```
      H   H   H   H   H
      |   |   |   |   |
  H — C — C — C — C — C — H
      |   |   |   |   |
      H   H   H   H   H     [1 mark]
```

d) Test: Add a few drops of bromine water to the gas and shake *[1 mark]*.
Observations: Gas A (propane) will have no effect. Gas B (propene) will change the bromine water from orange to colourless *[1 mark]*.

e) The C=C double bond is split *[1 mark]* and a bromine atom is added to each carbon atom *[1 mark]*.

f) $C_3H_8 + 5O_2 \rightarrow 3CO_2 + 4H_2O$
[1 mark for products and reactants, 1 mark for balancing]

g) i) cracking *[1 mark]*
ii) Gas B/propene, heptane, decane *[1 mark]*.

9 a) A reaction that gives out energy to the surroundings (usually in the form of heat) *[1 mark]*.

b) E.g. measure the temperature of some water, add the substance and stir, then measure the temperature every 30 seconds and record the lowest temperature reached *[1 mark]*. Repeat the experiment with other substances to determine which is the most effective *[1 mark]*. The same volume of water and mass/volume of substance should be used for each experiment *[1 mark]*.

c) $Fe_2O_3 + 3Ca \rightarrow 3CaO + 2Fe$
[1 mark for the correct reactants and products, 1 mark for correct balancing]

10 a)

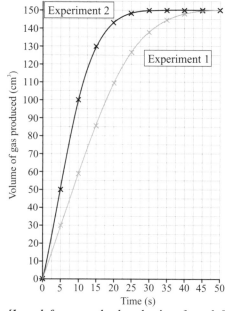

Rate of reaction = change in y ÷ change in x
= (135 − 65) ÷ (27.5 − 2.5)
= 70 ÷ 25 = **2.8 cm³/s**
(accept answers between 2 and 3 cm³/s)
[3 marks for correct answer, otherwise 1 mark for correctly drawn tangent, 1 mark for dividing change in y by change in x.]

b)

[1 mark for correctly plotted points, 1 mark for curve of best fit]

c) 7-8 seconds (to collect 75 cm³) *[1 mark]*
The total volume is 150 cm³, so you need to read off the value from 75 cm³ on your graph.

d) The rate of reaction decreases as the reaction proceeds *[1 mark]*.

e) It increases the rate of the reaction. The graph for experiment 2 has a steeper slope at the beginning. / The reaction is complete in less time *[1 mark]*.

f) Catalysts make reactions happen faster by providing an alternative reaction pathway with a lower activation energy *[1 mark]*.

11 a) Oxygen *[1 mark]* and water *[1 mark]* must be present.

b) C *[1 mark]*

c) i) sacrificial protection *[1 mark]*
ii) Magnesium is more reactive than iron *[1 mark]*, so the magnesium will be oxidised instead of the iron *[1 mark]*.

d) galvanising *[1 mark]*

12a) $M_r(Mg) = 24$
$M_r(MgCl_2) = 24 + (35.5 \times 2) = 95$
moles of $MgCl_2$ = mass $\div M_r = 7.60 \div 95 = 0.08$ moles
From the equation, 1 mole of $MgCl_2$ is produced from 1 mole of Mg. So 0.08 moles of $MgCl_2$ will be produced from 0.08 moles of Mg.
So mass of Mg $= 0.08 \times 24 = 1.92$ g
[3 marks for correct answer, otherwise 1 mark for correctly calculating the M_rs, 1 mark for correct number of moles of $MgCl_2$ and Mg.]

b) Test: test the gas with a lighted splint *[1 mark]*.
Observation: hydrogen produces a squeaky pop *[1 mark]*.

c) E.g. the hydrochloric acid/HCl was used in excess *[1 mark]*.

13a) Mass of Cu: $33.08 - 28.00 = 5.08$
Mass of O: $34.36 - 33.08 = 1.28$
Number of moles: Cu $= 5.08 \div 63.5 = 0.08$
O $= 1.28 \div 16 = 0.08$
Simplest whole number ratio:
$(0.08 \div 0.08) : (0.08 \div 0.08) = 1 : 1$
Empirical formula: CuO
[5 marks for correct answer, otherwise 1 mark for calculating the mass of Cu, 1 mark for calculating the mass of O, 1 mark for correct number of moles of each element, 1 mark for finding the simplest whole number ratio.]

b) i) percentage yield $= (1.20 \div 1.80) \times 100 = $ **66.7%** *[2 marks for correct answer, otherwise 1 mark for correct working.]*

ii) E.g. not all of the metal may have reacted *[1 mark]*.

Practice Paper 2C

1 a) i) Isotopes are different atomic forms of the same element, which have the same number of protons but a different number of neutrons *[1 mark]*.

ii) Cl is 25% ^{37}Cl and 75% ^{35}Cl *[1 mark]*
$A_r = (37 \times 25 \div 100) + (35 \times 75 \div 100) = 35.5$ *[1 mark]*

b) E.g.

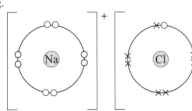

[1 mark for 8 electrons in sodium, 1 mark for 8 electrons in chlorine, 1 mark for the correct charges]

2 a) The forward and reverse reactions happen at exactly the same rate. / The concentrations of reactants and products remain the same. *[1 mark]*

b) The yield of ammonia will decrease *[1 mark]*. Increasing the temperature will favour the reverse/endothermic reaction which takes in energy *[1 mark]*.

c) The yield of ammonia will decrease *[1 mark]*. This is because lowering the pressure will encourage the reaction that produces more moles of gas (there are four moles of gas on the left-hand side of the equation, for every two moles on the right) *[1 mark]*.

d) i) M_r of ammonia $= 14 + (3 \times 1) = 17$
Number of moles of ammonia = mass $\div M_r$
$= 85 \div 17 = $ **5 moles**
[2 marks for correct answer, otherwise 1 mark for correct working.]

ii) Volume = moles $\times 24 = $ **120 dm³** *[1 mark]*
The molar volume of a gas is 24 dm³, so you need to multiply that value by the number of moles.

3 a) propanol/propan-1-ol *[1 mark]*

b) i) propanoic acid *[1 mark]*

ii) ester *[1 mark]*

iii) E.g. it is volatile *[1 mark]*.

c) i) $C_2H_5OH + 3O_2 \rightarrow 3H_2O + 2CO_2$
[1 mark for the correct reactants and products, 1 mark for correctly balancing the equation.]

ii) E.g. microbial oxidation / heating with potassium dichromate(VI) in dilute sulfuric acid *[1 mark]*

4 a) Any two from: e.g. fizzing increases from lithium to potassium / sodium and potassium melt, but lithium doesn't / a flame is only seen with potassium *[2 marks — 1 mark for each correct answer]*.

b) E.g. Group 1 elements further down the group have an outer electron in a shell that is further from the nucleus *[1 mark]*. So as you go down the group, the attraction between the outer shell electron and the nucleus becomes less and so the electron is more easily lost *[1 mark]*.

c) $2Li + 2H_2O \rightarrow 2LiOH + H_2$
[1 mark for the correct reactants and products, 1 mark for correctly balancing the equation.]

d) The student could put the wire loop in one of the unlabelled samples and then hold it in a blue Bunsen flame *[1 mark]*. If the flame turns crimson-red, the sample is lithium chloride, but if it turns lilac, the sample is potassium chloride *[1 mark]*.

5 a) Bonds broken $(2 \times 436) + 498 = 1370$ *[1 mark]*
Bonds formed $(4 \times 464) = 1856$ *[1 mark]*
Enthalpy change $= 1370 - 1856 = $ **−486 kJ/mol**
[1 mark for the correct value, 1 mark for the correct sign]

b) endothermic *[1 mark]*

c) D *[1 mark]*

6 a)

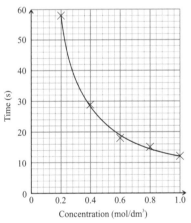

[1 mark for plotting points correctly, 1 mark for sensible curve of best fit.]

b) E.g. 23 s (accept 22-24 s) *[1 mark]*

c) Repeat the experiment and take the mean of the results *[1 mark]*.

d) The rate increases as the concentration increases *[1 mark]*.

e) At higher concentration there are more particles in a certain space / the particles are closer together *[1 mark]*. This means that collisions between particles happen more often / there are more frequent collisions / there are more collisions per second *[1 mark]*.

f) No. The magnesium has a larger surface area *[1 mark]*. This will increase the rate of the reaction *[1 mark]*, so it will take less than 18 seconds for 20 cm³ of hydrogen to form *[1 mark]*.

7 a) E.g. methyl orange / phenolphthalein *[1 mark]*

b) $H_2SO_{4(aq)} + Ca(OH)_{2(aq)} \rightarrow CaSO_{4(aq)} + 2H_2O_{(l)}$
[1 mark for the correct formula for calcium sulfate, 1 mark for correctly balancing the equation]

c) i) $(8.80 \div 1000) \times 0.050 = $ **0.00044 moles** *[1 mark]*

   ii) 0.00044 moles *[1 mark]*

From the equation you can see that one mole of H_2SO_4 reacts with one mole of $Ca(OH)_2$ so the number of moles of each will be the same.

   iii) 10 cm^3 ÷ 1000 = 0.01 dm^3

       concentration = moles ÷ volume

       0.00044 ÷ 0.01 = **0.044 mol/dm^3** *[1 mark]*

8 a) So the ions are free to move *[1 mark]* so they can carry the charge / conduct electricity *[1 mark]*.

  b) $2Cl^- \rightarrow Cl_2 + 2e^-$ *[1 mark]*

  c) The sodium ions are more reactive than the hydrogen ions, so hydrogen gas will be formed *[1 mark]*.

  d) sodium hydroxide *[1 mark]*

  e) Aluminium is more reactive than carbon (so the carbon will not be able to reduce the aluminium oxide) *[1 mark]*.

  f) E.g. aluminium has a low density, which makes it relatively light *[1 mark]*.

  g) $M_r(Al_2O_3) = (2 \times 27) + (3 \times 16) = 102$

      moles = mass ÷ M_r

      moles of $Al_2O_3 = 40.8 \div 102 = 0.400$ moles

      From the balanced equation, 2 moles of aluminium oxide produce 4 moles of aluminium.

      So, 0.400 moles of aluminium oxide will produce $(0.400 \div 2) \times 4 = 0.800$ moles of aluminium.

      $A_r(Al) = 27$, so mass of Al = $0.800 \times 27 = 21.6$ g

      [4 marks for correct answer, otherwise 1 mark for correctly calculating M_r of Al_2O_3, 1 mark for correctly calculating the number of moles of Al_2O_3 and 1 mark for working out how many moles of Al are made.]

9 a) i) The solid stops dissolving and remains at the bottom of the flask *[1 mark]*.

   ii) zinc chloride *[1 mark]* and water *[1 mark]*.

  b) E.g. do a titration to find out how much acid and alkali are needed for neutralisation *[1 mark]*. Add these volumes of acid and alkali together without indicator *[1 mark]*. Heat the solution to evaporate the water, leaving a dry sample of the salt *[1 mark]*.

  c) B *[1 mark]* and E *[1 mark]*

For this reaction you need to pick two soluble salts — one that contains Ba^{2+} and one that contains SO_4^{2-}.

Index

Index

CESI42